ANTIGRAVITY:
The Dream Made Reality

The Story of John R. R. Searl

By: John A. Thomas Jr.

Copyright © 1993 by John A. Thomas Jr.

All rights reserved. No part of this book may be reproduced or utilized in any form or by any means, electronic or mechanical, including photocopying, recording or by any information storage and retrieval system, without permission in writing from the publisher. Inquiries should be addressed to John A. Thomas Jr., 373 Rock Beach Road, Rochester, New York, 14617-1316.

ISBN 1 898827 99 0
Issue Date November 11, 1993

Published By: Direct International Science Consortium
13 Blackburn, Low Strand, Grahame Park Estate, London, NW95NG, England
373 Rock Beach Road, Rochester, New York, 14617-1316, U.S.A.

ABOUT THE TITLE

Prof. Searl has stated for the record that the title "Antigravity" is not technically correct. Although this term is used by the general public to describe a repulsion from the earth's gravity, scientific people will know that antigravity would be the opposite to gravity and would attract the earth's gravity instead of repelling it. The Inverse-G-Vehicle, using the Searl Effect Generator, creates it's own gravity field. This field is like the earth's field and because of this the two like fields repel each other. So instead of producing antigravity, the craft produces its own gravity.

ANTIGRAVITY: THE DREAM MADE REALITY
THE STORY OF JOHN R. R. SEARL
BY: JOHN A. THOMAS, JR.

This book contains information that was received by me from John R. R. Searl about his life and inventions. Searl has had an antigravity device since 1946. He also developed a generator of electricity that uses no input power as we know it.

There has been much written about Searl and his work but most of it is misinformation or guesswork. Many people have tried to duplicate his work but none have succeeded. All information in this book is correct and directly from the source, Prof. John R. R. Searl himself. This book is the story of a man who is trying to move the world into the future... and has been for years.

Published By:

John A. Thomas Jr.
373 Rock Beach Rd.
Rochester, New York
14617-1316
Phone: (716) 467-2694
Fax: (716) 338-2663

John A. Thomas Jr.
Author

Prof. John R. R. Searl
Inventor

Mr. Thomas has a technical background in electricity and process control. He has studied such varied topics as UFO's and Ancient Technology that has been lost or forgotten.

He has carried on the efforts of Mr. William Sherwood, formerly Professor Searl's contact and help mate in the National Space Research Consortium (NSRC).

He first contacted Professor Searl in 1990 and since that time has printed and distributed his books on "The Law of the Squares".

John has been a student of Professor Searl and has come to an understanding of "the square technology" which is the basis for the Searl Effect Generator (SEG) and the Inverse-G-Vehicle (IGV). This book is a reflection of that learning process.

John is presently Vice President of the Direct International Science Consortium (DISC) and is Technical Representative for Professor Searl.

When I first called Prof. Searl I was apprehensive as to how I would be received. I was delighted to find him very receptive and eager to talk about his technology. We became good friends in the years to follow. I have never met such a sincere and honest individual.

Prof. Searl looks at things differently from most people in that he equates everything to "The Law of the Squares". He is only interested in the Truth in all things. He has written his books to dispel all the mis-information and lies that have been written about him and his work. He is setting the record straight. These books tell of his life experiences as well as the technology that he has developed. After reading these books you may look at things differently, as I do now.

He is currently the President and Consultant Engineer of the Direct International Science Consortium (DISC).

Prof. Searl is truly trying to bring us into a better future through this method of thinking and the technology that it has produced.

INDEX

CHAPTER 1

This chapter will deal with John R.R. Searl's early days.

John's mother, Violet Gertrude Maud Pearce, was born of poor parents on December 22nd, 1911 at number 8 Bridge Cottages, Shaw Road, Newbury in the county of Berkshire. Little is known of the origin of his father Robert Henry Searl as no record of his birth can be found. It seems that Violet and her parents had moved to a farm to work and that Robert had also moved in and worked on that farm. The farm was a poor one and the pay was so little and the conditions so poor that they became ill. The local council had to rehouse them at the council houses, Hampstead Norrays, then in Berkshire. But Violet's father, William Alexander Pearce then age 48, died from his illness which he had gotten from the farm job. This left Robert the only man in the house.

Robert was serving in India when Violet and he were married by proxy on April 26th, 1930. He served in India for 2 years and received 2000 rupees for bravery. Their son was born on May 2nd, 1932 at the Downs, Newbury Road, Wantage, then in the county of Berkshire, by the name of John Roy Robert Searl. John was born 1 month early and had black curly hair. The Downs at that time was a workhouse, a place of disgrace. It has since been torn down and it's believed that John was the last baby to be born there. Today the hospital part of the workhouse is used for a stable for horses. Robert brought a very heavy shawl back from India to wrap the baby in. One day John's mom and dad took him for a walk wrapped up in this shawl. Somewhere along that road, John slipped unnoticed from that shawl, and did a head landing on the road surface. They had walked for over an hour before Violet checked to see why the baby was so quiet. John was nowhere to be found. She quickly retraced her steps and found John still in the road. After that John suffered from "fits" and Violet was told by the doctor that if they didn't stop in 2 years he would die.

Their second child, Iris, was born at home on June 28th, 1934 while still at the council houses. The last child born to them was Peter. He was born at 214 Newtown Road, Newbury in Berkshire. They then moved to 86 Northbrook street, Newbury, Berkshire. Robert claimed that Peter was not his child and one Friday evening he just never came home. After she was abandoned, she could not support the children. As a result, she left the children with her mother and went to work on a farm. Now it came to pass that the milkman seeing 4 days milk on the doorstep called the police who broke in and found the 3 children in a bad way. Violet was sentenced to jail for 3 months for neglect. An order was granted for the custody of the 3 children at the Public Assistance Institution until such time as the N.S.P.C.C. will apply for permission before a Juvenile Court to provide them with proper care and attention. An investigation ensued and it was found that the children had been left alone and in filthy conditions often. Violet claimed that after her husband abandoned her she just lost hope. A warrant was issued for Robert but he was never found.

An order was made that the children be placed in Dr. Barnardo's Homes until their 18th birthday. John, at the time was 4 years old, and soon lost contact with his brother and sister after that. He was put into foster homes, and was frequently beaten in some of them.

One account as recalled by John: My foster mother was very religious and belted my bum daily. Maybe she thought that was where the brains are kept. The only good thing that came out of it was my bum could have won a prize for being so well developed and firm. For special, she made you take a hot bath for 15 minutes, then made you stand up to have your bum changed from a smooth surface to a red hot mass of blisters until there was no more room for another blister. His childhood was not pleasant one.

John had a series of dreams that started when he was 4 ½ years old and ended when he was 10 years old. Something happened to opened his mind to the inspirational thinking that has followed him throughout his life. Perhaps it had something to do with his head injury as an infant. There have been cases recorded where an average person suddenly became a genius after sustaining a blow to the head. This may have caused the person to use more of the previously unused portion of his brain. Or the information could have been given to John from an unknown source. Or perhaps John is just an independent free thinker who does not accept things at their face value. John has stated that the technology that he has developed goes way beyond his knowledge and learning and that he has been inspired by some force to accomplish his task. He has used the dreams that were given to him to guide his way. When he comes to a point he cannot figure out he just goes to sleep at night and by morning he has the answer.

Everything in his life has directed him closer to his goal of saving mankind through the use of his marvelous technology. Things never seemed to come easy though. John knew that his dreams had some special meaning. The dreams started at age four and a half, but he didn't start to interpret these until he was 14. He had two dreams twice a year for six years. His description follows:

Dream 1: The mathematical aspect.

"I am playing a game of hop scotch...which of course is a set of eight squares...I find myself on square two, my pebble is on square three and I am in the act of going to hop over three into four, but I am instantly frozen with my right leg up in the air, and my left leg still firmly on the ground, via the foot of course.

KEY FACTS:

1....2 types of dreams, which are related.
2....There are always 8 squares.
3....I am always standing in square 2 and my feet are always in the same position.
4....My pebble is always on square 3.
5....There are 4 dreams a year.
6....There are 6 years of dreams.

In the first dream it is clear that I shall have something to do with very high energy levels of a solid structure, whose action is created by rotation. Because it is a solid structure it belongs to the third state of nature.

Nature operates here on earth in three prime states, which are:

1....GASES

2....LIQUIDS

3....SOLIDS

There is a 4th state in nature, but it is not available here on earth.

4....PLASMA

Thus in the dream its a pebble, a solid object, and being in square 3, which declares it as being an object of the third state of nature. Let's look at fact 1 and fact 3. There are 2 types of dreams, and I am always standing on square 2. Let us look again at my feet. The right is high to the left...translation...The right hand side is high in respect to the left hand side. It could mean that the right side can be classed as 1 while the left side can be classed a 0. Therefore, nature can only operate in two states, it can only be high or low. In plain talk, nature is binary in function, because I am about, or at least trying to hop over square 3, which is a function.   Why can I not cross over square 3? It is clear that the game has been operating quite normal, until this point is reached. To understand this point better, I will now fill in a bit more detail about this dream. Up to this point, all the children who go to school with me are present and have been playing this game with me. But at this point they all instantly vanish from my sight. Now, at the same instant an object appears at the top end of the game, which should not be there, as it has no relationship to the game. The object took the form of the village steam roller...that being, a large roller being driven by a steam engine. Only in this case this object was many times larger than normal and is racing towards me. Therefore, I have only got a short time to save myself from being crushed to death.

So, we can state the reason why I cannot cross three is the fact that it is making an absolute statement as follows:

STOP,   THINK,   ACT

You may think that it is myself which is going to be crushed to death...in this case, you are wrong...re-cap again...at the instant in which I am frozen, all the children that I know have vanished...I am all alone. This means...that my generation will not produce any more generations of children to replace them...you automatically say that they have produced them...I agree with you, but they will never draw their old age pension, or their children. In other words my generation is the end of the road unless we STOP, THINK, AND ACT.

In this troubled period I am all alone. Again in dream two I am all alone...WHY? Does this mean that I shall be the only person to be given the knowledge on what must be done to save all life? Does this mean that life as a whole has little chance to survive unless we prepare for the coming onslaught? Does history hold any past facts of such events...the answer is a positive, YES! Well developed groups have appeared on earth and vanished without a trace as to where they went. All we can conclude is that they were wiped out completely by a natural event. What dream one seems to state, is that the human race will be wiped out by a pressure force many times greater than normal, crushing everything in its path, unless you act now to prevent it."

There is much more explanation given in Prof. Searl's books "THE LAW OF THE SQUARES". There are presently 5 in the series.

These dreams came to a four and a half year old boy. I am amazed that they could be remembered and interpreted in the way that Prof. Searl has done. I can't remember dreams clearly from the night before many times, although I have had dreams that I can remember. Prof. Searl's dreams must have been vivid and clear. They appear to have been prophetic and made a lasting impression on his mind. The message of the dreams has unfolded throughout Searl's life. Each experience he has had opens new doors through the better understanding of the message of the dreams. John has told me that everything that has happened in his life has seemed to have a reason and everything seems to be guiding him towards his goal. His knowledge of THE LAW OF THE SQUARES has given him an understanding of the workings of nature and science. Not the accepted science of the universities, although he has educated himself in many of them, but the science that is in harmony with nature. John works with nature instead of against it. John refused to accept things just because he was told that they were true. He had to see for himself. For this reason he has been at odds with "respectable" accepted beliefs taught by the establishment. Science has not always been correct in its assumptions or "Laws" but the scientists of the day always believed that their way was the only way to think. At one time scholars and scientists believed that the world was flat, then, that the earth was the center of the solar system, then, that there were only certain ways to generate power, accepted ways, etc.. For this reason he was labeled a trouble maker in his youth and was labeled a "quack" by the scientific community when he tried to bring his technology to the world. He has been fighting the insecurity and irate self-righteousness of the scientific and engineering community because he doesn't have the diplomas and structured training and education that they have. He is not a member of their "club".

John's education as described by him...

"My education is not good, agreed. I started at an infant school at Thorndon, where I learned absolutely nothing. Well that may be a little bit of a lie...I did learn what it was like to get your bum spanked by the teacher, which was much better than when my foster mother did it. Then I moved along to the secondary school at Eye. Here I again learned nothing, well except what the cane felt like in an effort to teach me not to take bombs apart and make fireworks out of them. I actually learned more from what they were trying to tell me not to do then what they were trying to tell me to do. Then I continued my education at Russell-Cotes Nautical school where I learned that all the things I had been taught were actually opposite and that the bum could be used for other things besides spanking. I received top marks for seamanship.

From there I covered a range of work training from rewiring of electric motors to dispensing doctors prescriptions, to medical training and nursing, including the caring for the elderly. Then onto electrical and electronic wiring and repairs, to the prototype wiring work for the atomic works and wiring of the VICTOR BOMBERS MK.11 and V.C.10's as a private contractor. To the wiring of the first fully transistorized computer for the four large naval guns of NATO in Norway. I also covered the way to cut keys, fix locks, the building of T.V. and radio sets, and repair of them. I also covered everything about mechanical engineering from producing the machines from prints, to setup, to operating machines, to inspection of the finished product. This work also covered plating and treatment of various materials. Within this 40 years of practical experience, I undertook home courses on electronics 1,2,3 and 4 with B.I.E.E. plus 2 years on site training in radio communications at Reading University and 2 crash courses at the Open University, one of ROBOTICS FOR INDUSTRY and the other DIGITAL COMPUTERS FOR INDUSTRY. I have undertaken a flying training course to a higher standard than is normally required for private flying. I have experimented across a range of structures which the scientific man rejects as not possible, and proved them wrong. Those structures came from the LAW OF THE SQUARES. So to date, the best that I could achieve was a mere honorary degree of PROFESSOR of MATHEMATICAL STRUCTURES OF CREATION AND ENERGY. It's nothing much and not important...but at least it acknowledges my life's time work in the study of life and energy to research and development...making me the creator of a new TECHNOLOGY. The very first in this field of science. So I am sorry that I fail to meet your high standards of knowledge, but from my point of view, my knowledge serves all of my requirements to the fullest. I am pleased to state that I am learning something new every hour of my life.

Agreed, that my knowledge has not arrived from theory taught in schools. But it has been achieved by hard work in the practical field. At least I do have a very high practical experience which is worth it's weight in gold. Something that one needs to support ones theory. This puts me in a far better position to present my thesis upon a natural prime mover. You people of theory have not been able to put forward any real theory for such a prime mover. Your own statements upon this matter are a disgrace to your education. You may be good at spelling, grammar and english, but you are no bloody good at witnessing demonstrations of something which fails to conform to your knowledge.

I may not belong to your world of force to obtain results, and pollution, created through greed and destruction and hate. I belong to another world, which knows no hate, is not greedy, where all things in nature are appreciated and not destroyed. In your world you are causing nature to deteriorate and your square frame is now well and truly over loaded, and will soon collapse. For nature cannot forever continue to support your frame at the expense of other frames. Everything in nature has its' rights, and man is taking away the rights of other frames. Man's superior knowledge over all other creatures tends to make him greedy, with no care for other frames upon this earth, as long as he can make a quick buck, he doesn't care. There is nothing wrong in superior knowledge, if applied sincerely and honestly to better all mankind, including all creatures and plant life upon this planet. But alas, this is not the case. Far too often man's knowledge destroyed vast numbers of frames of other life forms, purely for gain or a kick. It appears to me, that education creates the very opposite of its objectives. Instead of producing products which can appreciate all of nature, it produces products for the destruction of nature. The one thing that man forgot is what I have been telling him since 1946; man will destroy himself, through his own greed. So man will for certain reap the rewards he certainly deserves."

John has said that he belongs to a world that knows no hate. He has observed organized religions and saw hypocrites. People going to church every Sunday, and forgetting everything that there religion teaches as soon as they go out the front door of the church. John recalls a poem that he heard once as a very young child at the infants school...

This poem represents his attitude toward life...

Abou Ben Adhem (may his tribe increase)
Awoke one night from a deep dream of peace,
And saw, within the moonlight in his room,
Making it rich, and like a lily in bloom,
An angel writing in a book of gold:
Exceeding peace had made Ben Adhem bold,
And to the presence in the room he said,
"What writest thou?" - The vision raised it's head,
And with a look made of all sweet accord,
Answered, "The names of those who love the Lord."
"And is mine one?" said Abou. "Nay, not so."
Replied the angel. Abou spoke more low,
But cheerily still; and said, "I pray thee, then,
Write me as one that loves his fellow men."
The angel wrote, and vanished. The next night
It came again with a great wakening light,
And showed the names whom love of God had blest,
And lo! Ben Adhem's name led all the rest.

It is John's belief that he may very well be the only man in the world able to save all mankind, but that will be explained later in this book.

CHAPTER 2

This chapter will deal with Prof. John R. R. Searl's LAW OF THE SQUARES. This is the basis for all the technology that has been developed by Prof. Searl. This has come to him through his dreams and his study to interpret them through the years. John has said in his lecture of 1986 in Munich, Germany that the law of the squares is really a very old technology. He states that when the Bible was edited by the church, that many books were not included. One man had written 144 books of which only a few survived and those were omitted also because they were not understood or accepted by the church of the time. These books contained information based on The Law of the Squares.

The squares are a numerical representation of matter and energy. There are three groups of squares and three only. They are:

GROUP 1 - ROTATE - All odd numbers belong to this group. That means half of all numbers are a group one class.

GROUP 2 - OSCILLATE - All even numbers that divide exactly by 4. That means half of all even numbers belong to this group.

GROUP 3 - OSCILLATE EXCEPT FOR THE CENTER CROSS WHICH ROTATES - Half of all even numbers belong to this group. All even numbers that do not divide exactly by 4.

There are numbers which nature does not use in its building blocks. These have been listed in "THE LAW OF THE SQUARES- BOOK 1"

The simplest GROUP 1 square that can be shown is a square 3. This consists of a block of three by three numbered squares. It is level 1 and includes 0 as its first number. The squares are shown in their original uniform layout and are numbered from top left down in columns from left to right (See Fig.1). If you add across any line of numbers you will get a random sum or output.

This block of numbered squares can be arranged so that all the rows of numbers, vertical, horizontal, and diagonal will add up to the same number. This square is called a RANDOM square because the position of the numbers appear random but the output is uniform, where in the original UNIFORM square the position of the numbers are uniform but the output appears random. In a random square 3, level 1, the sum of any row is 12. 12 is the smallest number for a smooth operation of an electric current. This is shown in the linear motor which uses 12 phases for its drive unit. Since we never use 0 in our work we shall start this square and all subsequent squares with Level 2, which starts with the lowest number of 1. All GROUP 1 squares have a single central square and they are made up of an odd number of squares. Thus they would be 3,5,7,9,11 etc.. If you take many of the same RANDOM squares and place them side by side you will see a pattern that continuously repeats itself throughout the matrix. GROUP 1's rotate.

GROUP 1 SQUARE LEVEL 1:

0	3	6
1	4	7
2	5	8

UNIFORM

7	0	5
2	4	6
3	8	1

RANDOM

GROUP 1 SQUARES LEVEL 2:

1	4	7
2	5	8
3	6	9

UNIFORM

8	1	6
3	5	7
4	9	2

RANDOM

Fig.1

1. The line value can be predetermined by adding the numbers of the square up on the diagonal from the top left to the bottom right.

2. The center number of a GROUP 1 is equal to the line value divided by the square size. Therefore, the center number of a square 3 level 2 would be, 15 divided by 3 or 5.

3. Square 3 consists of 2 squares. The center single number being the first square and the next square out or 2nd square consisting of the 8 numbers that surround the center square. The total of the 2nd square can be obtained by multiplying the center square by 8, which is the number of numbers that surrounds the center square. Thus, the total value of the 2nd square out is 40.

4. There are 8 different ways you can add different lines to get the line value. They are 3 vertical, 3 horizontal and 2 diagonal. These are called options. Thus, square 3 has 8 options.

5. The total of all the squares in a square is equal to the line value times the square number. Therefore square 3, level 2 total would be 15 times 3 or 45.

6. The four corner total is equal to the center square times 4. As the squares get larger there are additional rules involved but there are always numerical links between the parts of the square. With a little practice you can learn the pattern of numbers and then do all group 1 squares by yourself. Prof. Searl has shown up to square 25 in book 2 of THE LAW OF THE SQUARES. He has figured the squares to over square 100.

GROUP 2 SQUARES:

1	5	9	13
2	6	10	14
3	7	11	15
4	8	12	16

UNIFORM

1	12	8	13
15	6	10	3
14	7	11	2
4	9	5	16

RANDOM

Fig. 2

---

1. Group 2 squares are always even numbered squares, but not all even numbered squares are Group 2. Some are Group 3 squares.

2. Group 2 squares oscillate instead of rotating.

3. If you look at a Group 2 square in the Random state you will see that the numbers switch positions throughout the square. This switching shows the oscillation of the energy patterns within the square or between atoms. The square is a numerical representation of the interaction between different atoms within a structured mass.

4. There is a center block of 4 separate squares. This is called the kernel square. Notice that all Group 2 and Group 3 squares have a kernel square. John Searl's dream 1 states that when you are looking at a square, you are looking at 2 frames no matter what square you are looking at. (That squares are made from squares.) But the dream states more than that - it states that these 2 frames are at right angles to each other and held apart by 2 cross beams. So there are 2 prime states and a secondary state. So 3 conditions are present in a square.

The three frames of all kernels are:

1....SPACE FRAME

2....TIME FRAME

3....ENERGY FRAME

Let's look at the kernel square of a uniform square 4:

6	10
7	11

Now we examine the properties of this square:

1...VERTICAL- left 6+7=13 and right 10+11=21. Then subtract 13 from 21 to get a directional force of 8 to the left.

2...HORIZONTAL- top 6+10=16 and bottom 7+11=18. Then subtract 16 from 18 to get a directional force of 2 upwards.

3...DIAGONAL- top left to bottom right 6+11=17 and top right to bottom left 10+7=17. Then subtract 17 from 17 and get 0 showing that the square's energy is conserved.

There is no gain or loss thus this kernel is in harmony. From dream 1 Searl states: "We will have a lifting force of a value of 2 and a pushing or pulling force equal to the last value of the second column of the uniform square. We see that this holds true. We also see that the right hand vertical is more positive than the left hand vertical and the horizontal lower is more positive than their upper horizontal."

In Prof. Searl's book 1A he explains this in detail and also shows further switching of numbers to increase the thrust and lift of the square without changing the basic properties that keep the square in tune with nature. In John's words, "If a building block conforms to a mathematical kernel and its energy frame is conserved, and that kernel contains 4 different forces conforming to the requirements above, then if a similar piece of material is placed upon that material, it will experience a lifting force and a pushing/pulling force... For that is the LAW OF THE SQUARES.

GROUP 3 SQUARES:

This square has the properties of both the Group 1 and Group 2 squares as it both oscillates and rotates. There is a central cross which rotates in the Group 3 squares. The remaining squares oscillate. Group 3 squares are used to make flying machines as they put out a great amount of power.

The central cross is made up of the 2 vertical center rows and the 2 horizontal center rows of the square. The first Group 3 square is a square 6.

SQUARE 6 LEVEL 2:

UNIFORM

1	7	13	19	25	31	=	**96**
2	8	14	20	26	32	=	**102**
3	9	15	21	27	33	=	**108**
4	10	16	22	28	34	=	**114**
5	11	17	23	29	35	=	**120**
6	12	18	24	30	36	=	**126**

21   57   93   129 165 201 111

RANDOM

8	30	34	3	5	31	=	**111**
35	1	28	9	26	12	=	**111**
18	17	15	21	27	13	=	**111**
19	20	16	22	10	24	=	**111**
25	11	14	23	36	2	=	**111**
6	32	4	33	7	29	=	**111**

111   111   111 111 111 111 111

Fig. 3

Group 3 squares are the most complicated squares to do and explain. As you study the square you will see that there is a rotating action of the center cross and the same oscillating action as a Group 2 in the remaining 4 corners. You will have to do a little work to see it, but be persistent, you can do it.

The Random squares shown here are not the only answers to correcting a square to the Random state. Here are a few squares for you to compare.

SQUARE 4 LEVEL 2:

11	5	14	4	=	34
2	16	7	9	=	34
8	10	1	15	=	34
13	3	12	6	=	34

34   34   34   34   34

13	3	12	6	=	34
10	8	15	1	=	34
7	9	2	16	=	34
4	14	5	11	=	34

34   34   34   34   34

Fig. 4

The squares can be solved in many ways but only one way works the best in the construction of an energy producing device. John Searl developed his first SEARL EFFECT GENERATOR (SEG) back in 1946 at the age of 15.

The law of nature states that no TWO BODIES or PARTICLES can share the same SPACE FRAME within the same TIME FRAME. But the law of nature does state that TWO BODIES or PARTICLES CAN SHARE THE SAME SPACE FRAME at different TIME FRAMES. However, TWO OBJECTS cannot share the same TIME FRAME within the same SPACE FRAME. Thus, TWO OBJECTS can share the same TIME FRAME provided they occupy different SPACE FRAMES. These statements can be seen while studying the Law of the Squares.

Some other interesting facts:

There are TWO PRIME STATES within nature: **ENERGY AND MATTER**

Energy and matter are reversible. Energy can switch to matter and matter can switch to energy.

Nature operates upon TWO PRIME STATES: LOW .... 0 .... NO ...... RED
HIGH ..... 1 .... YES ..... GREEN

This simple rule of Nature is used by us in many ways, but within Nature it's used all the time. Therefore, Nature tends to be BINARY within its actions.

Nature sometimes makes a triangle agreement with its actions of functions: one input and two outputs or two inputs and one output. In the first case it's an inverted Y, it is not a mirror image. In the second case it is the original Y. We can see that Nature builds blocks which can be used either original, mirror or inverted.

In matter there are THREE PRIME STATES, which are: GAS, LIQUID AND SOLID. Within solids we have three states which are Conductors, Semiconductors and Nonconductors. The elements are the building blocks of Nature. Here again we can break them down to Nonmetals, Light Metals and Heavy Metals. In designing, many points have to be accounted for. That applies to Searl as well, as he wants to work with Nature and not against Nature.

All matter and all life conforms to THE LAW OF THE SQUARES. These are natures building blocks from the smallest particle to the largest universe. All energy exchange can be explained using this law. From chemical bonding to the production of natural energy.

"Modern man" has perverted the laws of nature and has only limited knowledge of how nature works and how man can work with nature, rather than destroy its beauty and balance.

Searl's Law of the Squares is the basis for an energy producing generator that works with nature and will not consume or harm any part of nature. Indeed it will help nature heal the earth from the damage that mankind has caused.

The Law of the Squares is explained in detail in a series of books written by Prof. John R. R. Searl. They are titled:

"THE LAW OF THE SQUARES"
(Book 1, 1A, 1B, 2, 3, 4, 5, 6, 7, 7A...)

These books have been written from 1990 to 1994 and are available through:

John A. Thomas, Jr.
373 Rock Beach Road
Rochester, New York
14617-1316
Phone: 716-467-2694
Fax: 716-338-2663

In these books is the key to a new technology and how to put it to use. This information has never been allowed out to the public in the past. Everything in the books is the TRUTH and there is no misinformation in them. They are copies of original manuscripts made by Prof. Searl and have not been changed or edited in any way. Through these books you will get to know the inventor as well as his technology. In Searl's words "You have to know the inventor in order to understand the invention." This book could be termed as a primer to Searl's books on the Law of the Squares as much of it has been taken from the original books.

In his book 2 he has shown up to square 25 and given the Go - No Go tables up to 8774. These tables and squares can be found nowhere else. Many properties and symmetries are given throughout the books. When you see and understand these you will be able to work out the squares for yourself without having to look at the books. The squares are the key to the SEG (Searl Effect Generator).

All the information needed can be taken from the square used for the work. This includes all sizes and dimensions as well as amounts of different elements used. The SEG is in perfect harmony with the squares and nature. It must be made correctly and it will only operate as a completed unit. Someone once broke one of the magnetic rollers to see what it was made of. In doing so he ruined it and the operation of the Searl Effect. The SEG works because of the exactness of ALL its components, in proportional content and dimensional size and exact frequencies used. These are all taken from the squares. Once completed, the SEG operates like a huge laser diode, a solid state device which starts at the atomic valance level and ends with an output of energy, both electric and magnetic, and in the flying craft it is also gravitational energy.

CHAPTER 3

This chapter will deal with Prof. Searl's early days and his first experiments with his SEG (Searl Effect Generator).

John was placed in a foster home when he was still very young. He was a very curious boy and wanted to know how everything that he saw worked and was eager to learn and understand everything he could. I asked John to describe his young days of work starting at age 14. Here is his telling of his early years.

John Searl (J.S.) - I started in electrical rewinding of motors. Stripping motors and rewiring them. Winding coils. I was actually starting a five year apprenticeship. But weeks later I left that and went into pharmacy. Learning to dispense doctor's prescriptions. And that of course REALLY was a key. Because in the time I was in the electrical trade I found out how electrical motors worked. What caused them to work, how they were wired, how to wind the coils, how to insulate them and so on. So I picked up very quick a key thing but you see I couldn't stay there. Because if I stayed there I'd be locked onto one narrow band. I had to go on to the medicine field to learn how chemicals are mixed together to produce certain results. And then from there I went on to medical training. All these changes occurred within a short time frame.

I was told by my boss at the chemist's shop that I was certainly qualified for something far better, having far more skills than what was required of me. He said he was holding me back. So he wrote a doctor to get me to see him, and he did. And he said, "Yes, I'll put you on the ward for a months trial," to see how I'd get on. So I went on the ward for a month and did so well that he put me in the lab for a month to see how I got along there. I did so well there that they wanted to pay for six years training at Oxford University. And when I left there I would be a brain surgeon. But my guardian stepped in and stopped my training. They put me down to an old people's rest home. There was about 45 old age women, bedridden. And the job was to help the night nurse on nights. Of course I learned a lot. I learned about old age and what problems came along and started questioning these problems. Now while at the hospital training, I learned a lot because I came in contact with the brain, kidneys, liver, heart, unborn babies and more. So I questioned my instructors very strongly about things. In fact I wrote an essay and they downed it. And it turned out a few years ago that I was right! They were wrong.

John Thomas (J.T.) - That was at the old age home?

J.S.- Yes. Now I doctored myself. I went down with the flu, a bronchitis flu, and I went and wrote a prescription and got the medicine and got back. And one day the matron went into my room to see if I was keeping it clean and tidy and saw this bottle of medicine and saw what it was. She came to me and asked how did I get it. I said, "I got it." She said, "You have no right to any medicine unless my doctor here says you can have it. This is poison and you shouldn't have it." So they called up the Homes, which were my guardians. They came running down and took me to the chemist's shop. The chemist got the prescription out. He said, "The prescription is right. Absolutely correct. I dished it out as stated and there was nothing wrong with the prescription and therefore as far as I'm concerned he was the authorized person to pick it up and I gave it to him. So I have not committed any crime."

So they whipped me off to London. I got fed up with sitting about so I went to the cinema to see a film. I was so impressed with it because I had just seen a film for the first time. I wanted to know how motion was done on film. So I went to the manager and asked him how do you do this? So he said, "Would you like to see how it's done?" So he took me up to the projection room and got the chief projectionist to show me about. And when he opened the arc lamp door he said, "You see the thin rod, carbon rod, and the thick one. The thick one is positive and the thin one is negative. And you see that the positive one has got a hole, a crater and the negative has got a point." He said, "The power comes from the positive and goes to the negative." And I said, "You're wrong. It goes from negative to positive." He said, "No, I've been in the theater a long time. It goes from positive to negative." So I said, "If it goes from positive to negative as you've said and not from negative to positive, how do you explain the crater in the positive? You've got a crater there because something is hitting it hard. It is knocking the stuff out. And it has a point on the other end because stuff is leaving it from the outside to the inside and it splits away." So when the boss saw how I was tearing his top man to pieces, and I'm only a kid, he asked me if I wanted a job! So I was given a job right away.

But within a couple of months a new law came out that people under 16 couldn't be in a cinema where X films are being shown. So that meant that he couldn't employ me on those weeks when they were shown. So he said to me that there was a cinema at Illford which was S class. They have two floor levels operating and they only show an X film on one floor. So when they show an X film they can always send you up to the next floor. It's got the latest equipment and that should really fascinate you.

Of course when I got there, the chap in charge, the chief projectionist, was also a ham operator! He felt sad for me because I was just an orphan. So he took me home and introduced me to his family and showed me all his ham equipment and told me about the things you have to do to become a ham operator, and he started teaching me. We got on very well and things started changing. They had a party at the cinema and wanted me to join them after the show to celebrate. And so I asked the Homes permission to stay late. They said, "You have to be back by 11." and well, we had hardly started the party after the show. So what happened was I stayed overnight. I went to sleep on one of the big couches in the lounge. And some of the usherettes slept on the couch as well. The couches were massive. You could get 4 or 5 of us on one of them. And they just threw curtains over us to keep us warm. And of course when I got back the next day they went mad, The Homes did. Stopped me from working there and things started going all wrong.

But as I look back on it today, I can see the picture now, when I look back. I was getting into a permanent fix and I musn't. I need a lot of experience across a wide field to do what I've got to do. I not only had to know what happened to people, I want to understand how they work, how they function, why this, why that. About materials, how you can do, what you can do, what part of materials will do this and how it functions.

So by the time I was about 30 I really knew everything about the atom. What you could do with it and what you can't do with it. I began to realize that a certain law applied. And that law was the SQUARES. These squares define everything. What you can and cannot do in nature.

J.T.- It sounds like you've had quite an experience John.

J.S.- Oh I had to go through a lot. I even had to take up flying. I hit a problem there when we were getting going. Every pilot that came to answer my advertisement (to test fly the Levity Disc), when they came to see the model tested, they said, "Oh, I wouldn't take that up! It turns too fast. Too sharp! You'll get killed!" So the question was no financier would back a project which wouldn't get off the ground. So I had to do something about it. I had to licence myself for flying. So that I could fly it. The trouble was it had to be more than just a private licence. So I had to buckle down and really get up to a commercial standard so that I'd be able to test fly it myself. And that's what I did. I hammered it, and hammered it and got the standard required.

J.T.- You never did get to test fly it though did you?

J.S.- No, We got the land ready to build a three seater and then the check promised was stopped by the Prime Minister of New Zealand. It was in the paper. We have the paper cutting. "John will have to find his money elsewhere. The prime minister has stopped the check and told the people to invest the money in marsh gas."

J.T.- Oh well.

J.S.- So the check didn't come. So we had to forget it. We did work hard. We got everything ready to go ahead. We had to move trees. We had to move debris. We had to level the ground off for the building of this three manned craft. As far as I was concerned, we brought in heavy tackle equipment from miles away and it cost quite a packet to get it in and do the job and get it back again. But we couldn't build it. That was the trouble. It was a sad thing. But of course I always get kicked in the pants about it. Everybody said, "You said you were going to build this three manned craft and you didn't!"

J.T.- Well what are you going to do without money?

J.S.- The point is that they don't look at it in the proper light. They said, "You said you were going to do this." I said that I'd do it if we had the money. If I'd had the money, I wouldn't have been asking for the money. But the thing is, today, things are moving slow. But I find that if I try to push people, I lose everything. They stop because they can't keep up with the pace. And I sit back here fiddling with my fingers, but annoyed about it myself. I'm annoyed that I'm not racing as I was years back. And time's running out.

John had many jobs and experiences as you can see, and what does he mean by "Time's running out"? This will be explained later in the book. I was curious as to when he first started building his first SEARL EFFECT GENERATOR. In his books he had this technology since 1946. So I asked him to tell about his first units. This is his reply.

J.T.- You said that you were just 15 years old when you made your first SEG?

J.S.- Yes, well when we say the first one, it's an object which shot off the table when we started it up. It bashed up against the wall. The sparks flew everywhere, but that was the beginning. I destroyed the house with it eventually. When we tried to make them a little bit bigger, it just shot through the ceiling! The ceiling came all down and it tore through the roof which fell in. We had to move because there was so much damage that the house was unfit to live in!

J.T.- That must have made a big hit with everybody!

J.S.- Yes! It did! Well there were a little later ones, much bigger, we put up and they got shot at by an RAF (Royal Air Force) chap that said I was frightening his pigeons.

J.T.- Oh, really! He shot at it?

J.S.- Yes! He shot at ME!!

J.T.- Oh no.

J.S.- Yeah, there were bullet holes in the building. A bullet shot past me.

J.T.- That was kinda scary!

J.S.- Yes. Oh, we had plenty of fun. I should write everything down that happened. It's shocking that I'm still alive today.

J.T.- What building were you living in then?

J.S.- We had a shed. The old man who took me in was dying of cancer. The hospital gave him about 6 to 8 weeks to live, so he begged to go home. So they brought him home and his wife thought it would be nice to have a lodger to help out. And back then I was lucky enough to want an accommodation.

I arrived in the area so they took me in. And when I told him about the things I had in my mind, he said "John if you can make people look up in the sky, that would be a great achievement because everyone who walks around here, walks with their head down, looking at the ground," Well I said, " That should be no problem." But I said that I would need a shed and materials. He called his son up and said, "George, take John down to the market and get everything he wants." And things really got going and we started building 6 footers and 8 footers and 12 footers. But then we really got down to the job of discovering that there was no way of stopping these things from going up! Of course we eventually did learn, but my word, it took some effort!

J.T.- So you went down to buy all this stuff. You bought all the chemicals?

J.S.- Yes, he paid for everything.

J.T.- So the first one that actually took off, that actually left the ground, was a magnetic motor.

J.S.- Yes. They were all magnetic motors. The trouble was, they weren't intended to fly! That was the bug!

J.T.- Yes, I imagine that was quite a surprise!!

J.S.- Yes that was a surprise package. There were good people who were so excited by it, they paid for more to be done. And slowly we broke out the problems step by step. If it hadn't been for those good people, well I would have had to give up then because I couldn't afford to carry on - throwing money up in the sky and losing it.

I asked John to describe what happened when the first units went airborne.

FIRST UNITS THAT WENT AIRBORNE

J.S.- Well you can't control the little things at all. All that happens is that once they get the speed up to get to the superconductor stage, it lifts. And it lifts to a given height. It's hard to determine just how high that is. It's higher than the buildings around and higher than the trees that were around there. And then there's what we call a "rest section", where they seem to rest. And then suddenly they get very bright. The glow gets brighter and brighter and brighter. It's obviously getting very superconductive. There is an immense plasma building up all around it. Then electrical appliances switch on. Televisions and radios turn on by themselves. This happens all around as the power leaks down cables and aerials and things like that. And suddenly it shoots off. It just goes off, up and up and up, until it's lost. You can't see the light glow or anything anymore. So we have to assume that they have gone right out into space.

J.T.- And that will go automatically with no load coils or anything.

J.S.- Yes, it will just go on and on until it balances out with the forces of the planet. And then it will orbit. So we don't know where the bits have gone to. Someday, who knows, somebody may find them!

J.T.- That would be quite a find!

J.S.- Yes, Well of course after we'd done six of them, the old boy who paid the bills died. So work literally stopped for awhile. So then I formed a party of old retired people who had money, and we started looking at the problem of building the body. Working on the body shape, trying to work out ideas on how we could control this. And then we did. We were successful in the end, because a lot of things happened while I was experimenting. I found out how it cools an iron down which was red hot, and it would turn icy cold. So we learned bit by bit, by shear experimentation, chance you could say. Then again most of the big experiments were just chances that the inventor hit upon. They were probably looking for something different! And then hit on this and said, "Oh, that's interesting!" And then developed it. And that is really what sort of happened in my case. It was just shear luck that while you were trying something, something else happened. And that gradually let you build up the picture of what was going on!

Once we understood what was going on, then it was easier to try to put together a structure that would allow you to make use of it. I agree, at the time, we could not see how to use it as a domestic power plant. We could see it as a flying machine. And that is what we worked on. But once we mastered the holding of it and we could hold it at low heights and keep it there stationary against all winds. Then you see I was winning! But the thing was, we couldn't stop the motor!

We were never able to stop that until I was lecturing in Canada. And it was on the TV program that I was doing, that the camera came forward, and for the first time ever, the rollers stopped. And I was quite embarrassed. And yet it was the greatest miracle of the lot. Because when they pulled back to show my face, the thing started off again. And then I knew instantly what I had to do. The frequency of the camera was the key to stopping it.

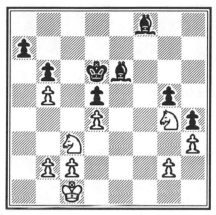

54.b3?!

Better is 54.Kd2 Bg7 55.Ne2 Bd7 with an equal position.

54...Bg7 55.Ne2 Bd7 56.c4 Be6 57.Ne3 g4

Opening up the h6-e3 diagonal.

58.hxg4

If 58.Nxg4, then Black is slightly better after 58...dxc4 59.bxc4 Bxc4.

58...Bh6 59.Kd2 dxc4 60.bxc4 Bxc4 61.Kc3!

Not 61.Nc3 Ke6 with a large advantage to Black.

61...Bxe2   62.Nf5 +   Ke6 63.Nxh6 Kf6!

Not 63...Bxb5 64.Nf5 Kf6 65.Nxh4 Kg5 66.Nf3 + Kxg4 67.Ne5 + with an equal position.

64.d5?

Correct is 64.Kb4. The position is equal after 64...Kg5 65.Nf7 + Kxg4 66.d5 or 64...Bf1 65.d5 Bxg2 66.d6. After the text Black is winning.

64...Bxb5 65.Nf5 Kg5 66.Nd6 Ba6 67.Kd4 Kxg4 68.Ke5 b5 69.Nf5 b4 70.d6 Bc8 71.Ne7 Bd7 72.Kd4 Kg3 73.Ng6 a5 74.Ne5 Be6 75.Ke3 Bc8 0-1

Dutch

Illustrative Game 26

IM Chris Ramayrat

FM Paul Whitehead

San Francisco 1987

1.d4 f5 2.Nc3 Nf6 3.Bg5 d5 4.Bxf6 exf6 5.e3 c6 6.Bd3 Bd6 7.Qf3 g6 8.h3

The break g2-g4 is in the cards.

8...O-O?!

Castling is premature, as Black's King may be open to attack here. Better is 8...Qe7.

9.O-O-O

9.g4 would be met by 9...fxg4 10.hxg4 f5.

9...a5 10.h4 h5?!

Further weakening the Kingside. Better is 10...Qe7 11.h5 Na6 12.hxg6 hxg6 as 13.Qh3 can be met with 13...Qg7.

11.Nh3 Kg7 12.Nf4 a4 13.Rh3 a3 14.b3 Rh8 15.Nce2 Na6 16.c3 Nc7 17.Rg1

The purpose of this Rook move will be made clear on move 21.

17...Qe7 18.Rg3 Rh6

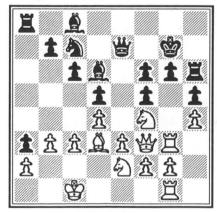

19.Nxg6! Rxg6 20.Rxg6 + Kxg6 21.g4 Kf7

Not 21...hxg4 22.Qxg4 +.

22.gxf5 Ke8 23.Qxh5 + Kd8

24.Qh8+ Ne8 25.h5

Black's King is safe but his pieces are blocked in and he will not be able to stop the h-pawn.

25...b5 26.h6 Ra7 27.Rg8 Bd7 28.h7 Qf7 29.Rg7 Qxg7 30.Qxg7 Nxg7 31.h8=Q+ Ne8 32.f3 b4 33.e4 dxe4 34.fxe4 bxc3 35.e5 Be7 36. Nxc3 c5 37.e6 cxd4

If 37...Bc6, then 38.d5 Ba8 39.Bb5

1-0

Illustrative Game 27

NM Cyrus Lakdawala
FM Tibor Weinberger

Pasadena 1987

1.d4 f5 2.Nc3 d5 3.Bg5 c6 4.e3 Qb6 5.Bd3 e5

Also possible is 5...Qxb2 6.Nge2 with an unclear position. Black first sacrifices a pawn so that his King Bishop can be developed. See his 7th move.

6.dxe5 Qxb2 7.Nge2 Bb4

This would be strong if 8.Kd2 were forced.

8. O-O Bxc3 9.Rb1 Qxa2

If 9...Qa3, then 10.Rb3 regains the piece. Also bad is 9...Qxb1 10.Qxb1 Bxe5 11.Bxf5 Bxf5 12.Qxb7.

10.Nxc3 Qa5 11.Nb5!

This sacrifice is strong because Black is so far behind in development.

11...cxb5 12.Bxb5+ Nc6 13.Qxd5 Qc7 14.Rfd1

White threatens 15.Qc4 followed by 16.Rd8+ as well as 15.Bd8 Qd7 16.Qc5 Qe6 17.Rd6.

14...Nge7 15.Bxe7 Kxe7 16.Qc5+ Kf7 17.Rd6 Be6 18.Bxc6 bxc6 19.Rxc6 Qd8 20.Rb7+ Kg8 21.Rd6 Qf8

No better are 21...Qc8 22.Qxc8+ Bxc8? 23.Rd8# nor 21...Qe8 22.Qc7 Bf7 23.e6.

22.h3 h5 23.Qc6 Rc8 24.Qa6 f4?

Also bad is 24...Bf7? 25.Rxf7 Kxf7 26.Qa2+. However, White's win is not clear after 24...Bc4 25.Rxg7+ Kxg7 26.Rd7+ Bf7 27.Qf6+ (if 27.e6, then 27...Rh6) 27...Kg8 28.e6 Rh7 29.e7 Qe8 30.Rd8.

25.Rxe6 fxe3 26.fxe3 Rxc2 27.Rf6

Stopping Black's counterattack.

27...Qe8 28.Re6 Qc8 29. Rxg7+ Kf8

If 29...Kxg7, then 30.Re7 mates.

30.Qd6+ 1-0

B) 1.d4 e6 2.Nf3 f5 3.g3 Nf6 4.Bg2 d5

The Stonewall variation. If 4...Be7, then after 5.O-O O-O 6.b3 White has a fine position as demonstrated in the following variations:

a) 6...d5 7.Nbd2 c6 8.Ne5 Nbd7 9.Nd3 Qe8 10.e3 b6 11.Bb2 Ba6 12.Nf3 Bd6 13.Rc1 Rc8 14.c4 Bauza–Trompovsky, Montevideo 1954.

b) 6...Ne4 7.Bb2 Bf6 8.Nbd2 c5 9.e3 Nxd2 10.Qxd2 d6 11.c4 Nc6 12.Rfd1 Bauza–Estrada, Montevideo 1954.

c) 6...d6 7.Bb2

c1) 7...Nbd7 8.Qd3 Ne4 9.Nfd2 d5 10.f3 Nxd2 11.Nxd2 Nf6 12.e4 Bd7 13.c4 c6 14.Rae1 Model–Sergejez, USSR 1927.

c2) 7...Qe8 8.Ne1 Nc6 9.Nd3 g5 10.Nd2 Qg6 11.c4 Nd8 12.e3 Bd7 13.Qe2 Ne4 14.f3 Nxd2 15.Qxd2 Nf7 16.Qe2 Bf6 17.Rad1 Barcza–Walther, Zurich 1959.

5.O-O c6 6.c4 Bd6

This is the modern way of playing the Stonewall Dutch. One idea is that if White plays 7.b3 with the idea of 8.Ba3, Black can prevent this with 7...Qe7. On the older 6...Be7, then 7.b3 followed by 8.Ba3 is good.

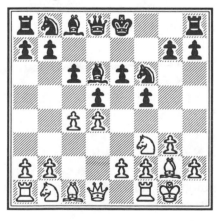

7.Bf4

White wants to exchange off dark-squared Bishops, even at the cost of weakening his Kingside pawn structure.

7...Bxf4

Black should not pass up the opportunity to double White's pawns. Inferior is 7...O-O. See Illustrative Game 28.

8.gxf4

The altered pawn structure limits the options of both sides. Black can no longer break with ...e6-e5. On the other hand, White can no longer play f3 and e4.

8...O-O

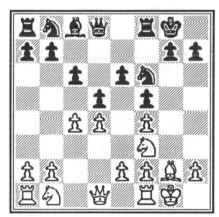

9.e3

White has several other possibilities here as well:

a) For 9.Nbd2, see Illustrative Game 29.

b) For 9.Qb3, see Illustrative Game 30.

c) Georgadse–Kransenkov, Tbilisi 1987 continued 9.Nc3 Ne4 10.e3 Nd7 11.Rc1 Qe7 12.Qe2 Kh8 13.Kh1 Ndf6 14.Ne5 Bd7 15.Nxe4 Nxe4 16.Rg1 Be8 17.Bxe4 fxe4 18.Rg5 Rf5 19.Qg4 with a large advantage to White.

9...Nbd7

Black has also tried:

a) 9...Bd7 10.Ne5 Be8 11.Bf3 h6 12.Kh1 Kh7 13.Rg1 Nbd7 14.cxd5 exd5 15.Nd3 Ne4 16.Nc3 Rg8 17.Rg2 Nf8 18.Bh5 Qh4 19.Bxe8 Rxe8 20.Nxe4 dxe4 21.Ne5 Rd8 22.Qa4 with a big advantage to White, Brenninkmeijer–Winants, Holland 1989.

b) 9...Kh8 10.Qc2 Ne4 11.Ne5 Nd7 12.c5 a5 13.f3 Nef6 14.Nc3 Nh5 15.Rad1 Nxe5 16.fxe5 f4 17.e4 Qg5 18.Kh1 Bd7 19.Bh3 Qh6 20.Qg2 g5?! 21.exd5 cxd5 22.Nxd5 with a large advantage to White, Beliavsky–Karlsson, Novi Sad Olympiad 1990.

10.Ne5

For 10.Qe2, see Illustrative Game 31.

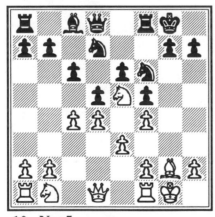

10...Nxe5

Alternatives are:

a) 10...Ne4 11.Nd2 Nxe5 12.dxe5 Bd7 13.Qe2 Nxd2 14.Qxd2 Be8 15.cxd5 cxd5 16.Rfc1 Bc6 17.Rc5 Kh8 18.b4 a6 19.a4 Rg8 20.Kh1 Qh4 with chances for both sides, Mikhalchischin–Dreev, Pavlodar 1987.

b) 10...Qe7 11.Qc2 Nxe5 12.dxe5 Ng4 13.h3 Nh6 14.Nd2 Nf7 15.Nf3 h6 16.Nd4 Nh8 17.Rac1 Ng6

18.Kh2 Nh4 19.Bh1 Bd7 20.Rg1 with better chances for White, Mikhalchischin–Tibensky, Trnava 1988.

11.dxe5

See Illustrative Game 32.

Illustrative Game 28
GM Alexander Beliavsky
IM Evgeny Bareev
USSR Championship 1987

1.d4 f5 2.c4 Nf6 3.g3 e6 4.Bg2 d5 5.Nf3 c6 6.O-O Bd6 7.Bf4 O-O

It is better to ruin White's pawn structure with 7...Bxf4.

8.Bxd6 Qxd6 9.Qc2 b6 10.Na3

White develops his Knight here as at c3 it would block the c-file. Later the Knight may go to b5.

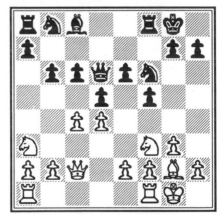

10...Na6 11.Rac1 Bb7 12.cxd5 cxd5

Not 12...exd5 13.Qxf5.

13.Nb5 Qe7

If 13...Qb4, then 14.Qb3 Qxb3 15.axb3 threatening Nd6 and Ng5.

14.Qa4 Ne8 15.Rc3 Nec7 16.Nxc7 Nxc7 17.h3

White feels that the c-file is not enough to have a decisive effect, therefore he switches his attention to the Kingside.

17...Rfc8 18.g4 g6

18...f4 would have allowed White to open the e-file with 19.e3. Perhaps it would have been better to try 18...fxg4 19.hxg4 a6 followed by 20...Nb5.

19.gxf5 gxf5 20.Ne5 Ne8 21.Rg3+ Kh8 22.Kh2 Nf6 23.Rg1 Rc7 24.Bf3 Bc6 25.Qb3

Of course not 25.Nxc6 as 25...Qd7 26.Rc1 Rac8 wins back the piece.

25...Rg8 26.Bh5

Threatening 27.Nf7, winning the Queen.

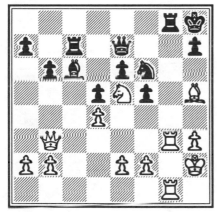

26...Qf8

Of course not 26...Rxg3 27.Qxg3 Nxh5 28.Qg8#. Also bad is 26...Be8 27.Rxg8+ Nxg8 28.Qg3 Nf6 29.Bxe8 Qxe8 30.Ng6+ hxg6 31.Qxc7 winning the Exchange.

27. Rxg8+ Nxg8 28.Qg3

Threatening 29.Ng6+ hxg6 30.Qxc7 gxh5 31.Qxc6.

28...Bb5 29.Qh4 Nf6

If 29...Nh6, then 30.Bf7 Rxf7 (or 30...Nxf7 31.Qf6+) 31.Qxh6 Qxh6 32.Nxf7#. If 29...Qh6, then 30.Nf7+ Rxf7 31.Bxf7 Qxh4 32.Rxg8#. Finally if 29...Be8, then

30.Bxe8 Qxe8 31.Ng6+ Kg7 32.Ne7+ wins.

30. Bf7 1-0

There is no way to stop the threats of 31.Qxf6+ and 31.Ng6+.

Illustrative Game 29

IM Jonathan Levitt
IM Jon Tisdall

London 1990

1.d4 f5 2.Nf3 Nf6 3.g3 e6 4.Bg2 d5 5.O-O Bd6 6.c4 c6 7.Bf4 Bxf4 8.gxf4 O-O 9.Nbd2 Bd7

H.Olafsson–Dolmatov, Soci 1988 ended in a draw after 9...Qe7 10.Rc1 Bd7 11.Ne5 Be8 12.Qb3 Bh5 13.e3 Kh8 14.Rc3 Na6 15.Qa3 Nb4 16.c5.

10.Qb3

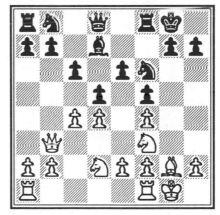

10...b5?!

Better is 10...Qb6 11.e3 Be8 12.Qxb6 axb6 13.Ne5 Bh5 14.Bf3 Bxf3 15.Ndxf3 Na6 16.a3 Nc7 17.Rfd1 Rfd8 18.Rac1 Kf8 19.Kf1 dxc4 20.Rxc4 Ncd5 with a solid position, Nikolik–Salov, Leningrad 1987.

11.c5

Fixing a weakness at c6 and making it difficult for Black to develop his Queen Knight

11...a5 12.Ne5 Be8 13.Kh1

Preparing to utilize the g-file.

13...Ra7?!

13...Bh5 would have limited White's options.

14.Rg1 Bh5 15.Bf3 Bxf3+ 16.Ndxf3 Ne4 17.Rg2 Qc8 18.Rag1 Re7 19.Ng5 Nd7

If 19...Rf6, then 20.Qh3 Rh6 21.Qxh6 gxh6 22.Nxe4+ Kh8 23.Nf6 wins. If 19...Nf6, then 20.Qh3 Nbd7 21.Nxe6 Rxe6 (21...Nxe5 22.Nxf8) 22.Rxg7+ Kh8 23.Qxh7+! Nxh7 24.Rg8+ Rxg8 25.Nf7#. Finally if 19...Nxg5, then 20.Rxg5 Rf6 21.Qg3 Qf8 22.h4 leaves White with a decisive advantage.

20.Nxh7!

Not 20.Nxe6 Nxf2+.

20...Kxh7

If 20...Nxe5, then 21.Nxf8 Ng4 22.Ng6 wins.

21.Ng6 Qd8 22.Qh3+ Kg8 23.Qh8+ Kf7 24.Nxf8 Nxf8 25.Rxg7+ Ke8 26.Qxf8+ 1-0

Illustrative Game 30

GM Mikhail Krasenkov
GM Evgeny Gleizerov

Poland 1993

1.d4 e6 2.c4 f5 3.g3 Nf6 4.Bg2 c6 5.Nf3 d5 6.O-O Bd6 7.Bf4 Bxf4 8.gxf4 O-O 9.Qb3 b6 10.Nc3 Bb7 11.Rac1 Ne4 12.Nxe4?!

Better is 12.Rfd1.

12...fxe4 13.Ng5 Rf6 14.cxd5 cxd5

Not 14...exd5 15.Nxe4.

15.Bh3 Qd7 16.f5 exf5 17.Nxe4 Rh6 18.Ng5 Nc6 19.Qd3 Rf6 20.f4 Re8 21.e3 Qe7 22.Rfe1 h6 23.Nf3 Qe4?

Better is 23...Nb4 24.Qb3 Qe4 25.Qxb4 Qxf3 26.Bg2 Rg6 27.Qd2 with a slight advantage to White.

24.Qxe4 dxe4 25.Ne5 Nxe5 26.dxe5

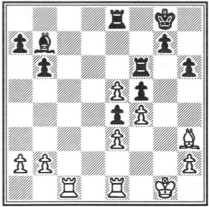

White has a large advantage in the ending because of his active Rooks, passed e-pawn and better Bishop.

26...Rf7 27.Red1 Bc8 28.Bf1 Be6 29.b3 Rfe7 30.Rd6 Kf8 31.Bb5 Rb8 32.h4 Rbb7

32...Ra8 would have held out longer.

33. Rd8+ Kf7 34.Bc6 Rec7

If 34...Rbc7, then 35.Be8+ wins.

35.Rdd1 1-0

If 35...Rb8, then 36.Be8+ wins.

GM Alexander Beliavsky
GM Artur Yusupov

Linares 1989

1.d4 e6 2.c4 f5 3.g3 Nf6 4.Bg2 d5 5.Nf3 c6 6.O-O Bd6 7.Bf4 Bxf4 8.gxf4 O-O 9.e3 Nbd7 10.Qe2 Kh8 11.Nc3 Qe7 12.Kh1

Both sides prepare to move their Rooks to the g-file.

12...Rg8 13.cxd5 exd5 14.Bh3 Ng4 15.Rg1 Ndf6 16.Rg2 Be6 17.Rag1 Raf8

Black is set-up defensively, but he is unable to generate any serious counterplay.

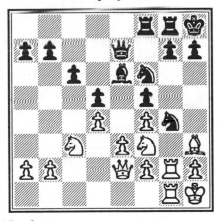

18.a3

White prepares to gain space on the Queenside.

18...Bd7 19.b4 Be8

Black is preparing to bring his bad Bishop outside the pawn structure. White's next move is necessary before Black can play ...Bh5.

20.Bxg4 Nxg4 21.Rg3 Bh5 22.Qb2 Nf6 23.Ne5

Black cannot be allowed to exchange off his bad Bishop.

23...Ng4 24.f3 Nxe5 25.dxe5 h6

26.Ne2 b6 27.Nd4 c5 28.Nb5 Kh7 29.Nd6 g5 30.Qc2 Qe6 31.Rh3 Qg6 32.fxg5 hxg5 33.e6

With the advance of this unescorted pawn, Black's position falls apart.

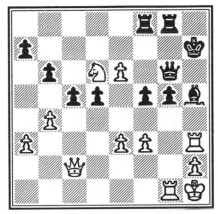

33...Kh6 34.Nf7+ Rxf7 35.exf7 Qxf7 36.bxc5 bxc5 37.Qxc5 Rg6 38.Qd4 Rg8 39.Rc1 Qe6 40.Rg3 g4 41.Qf4+ 1-0

GM Alexander Beliavsky
GM John van der Wiel

Amsterdam 1990

1.d4 e6 2.c4 f5 3.g3 Nf6 4.Bg2 d5 5.Nf3 c6 6.O-O Bd6 7.Bf4 Bxf4 8.gxf4 O-O 9.e3 Nbd7 10.Ne5 Nxe5 11.dxe5

Stronger than 11.fxe5, which Beliavsky played against Salov in 1987. White will put pressure along the c- and d-files and will have a strong outpost for his Knight at d4.

11...Nd7 12.Nd2

The Knight is heading to d4 via b3.

12...Qe7 13.Rc1 Rd8

Black has a lot of problems in this position. His Queenside is undeveloped and he is weak on the dark squares. It is difficult for him to activate his pieces. One point behind the text move is to free the f8-square for the Knight so that it can maneuver to g6 and h4.

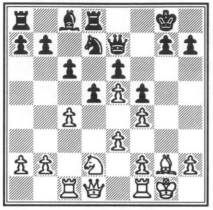

14.Qc2 Nf8 15.Nb3 Ng6 16.cxd5 exd5 17.Nd4 Nh4 18.Bh3 g5 19.Kh1

Not 19.fxg5 f4 or 19.Nxf5 Bxf5 20.Bxf5 gxf4 or 19.Bxf5 gxf4.

19...g4 20.Rg1 h5 21.Bf1 Rf8 22.f3 Rf7 23.Qf2 Ng6

Not 23...c5 24.Rxc5 Qxc5 (if 24...Nxf3, then 25.Rxc8+) 25.Qxh4 with a winning attack.

24.Bd3 Kg7

24...c5 still fails: 25.fxg4 hxg4 26.Nxf5 Bxf5 (if 26...Rxf5, then 27.Rxg4) 27.Bxf5 Rxf5 28.Rxg4 Kh7 29.Rcg1 followed by 30.Qg3 with a mating attack.

25.b4 a5

Not 24...Qxb4 due to 25.e6 winning the f5-pawn.

26.Qc2 Nh4

Black's Kingside falls apart after 26...axb4 27.Bxf5.

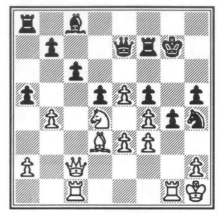

27.b5 cxb5 28.Qf2 Kf8

If 28...b4, then 29.e6 Rf8 30.Rc7 Qxc7 31.Qxh4 is hopeless for Black.

29.Bxb5 Nxf3 30.Nxf3 gxf3 31.Qxf3 Be6 32.Rg6 d4 33.Rcg1 Qc5 34.Rxe6 Qxb5 35.Qg2 1-0

Conclusion: After 1.d4 f5 2.Nc3, Black's most promising variation is 2...d5 3.Bg5 (3.e4 is interesting) 3...c6 4.e3 Qb6. The pawn sacrifice 5.Bd3 is unclear and Black is fine after other moves. 2...Nf6 3.Bg5 d5 4.Bxf6 (4.f3 is interesting) 4...exf6 is also solid. Other variations are bad for Black.

If Black plays a Stonewall, then the position after 1.d4 e6 2.Nf3 f5 3.g3 Nf6 4.Bg2 d5 5.O-O c6 6.c4 Bd6 7.Bf4 is good for White, as Beliavsky has demonstrated in his games.

Chapter 3

Black plays a Pirc/Old-Indian set-up

1.d4 d6 2.e4 Nf6 3.Nc3 g6

For the modern 3...a6, see Illustrative Game 33 or 3...c6, see Illustrative Game 34.

4.Nf3

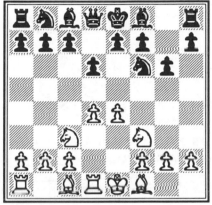

This position could arise after 1.d4 Nf6 2.Nf3 d6 3.Nc3 g6 4.e4.

4...Bg7 5.Be2 O-O 6.O-O Bg4 7.Be3

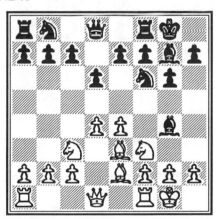

a) For 7...Nbd7, see Illustrative Game 35.

b) For 7...Nc6, see Illustrative Game 36.

Illustrative Game 33

NM Jeremy Silman
GM Duncan Suttles
Lone Pine 1975

1.e4 g6 2.d4 d6 3.Nc3 a6

The idea of this move is to determine whether White will allow Black to expand on the Queenside with ...b5 or stop it with a4. In the latter case Black will try to steer the opening into a position where the weakening of the b4-square is important.

4.a4

4.Nf3 and 4.f4 are worth considering.

4...Bg7 5.Nf3 Bg4 6.Be3

If 6.Bc4, then Black planned to play 6...e6.

6...Nc6 7.Be2 e5 8.d5

If 8.dxe5 then 8...dxe5 9.Nd5 Nf6 10.Bg5 Be6 is good for Black, as ...a6 prevents 11 Bb5. After the text Black will break with ...f7-f5.

8...Nce7 9.Nd2 Bc8 10.O-O f5 11.f4

Opening the center before Black has castled is a good idea.

11...exf4

Better than 11...Nf6 12.fxe5 dxe5 13.Nc4 followed by d6.

12.Bxf4 Nf6 13.Bc4 O-O 14.e5?!

Trying to take advantage of the Black King being placed on the a2-g8 diagonal, but this move fails tactically.

14...Ng4 15.Nf3

15.e6 is met by 15...Bd4+.

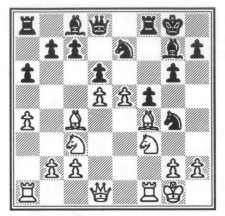

15...dxe5 16.Bg5

If 16.d6+, then after 16...Kh8 17.dxe7 Qxe7 Black regains his piece because of the double threat of ...exf4 and ...Qc5+.

16...Kh8 17.h3 Nf6 18.Nxe5 Qd6 19.Bf4 Qb6+ 20.Kh1 Nh5 21.Bh2

Not 21.d6 because of 21...cxd6 22.Nf7+ Rxf7 23.Bxf7 Nxf4 24.Rxf4 Qxb2 winning.

21...f4 22.d6 cxd6

Also possible is 22...Nf5 although White has some initiative after 23.Qd5 Nf6 24.Qd2 Nxd6 25.Bxf4. Therefore Black decides to sacrifice the Exchange.

23.Nf7+ Rxf7 24.Bxf7 Nf5 25.Re1 Bd7 26.Nd5 Qf2

Not 26...Qxb2 because of 27.Rb1 followed by 28.Nb6.

27.Ra3 Rf8 28.Be6

Better is first 28.Bg1.

28...Bxe6 29.Rxe6 Nhg3+ 30.Bxg3 Nxg3+ 31.Kh2

Or 31.Rxg3 hxg3.

31...Nf1+ 32.Kh1 Bd4 33.Ne3 Bxe3 34.Raxe3 Nxe3 0-1

Illustrative Game 34

GM Alex Yermolinsky
IM Georgi Orlov

Seattle 1994

1.Nf3 d6 2.e4 Nf6 3.Nc3 c6 4.d4 Bg4 5.h3 Bh5 6.Bd3 e6 7.Be3 Be7 8.Qe2 d5 9.exd5 Bxf3

Exchanging off his bad Bishop.

10.Qxf3 cxd5 11.O-O Nc6 12.Ne2 O-O 13.c3 a6

Preparing the minority attack.

14.Rad1

Played against ...e5.

14...Rc8 15.Rfe1 Na5 16.Ng3 Nc4 17.Bc1 b5 18.Re2 a5 19.Rc2 Nd6 20.b3

In order to meet ...b4 with c3-c4.

20...Qd7 21.Bf4 Nfe8 22.Be5 f5

Stopping White's Kingside attack but weakening the e6-pawn.

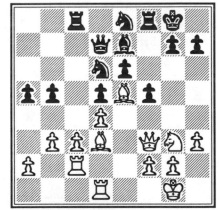

23.Qe2 b4?!

Prematurely opening up the position.

24.c4 Ne4 25.cxd5 Rxc2 26.Qxc2 exd5 27.f3 Nxg3 28.Bxg3

Black is under some pressure and is having trouble activating his pieces because of the weak f5-pawn. White is threatening Rc1 and Qc6.

28...Bd6 29.Bxd6 Qxd6

Giving up the f5-pawn, but 29...Nxd6 30.Qc5 is also bad.

30.Bxf5 g6 31.Bd3 Nf6 32.Bf1 Re8 33.Qc5 Qe6 34.Qxa5 Qe3+ 35.Kh1 Nh5 36.Qxd5+ Kg7 37.Qd6 Kh6 38.d5 Ra8 39.Kh2 Rxa2 40.Qf8+ Kg5 41.d6 Qe5+ 42.f4+ 1-0

Illustrative Game 35

GM Anatoly Karpov
GM John Nunn

Tilburg 1982

1.e4 d6 2.d4 Nf6 3.Nc3 g6 4.Nf3 Bg7 5.Be2 O-O 6.O-O Bg4 7.Be3 Nbd7 8.h3 Bxf3 9.Bxf3 e5 10.g3 c6 11.Bg2 Qa5 12.Qd2

White is planning 13.Rad1 followed by Nd5.

12...Rfe8 13.Rad1 b5 14.a3 Nb6?! 15.b3! Nfd7

If 15...Qxa3, then 16.Nxb5 cxb5 17.Ra1 Qb2 18.Rfb1 exd4 (or 18...Nxe4 19.Bxe4 exd4 20.Bf4) 19.Rxb2 Nxe4 20.Qxd4 Bxd4 21.Bxd4 with a large advantage to White.

16.Ra1!

Karpov has an uncanny ability to control the important squares and slowly squeeze his opponent.

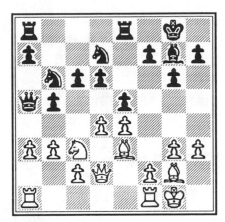

16...Nf8

With the idea of 17...Ne6.

17.d5 Rac8 18.Rfd1

With the idea of 19.dxc6 Rxc6 20.Nd5.

18...c5 19.Bf1 c4 20.a4 cxb3

If 20...b4, then 21.Na2 c3 22.Qd3 gives White a decisive advantage.

21.Nxb5 Qxd2 22.Rxd2 Rxc2

If 22...b2, then 23.Rb1 Nxa4 24.Nxd6 Rb8 25.Nxe8 Nc3 26.Rxb2 wins. If 22...bxc2, then 23.Rc1, threatening 24.Nxd6, 24.Nxa7, and 24.a5, wins.

23.Rxc2 bxc2 24.a5 Nc8 25.Rc1 Nd7 26.Rxc2 Nc5 27.Nxd6 Nxd6 28.Rxc5 Nxe4 29.Rc7 Bf8 30.a6 Rd8 31.Rxa7 1-0

Illustrative Game 36

GM Robert Hübner
GM Vassily Ivanchuk

Novi Sad Olympiad 1990

1.e4 d6 2.d4 Nf6 3.Nc3 g6 4.Nf3 Bg7 5.Be2 O-O 6.O-O Bg4 7.Be3 Nc6 8.Qd2

Also possible is 8.d5 Bxf3 9.Bxf3 Ne5 10.Be2 c6 11.a4 Qa5 12.Ra3 Rfc8 13.Rb3 Rab8 14.Qd4 with a better position for White, Ehlvest–M.Gurevich, Reggio Emilia

1989/90.

8...e5 9.d5 Ne7 10.Rad1 Ne8?!

Better is 10...Nd7, in order to fight for the strategically important square e5.

11.Ng5 Bxe2

If 11...Bd7, then 12.f4 is better for White.

12.Nxe2 h6 13.Nh3 Kh7 14.f4 exf4 15.Rxf4 Ng8

This is necessary in order to prevent Rh4 and protect h6. If 15...f5, then White will play 16.Rh4 Ng8 17.Ng5+ Kh8 18.Nd4 (hitting the weakness at e6) 18...Bxd4 19.Bxd4+ Nef6 20.Ne6.

16.Rdf1 Qe7 17.Bd4 Be5 18.R4f3 Nef6

In order to move the Knight to d7 where it will control the e5-square, thus admitting that his 10th move was a mistake.

19.Nf2 Nd7 20.Nd3

White also fights for the important e5-square.

20...Bxd4+ 21.Nxd4 Ndf6

White is also better after 21...Ne5 22.Nxe5 dxe5 (not 22...Qxe5? 23.Rxf7+) 23.Nb3 followed by c2-c4-c5.

22.Qb4

Threatening e4-e5. After 22.Qf2 Qxe4 23.Rxf6 Nxf6 24.Qxf6 Qxd5 the position is only unclear.

22...Qxe4

Not 22...Nxe4 because of 23.Re3 f5 (or 23...Rae8 24.Nf2 f5 25.Ne6) 24.Ne6 Rfb8 25.Rxe4 fxe4 26.Qxe4 followed by Ndf4, breaking through at g6.

23.Rxf6 Nxf6 24.Rxf6 Qxd5?

Correct was first 24...a5 and only after 25.Qc3 should he play 25...Qxd5.

25.Nf5!

White breaks through at the h6-weakness. There is no defense to Qh4.

25...gxf5 26.Qh4 Kg8 27.Rxh6 f6 28.Qh5 1-0

Conclusion: Against the Pirc Defense, the classical formation should ensure a slight advantage.

Chapter 4

1.d4 d5 2.Nf3

We examine **A)** 2...c5, **B)** 2...Bf5, **C)** 2...Nc6 and **D)** 2...Nf6.

A) 2...c5 3.dxc5 e6

White gets too far ahead in development after 3...Qa5+ 4.Nbd2 Qxc5 5.e4.

4.e4 Bxc5

a) For 5.Nc3, see Illustrative Game 37.

b) For 5.Bb5+, see Illustrative Game 38.

c) For 5.exd5, see Illustrative Game 39.

Illustrative Game 37

GM Ulf Andersson
GM Yasser Seirawan

Brussels 1988

1.Nf3 d5 2.d4 c5 3.dxc5 e6 4.e4 Nf6

Not 4...dxe4 5.Qxd8+ Kxd8 6.Ng5.

5.Nc3 Bxc5 6.Bb5+ Nc6 7.Bg5 d4

The start of some sharp tactics.

8.e5

Of course not 8.Ne2? Qa5+. Also 8.Bxc6 bxc6 9.Ne2 Qb6 is good for Black.

8...Qb6

Not 8...dxc3 9.Qxd8+ Kxd8 10.exf6.

9.exf6 dxc3 10.fxg7 Bxf2+ 11.Ke2 Qxb5+ 12.Kxf2 Rg8 13.Bf6 Qc5+ 14.Ke1 cxb2 15.Rb1

Of course not 15.Bxb2 Qb4+.

15...Qf5 16.Bxb2 e5

Under all circumstances Black must eradicate the g7-pawn.

17.Qe2 f6 18.Rf1 Qh5 19.Rd1 Rxg7

Black's position is very promising. He is a pawn ahead and White's King is stuck in the center.

20.Rd6 Bd7

20...Rf7 is also possible. However, Black decides to give back the pawn in order to get his King to safety.

21.Rxf6 O-O-O 22.Rf2

Black is hoping to take advantage of White's open King. However, Andersson characteristically defends very well.

22...Re7 23.Qe4 Re6 24.Rxe6 Bxe6 25.Rd2 Re8

Exchanges favor White as then his King would become more secure.

26.a3 Bf5 27.Qd5 Kb8 28.h3

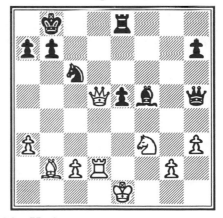

28...Ka8

An incredible blunder. Black would have still had some advantage after 28...Qg6.

29.g4 Bxg4 30.hxg4 Qh1+ 31.Ke2

Black has no compensation for

45

the lost piece.

31...Nd4+ 32.Bxd4 Qg2+ 33.Bf2 1-0

Illustrative Game 38

GM Lubomir Ftacnik

GM Yasser Seirawan

Haninge 1990

1.Nf3 d5 2.d4 c5 3.dxc5 e6 4.e4 Bxc5 5.Nc3 Ne7 6.Bb5+ Nbc6 7.O-O O-O 8.exd5 exd5

In exchange for the isolated pawn, Black has been able to develop quickly.

9.Bg5 h6 10.Bh4 a6

Because of what follows, perhaps better is 10...Bg4.

11. Bxc6

Giving up the two Bishops in order to give Black weak hanging pawns.

11...bxc6 12.Na4 Ba7 13.c4

Threatening to win a pawn with 14.cxd5 cxd5 15.Bxe7 Qxe7 16.Qxd5.

13...f6

An ugly move to make, but Black had to break the pin. 14...Nf5 is now threatened.

14.cxd5 cxd5 15.Bg3 Nf5 16.Bc7 Qd7

Of course not 16...Qxc7 17.Qxd5+.

17. Rc1?

Overlooking a nice tactical shot. Better is 17.Bb6.

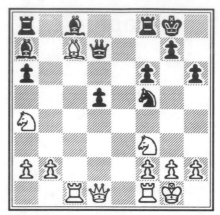

17...Ne3!

Taking advantage of the unique geometry of the position, especially the poor positions of the c1-Rook, the c7-Bishop, and the a4-Knight.

18.fxe3 Bxe3+ 19.Kh1 Bxc1 20.Nb6

Of course if 20.Qxc1, then 20...Qxa4.

20...Qxc7 21.Nxa8 Qc6 22.Qxc1 Qxa8 23.Nd4

The smoke has cleared. White has lost a pawn, but still has some positional advantages, especially the better minor piece.

23...Re8 24.Qc5 Qb7 25.b3 Kh8 26.h3 Qf7 27.Kh2 Qh5 28.Qc3 Bd7 29.Re1 Re5 30.Nf3?

Short on time, White drops another pawn.

30...Rxe1 31.Qxe1

31.Nxe1 Qe2 is also hopeless.

31...Bxh3 32.Nd4

Losing yet another pawn.

32...Bxg2+ 0-1

If 32.Kxg2, then 32...Qg4+. Each side had a minute left for the last 8 moves.

GM Jose Capablanca

GM Akiba Rubinstein

Berlin 1928

1.d4 d5 2.Nf3 c5 3.dxc5 e6 4.e4 Bxc5 5.exd5 exd5 6.Bb5 +

The Bishop is probably better placed at e2.

6...Nc6 7.O-O Nge7 8.Nbd2 O-O 9.Nb3 Bb6 10.Re1

This weakens the f2-square. Worth considering is 10.Bf4.

10...Bg4

Threatening 11...Bxf2+ 12.Kxf2 Qb6+.

11.Bd3 Ng6 12.h3 Bxf3 13.Qxf3 Nce5 14.Qf5 Nxd3 15.Qxd3

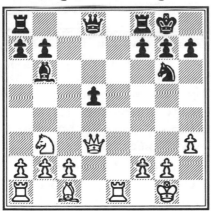

We quote Euwe from *The Middle Game in Chess:*

"In the diagrammed position a vital decision confronts Black: whether or not to push his d-pawn to the 4th rank. Generally this is good policy, leading to greater freedom of movement. In this particular case, things are rather different, as we shall see. The best line was 15...Qf6 16.Rf1 Rad8, after which Black, with his actively placed pieces, has a very good game."

15...d4?

"Here the advance only makes things more difficult for Black. At d4 the pawn comes under persistent pressure, which has the effect of reducing Black's Bishop to a second-rate piece. Another great handicap is that he cannnot - or at any rate can only with great difficulty - get control of d3, the blockade square."

16.Bd2 Qf6 17.Re4

White begins to pressure the isolated d-pawn.

17...Rad8

If 17...Ne5, then 18.Qg3 Rfe8 19.Rae1.

18.Rae1 Qc6 19.g3

Limiting the action of Black's Knight.

19...Rfe8 20.Ba5!

21.Bxb6 axb6 22.Rxe8+ Rxe8 23.Rxe8+ Qxe8 24.Qxd4 is threatened.

20...Rxe4 21.Qxe4 Nf8

Allowing White to penetrate to the seventh rank with his Rook. Capablanca suggested 21...Qxe4 22.Rxe4 f5 23.Re2 Rd7 as better, although White still has the advantage after 24.Re8+ Kf7 25.Rb8 Bxa5 26.Nxa5.

22.Qxc6 bxc6 23.Re7

Threatening 24.Rxa7 Bxa7 25.Bxd8.

23...Rd5

23...d3 offered more resistance. If 24.cxd3, then 24...Rxd3 25.Bxb6 axb6 26.Rb7 b5 27.Rc7 Rd1+ 28.Kg2 Rb1 offers Black good drawing chances. Instead White should keep the advantage with 24.Rxa7 Bxa7 25.Bxd8 dxc2 26.Bg5.

24.Bxb6 axb6 25.Rb7 Nd7 26.Rc7 Rd6

If 26...c5, then 27.Rc8+ Nf8 28.Rb8 c4 29.Nd2 b5 30.Kg2 g6 31.Kf3 Kg7 32.Ke4 is decisive.

27.Rc8+ Nf8 28.Nd2 c5

If 28...d3, then 29.cxd3 Rxd3 30.Nc4 b5 31.Na5 Rd2 32.Nxc6 threatening 33.Ne7+.

29.Nc4 Re6 30.Rb8 Re1+ 31.Kg2 g5

If 31...Rc1, then 32.Nxb6 threatening Nd7.

32.a4 Ra1

If 32...Rc1, then 33.Na3 followed by 34.Rxb6.

33.Nxb6 Kg7 34.Rc8 Ne6 35.Nd7 Rxa4 36.Nxc5 Rb4 37.Nd3 Rb5 38.Kf3 h6 39.b4 h5 40.g4 hxg4+ 41.hxg4 f6 42.Rc4 Kf7 43.Nc5 Nd8 44.Nb3 1-0

B) 2...Bf5 3.c4 e6

a) For 4.cxd5, see Illustrative Game 40.

b) For 4.Qb3, see Illustrative Game 41.

Illustrative Game 40
GM Jon Speelman
GM Nigel Short

Hastings 1988/89

1.Nf3 d5 2.d4 Bf5 3.c4 e6 4.cxd5 exd5 5.Qb3 Nc6 6.Nc3

Not 6.Qxb7 Nb4.

6...Bb4 7.Bf4 a5 8.a3 a4 9.Qd1 Bxc3+ 10.bxc3 Nf6 11.Bg5 h6 12.Bxf6 Qxf6 13.e3 O-O 14.Bb5 Ra5 15.Be2 Ne7 16.O-O Ng6 17.Ra2 b5

Preventing c3-c4 and locking up the Queenside. Instead White will try to break with e3-e4.

18.Qd2 Rfa8 19.Ne1 Nf8 20.f3 Qd6 21.Nd3 Nd7 22.Raa1 c6 23.Nf2 Nf6 24.Bd3 Bxd3 25.Qxd3 Nd7 26.e4 Qg6 27.Rae1 R5a7 28.f4 dxe4 29.Nxe4 Qf5 30.Qf3 Nf6 31.Nxf6+ Qxf6 32.Re5

White's position is quite strong: he has the open e-file, a target at c6, and a potential pawn storm with g2-g4. Black demonstrates an important defensive lesson: he sacrifices a pawn in order to activate his pieces.

32...Re7! 33.Rxb5 cxb5 34.Qxa8+ Kh7 35.Qd5 Re3 36.Qxb5

If 36.Rf3, then Black has a dangerous attack after 36...Re1+ 37.Kf2 Ra1 38.Qxb5 Qh4+.

36...Rxc3 37.Qxa4 Qf5!

Black does not worry about trying to regain his lost material with 37...Rd3. Instead he concentrates his forces on an attack against the White King. He intends ...Qe4 and ...Rc2.

38.Qe8 Rxa3 39.Qe5 Qd3 40.f5 Ra4 41.h3 Draw

Illustrative Game 41
GM Mikhail Botvinnik
GM Vassily Smyslov
World Championship Moscow 1954

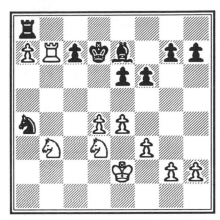

1.d4 d5 2.Nf3 Bf5 3.c4 e6 4.Qb3 Nc6 5.Bd2 dxc4?

Better is 5...Rb8 6.e3 Nf6 7.Nc3 Be7 with equality.

6.Qxb7 Nge7 7.Qb5 Rb8 8. Qa4 Rxb2 9.Na3 Qd7 10.Nxc4 Rb8 11.e3 Nb4

If 11...Nd5, then 12.a3 is good for White.

12.Qxd7+ Kxd7 13.Bxb4 Rxb4 14.Nce5+ Ke8 15.Bd3 f6 16.Bxf5 Nxf5

Better is 16...exf5 17.Nd3 Rb6 18.Ke2 Nd5.

17.Nd3 Rb6 18.Ke2 Ba3 19.Nd2 Nd6 20. Rhb1 Nc8

Not 20...Kd7? 21.Rb3 Rxb3 22.axb3 Nb5 23.b4 winning.

21.Nc4 Rxb1 22.Rxb1 Be7 23.Rb8 Kd8

Not 23...Kd7? 24.Ne5+! fxe5 25.Nxe5+ Kd8 26.Nf7+ winning.

24.a4 Re8 25.a5 Kd7 26.a6 Bf8

If 26...Nb6 or 26...Nd6, then 27.Ne5+! winning.

27.Rb7 Be7

If 27...Nb6?, then 28.Nxb6+ axb6 29.a7 Ra8 30.Rb8 winning.

28.Na5 Bd6 29.e4 Bf8 30.f3 Nb6 31.Rxa7 Rb8 32.Nb3 Na4 33. Rb7 Ra8 34.a7 Be7

35.Ke3?!

Better is 35.f4 Kc8 36.Na5 Kd7 37.e5 Nb6 38.Nc5+ Bxc5 39.dxc5 Nd5 40.c6+ Kc8 41.Nc4 Nxf4+ 42.Kd2 fxe5 43.Nd6+ winning.

35...Kc8 36.Na5 Kd7 37.g3 Nb6 38.Nb3?

Correct is 38.Nc5+ Bxc5 39.dxc5 Nc8 40.c6+ Kd6 41.Rb8 Rxa7 42.Nc4+ Kc5 43.Rxc8 Kxc4 44.Rh8 winning.

38...Kc8 39.Rb8+

Not 39.Na5? Nc4+ winning. If 39.Nbc5, then 39...Bxc5 40.Nxc5 Nd7 is equal.

39...Rxb8 40.axb8=Q+ Kxb8 41.Nbc5

The sealed move. White could have retained a slight advantage with 41.Ndc5 e5 42.d5.

41...e5 42.dxe5 fxe5 43.f4 Nc4+ 44.Kf3 exf4 45.gxf4 g6 46.e5 c6 47.Nb3 Kc7 48.Ke4 Kb6 49.f5 gxf5 50.Kxf5 Ne3+ Draw

C) 2...Nc6

a) For 3.g3, see Illustrative Game 42

b) For 3.Bf4, see Illustrative Game 43.

Illustrative Game 42
GM Jan Smejkal
GM Jakob Murey

New York 1986

**1.Nf3 Nc6 2.d4 d5 3.g3 Bf5
4.Bg2 Qd7 5.c4 e6**
Worth considering is 5...dxc4
6.O-O Bh3.

**6.O-O dxc4 7.Nbd2 O-O-O
8.Nxc4 f6**
Not 8...Nxd4? 9.Nxd4 Qxd4
10.Qb3 winning.

9.Qb3 Nge7 10.Re1 Qd5?
Correct is 10...Be4.

11.Qa4
11.Nfe5 Be4 leads to nothing.

**11...Be4 12.Ncd2 Bg6 13.Nb3
Qd6**
If 13...Be4, then 14.Nc5
threatening 15.Qb5 winning.

**14.Nc5 Nd5 15.Qb5 Nb6 16.Be3
a6 17.Qb3 Re8 18.Rac1 Na5
19.Qb4 Nc6 20.Qb3 Na5
21.Qb4 Nc6 22.Qa3 Nd5
23.Bd2 Qd8 24.b4 Bxc5
25.Rxc5 Nb6 26.e4?!**
26.b5 gives White a winning attack.

**26...Nxd4 27.Nxd4 Qxd4 28.Bc3
Qd7 29.b5 axb5 30.Rb1 Qd6
31.Bb4 Qd4 32.Rbc1 c6 33.Qa7**
White's attack is unstoppable.

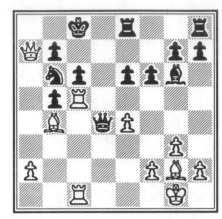

33...Re7
33...Qxb4 is also met by
34.Rxc6+.

**34.Rxc6+ Kd8 35.Bxe7+ Kxe7
36.Rxb6 1-0**

Illustrative Game 43
GM Loek van Wely
IM Alexander Morozevic

Tilburg 1993

**1.d4 d5 2.Nf3 Nc6 3.Bf4 Bg4
4.c4 e6 5.e3 Bb4+ 6.Nc3 Nge7
7.Rc1 O-O 8.Bd3 Ng6 9.h3 Bh5**
9...Nxf4 10.hxg4 is better for
White.

**10.Bh2 Nh4 11.g4 Nxf3+
12.Qxf3 Bg6 13.Bxg6 hxg6
14.cxd5 exd5 15.Kf1 Ne7
16.h4?!**
Better is first 16.Ne2.

16...Bxc3 17.Rxc3 c6
Black has equalized.

18.h5 g5 19.h6?!
Correct is 19.Bg3.

19...f6
Not 19...gxh6 20.Qh3.

**20.hxg7 Kxg7 21.Bg3 Qd7
22.Kg2 Rh8 23.Rcc1 Rxh1
24.Rxh1 Qe6 25.Qe2 Re8 26.f3
Ng6 27.Re1 f5 28.gxf5 Qxf5
29.e4 Qd7**

Threatening 30...dxe4 31.fxe4 Qxd4.

30.Qe3?

Correct is 30.Qf2.

30...dxe4 31.Kg1

31.fxe4 Qg4 and 31.Qxg5 Qxd4 are both much better for Black.

31...Qf5 32.fxe4 Qg4 33.d5 cxd5 34.Qc3+ Kh6 35.cxd5 Rc8 36.Qe3 Rd8

Better is 36...Nf4 37.Rf1 Rc2 with a winning advantage.

37.d6?

37.Rf1 would have held out longer, although Black has a large advantage after 37...Rxd5. White was very short on time.

37...Rxd6 38.Qf2 Nf4 39.Kf1 Rf6 40.Re4 Qd1+ 0-1

D) 2...Nf6 3.Bf4

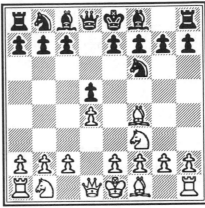

We will examine five moves:
  D1) 3...c5, D2) 3...Bf5, D3) 3...Bg4, D4) 3...c6, and D5) 3...e6.

  D1) 3...c5

  4.e3

a) Worth considering is 4.c3

a1) 4...Qb6 5.Qb3

a11) 5...c4 6.Qc2 g6 7.Nbd2 Bf5 8.Qc1 h6 9.h3 g5 10.Be5 Nbd7 11.g3 Nxe5 12.Nxe5 e6 13.Bg2 Qc7 14.O-O Bd6?! (14...Bg7) 15.Nexc4 dxc4 16.e4 Bg6 17.e5 is slightly better for White, Chernikov–Fedorov, USSR 1981.

a12) 5...e6 6.h3 cxd4 7.cxd4 Qxb3 8.axb3 Nc6 9.e3 Bd7 10.Nc3 Rc8 11.Bd3 Nb4 12.Bb1 Bb5 13.Kd2 Ba6 14.Rc1 Nd7 15.Ne1 f6 16.Nd3 e5 17.dxe5 Bxd3 18.Bxd3 fxe5 19.Bg3 unclear, Santos–Aleksandrov, European Team Championship, Debrecen 1992.

a2) 4...Nc6?! 5.dxc5 g6 6.g3 Bg7 7.Bg2 O-O 8.O-O Ne4 9.Ng5 f5 10.Nxe4 fxe4 11.Qd2 Ne5 12.Na3 Be6 13.Rad1 Qa5 14.c4 Qxd2 15.Rxd2 dxc4 16.Bxe4 Rac8 17.Be3 Ng4 18.Bxb7 with a winning advantage to White, Granda Zuniga–Bönsch, Capablanca Memorial 1987.

  b) 4.dxc5 e6 5.e3 Bxc5 6.c4 O-O

7.Nc3 Nc6 8.a3 Re8 9.Ne5 Bd6 10.Nxc6 bxc6 11.Bxd6 Qxd6 12.Be2 Rb8 13.b4 a5 14.bxa5 Qe5 15.Qd4 Qxd4 16.exd4 e5 with a slight advantage to Black, Grooten–Van der Werf, Wijk aan Zee 1993.

4...Nc6

4...Bg4 5.Nbd2 Nc6 6.c3 e6 7.Qa4 Bxf3 8.Nxf3 Qb6 9.Qb5 (9.Rb1 Be7 10.Bd3 O-O 11.O-O Rfd8 is equal, Keres–Reshevsky, Kemeri 1937) 9...Qxb5 10.Bxb5 a6 11.Be2 is slightly better for White, Herzog–Nogueiras, Lucerne Olympiad 1982.

5.c3

5.Nc3 (with the idea of 6.Nb5):

a) 5...Bg4 6.dxc5

b) 5...Qa5 6.Bb5 Ne4 7.O-O Nxc3 8.Bxc6+ bxc6 9.bxc3 Qxc3 10.Ne5 cxd4 11.exd4 Bf5 12.Rb1 f6 13.Nd3 Qxd4 14.Rb4 Qc3 15.Rb7 Rd8 16.Rxa7 e5 17.Re1? (17.Bd2 with a slight advantage to Black) 17...e4?? (17...Bxd3 gives Black a winning advantage) 18.Ra4! with a winning advantage to White, Meduna–Yakovich, Sochi 1986.

c) 5...cxd4 6.Nb5!? (6.exd4 Bg4 is equal) 6...Qa5+ 7.Qd2 (7.c3 dxc3 8.bxc3 Bg4 with a slight advantage to Black) 7...Qxd2+ 8.Kxd2 dxe3+ 9.fxe3 Kd7! 10.Rd1 (10.Nc7 e5!) 10...e6 11.c4 (11.Nc7! Rb8 12.Nb5 is equal) 11...Bc5! 12.Kc1?! (12.Nc7!) 12...a6 with a slight advantage to Black, Rakic–Cvetkovic, Yugoslavia 1991.

5...Qb6 6.Qb3

6.Qc1 Bf5 7.Nbd2 Rc8 (perhaps better is 7...e6) 8.dxc5 Qxc5

a) 9.Nb3 Qb6 10.Qd2 e6 11.Bd3 Be4 12.Qe2 Be7 13.O-O O-O 14.Bg5 is equal, Capablanca–

Maroczy, New York 1924.

b) 9.Qd1 Qb6 10.Qb3 Qxb3 11.axb3 Nh5 12.Bb5 Nxf4 13.exf4 a6 14.Bxc6+ Rxc6 15.Nd4 is slightly better for White, Knezevic–Osmanovic, Sarajevo 1981.

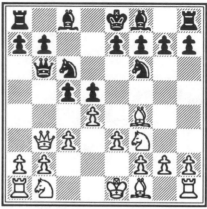

6...c4 7.Qxb6

7.Qc2 Bf5 8.Qc1 h6 9.Nbd2 Qd8 10.b3 cxb3 11.axb3 e6 12.Ne5 Nxe5 13.Bxe5 Nd7 14.Bg3 Be7 15.Be2 O-O 16.O-O a6 17.c4 Bb4 18.c5 e5 19.Nf3 Bg4 20.h3 Bh5 21.Qd1 e4 22.Ne1 Bxe2 23.Qxe2 Nb8 24.Nc2 Nc6 25.Bd6 Re8 26.Qh5 Qg5 27.Qxg5 hxg5 28.f3 g6 29.fxe4 Rxe4 30.Rf3 Ba5 31.Raf1 f5 32.g4! is slightly better for White, Lputian–Yakovich, Moscow 1992.

7...axb6 8.Na3

8.a3 b5 9.Ne5 e6 10.b4?! (better is 10.Nbd2, although Black is better after 10...b4) 10...Nh5 11.Nxc6 Nxf4 12.exf4 bxc6 and the a-pawn is very weak. Black went on to win after 13.Nd2 f6 14.Nf3 Bd6 15.g3 O-O 16.Be2 Rf7 17.Kd2 Rfa7 in Kovacevic–Ribli, Bugojno 1984.

8...Ra5

a) Worth considering is 8...e6 9.Nb5 Kd7.

b) For 8...e5, see Illustrative Game 44.

9.Bc7 Bf5

a) 9...e5?! 10.Nc2 e4 11.Nd2 Ra6 12.a4 is slightly better for White, Kovacevic–Kristensen, Thessaloniki Olympiad 1988.

b) 9...e6 10.Nc2 (10.Bxb6 Ra6 11.Bc5 Bxc5 12.dxc5 Ra5) 10...Kd7 11.Bf4 b5 12.a3 is slightly better for White.

The text move prevents Nc2.

10.Bxb6

If 10.Nh4, then 10...e6 11.Nxf5 Bxa3 12.Nxg7+ Kd7 13.Bxb6 Bxb2 is strong.

10...Ra6 11.Bc7

If 11.Bc5, then 11...b6.

11...Kd7 12.Nb5 e6 13.Be2

Better is 13.Bg3 Be7 14.Ne5+.

13...Be7 14.Bd1 Rha8 15.a4 Na7

with a slight advantage to Black, Legky–Cvetkovic, Vrnjacka Banja 1989.

D2) 3...Bf5

Black can unsuspectingly get into danger with this move.

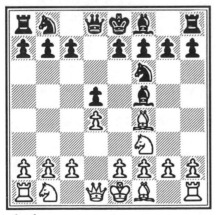

4.c4

4.e3 e6 5.c4? Bxb1 6.Rxb1 (6.Qxb1 Bb4+ with a slight advantage to Black, Z. Nikolic–Djukic, Nis 1981) 6...Bb4+ 7.Ke2

dxc4? 8.Qa4+ Nc6 9.Ne5 Nd5 10.Nxc6 Qd7 11.Bg3 Qxc6 12.Qxc6+ bxc6 13.Kf3 is slightly better for White, Hulak–Rowley, New York 1989.

4...c6

a) 4...e6 5.Qb3 is strong for White.

b) 4...dxc4 5.Qa4+ c6 6.Qxc4 Nbd7 7.Nc3 e6 8.a3 Be7 9.g3 Nb6 10.Qb3 O-O 11.Bg2 Nfd5 12.Bd2 Nxc3 13.Bxc3 Be4 14.O-O Draw, Meduna–Lechtynsky, Czechoslovakian Championship, Prague 1992.

5.e3 e6 6.Nc3 Nbd7 7.Qb3 Qb6 8.c5 Qxb3 9.axb3 a6 10.b4 Rc8

White was threatening 11.b5. 10...O-O-O? would be met with 11.Rxa6 bxa6 12.Bxa6 mate. Here White has only one dangerous plan: Nf3-d2-b3-a5 and Black's b-pawn will be difficult to defend. Black has two possible defenses: to exchange the Knight with ...Be7-d8 or defend the pawn with the Rook. The text move may not be Black's best. Worth considering is 10...Rd8 11.h3 Be7 12.Nd2 Nf8 13.Nb3 Ng6 14.Bh2 O-O 15.Na5 Rd7. The question is whether White could then successfully advance his Queenside pawns after a sacrifice on a6 or c6. Otherwise Black would have successfully solved his opening problems, as ...Bd8xa5 could then follow. See Illustrative Game 45.

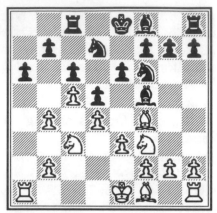

D3) 3...Bg4
4.Nbd2 e6 5.e3 Bd6

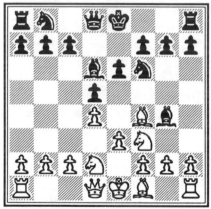

6.Bxd6

6.Bg3 O-O 7.c3 Ne4 8.Qb3 Nxg3 9.hxg3 Nd7 10.e4 dxe4 11.Nxe4 Be7 12.Bd3 Bf5 13.O-O-O Qc8 14.Qc2 h6 15.Nh4 Bxe4 16.Bxe4 Rd8 17.Qe2 c5 is equal, Kovacevic–Mantovani, Mendrisio 1988.

6...Qxd6 7.c4 Nbd7 8.Qb3 Rb8 9.h3 Bh5 10.cxd5 exd5 11.Rc1 O-O 12.Bd3 c6 13.O-O Rfe8 14.Nh4 Bg6 15.Nxg6 hxg6 16.Rc3 a6

This position was reached in Kovacevic–Timman, Indonesia 1983. White should play 17.Rfc1 g5 18.Qd1 with an equal position. Instead the game continued 17.Qc2?! g5 18.Qd1 g6 19.Qf3 Kg7 20.Rb1

Rh8 21.Nf1 Qe6 22.Ng3 Rh4 with a slight advantage to Black.

D4) 3...c6
4.e3

4.c3 g6 5.h3 Bg7 6.Nbd2 O-O 7.e3 Bf5 8.Be2 Nbd7 9.Qb3 Qc8 10.g4 Be4 11.Rg1 Bxf3 12.Bxf3 a5 13.a4 e5 14.dxe5 Nc5 with a slight advantage to Black, Pribyl–Yudasin, Leningrad 1989.

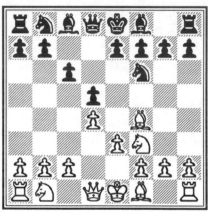

4...Qb6

4...Bg4 5.c4 Nbd7 6.Nbd2 e6 7.Bd3 Nh5 8.Bg3 Nxg3 9.hxg3 Bd6 10.Qb3 Rb8 11.Nh2 Bh5 12.Nhf1 Nf6 13.f3 Bg6 14.Bxg6 fxg6 15.g4 O-O 16.O-O-O is slightly better for White, Kovacevic–Bisguier, New York 1989.

5.Qc1 Bf5 6.c4 Na6 7.a3 Nh5 8.c5 Qd8 9.Nbd2 f6 10.b4 g5 11.Bg3 Nxg3 12.hxg3 Nc7 13.Qc3 Kf7 14.Bd3 Qd7

Equal, Hulak–Kuligowski, Wijk aan Zee 1983.

D5) 3...e6
4.e3 c5

For 4...Be7, see Illustrative Games 46 and 47.

b) 4...Bd6

b1) 5.c3

54

b11) 5...Nbd7 6.Bd3 O-O 7.Nbd2 Re8?! 8.Ne5 Nf8 9.Bg5 Be7 10.f4 N6d7 11.Bxe7 Qxe7 12.O-O f6 13.Nef3 e5?! 14.Qb3 c6 15.fxe5 Kh8 16.Rae1 fxe5 17.e4 is slightly better for White, Sakovich–Varna, USSR 1982.

b12) 5...Bxf4 6.exf4 O-O 7.Nbd2 Qd6 8.Ne5 c5 9.dxc5 Qxc5 10.Bd3 Nc6 11.O-O Qb6 12.Rb1 Qc7 13.Qe2 b6 14.Rfe1 is slightly better for White, Stoppel–Zobisch, Austria 1982.

b2) 5.Bg3

b21) 5...Ne4 6.Bd3 f5 7.Ne5 O-O 8.f3 Nxg3 9.hxg3 Bxe5 10.dxe5 Qg5 11.Kf2 Nd7 12.f4 Qg6 13.g4 is slightly better for White, Augustin–Szilagyi, Stary Smokovec 1976.

b22) 5...Nc6 6.c4 Bxg3 7.hxg3 Qe7 8.Nc3 Bd7 9.a3 a6 10.Rc1 dxc4 11.Bxc4 e5 12.d5 Na7 unclear, Gulko–Kupreichik, USSR 1982.

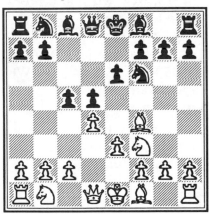

5.c3 Nc6

Or immediately 5...Bd6 6.Bb5+?! (6.Bg3) 6...Nc6 7.Qa4 Bxf4 8.exf4 Qb6 9.Nbd2 O-O 10.dxc5 Qxc5 11.O-O Bd7 12.Bxc6 bxc6 13.Qd4 Qe7 14.b4?! c5 with a slight advantage to Black, Seirawan–Alburt, USA 1990.

For 5...Qb6, see Illustrative

Game 48.

6.Nbd2 Bd6

a) 6...Qb6 7.Qb1 (weak is 7.Qb3?! c4 8.Qxb6 axb6 9.h3 b5 10.a3 b4 11.cxb4 Bxb4 12.Rc1 Be7 13.Be2 Nd7 14.O-O Nb6 with a slight advantage to Black, Trombik–Drasko, Prague 1984) 7...Be7 8.Bd3 Bd7 9.h3 Rc8 10.a4 h6 11.Ne5 cxd4 12.exd4 Nxe5 13.Bxe5 O-O 14.O-O a5 15.Qc2 Ne8 16.Rae1 Nd6 17.Re3 is slightly better for White, Hulak–Franzoni, Lucern Olympiad 1982.

b) 6...Be7 7.Ne5 O-O 8.Bd3 Bd7 9.Qf3 Ne8 10.Qh3 g6 11.Ndf3 Nxe5 12.Nxe5 f6 13.Nxd7 Qxd7 14.O-O c4 15.Bc2 Bd6 16.Bh6 Rf7 17.e4 is slightly better for White, Knezevic–Cekro, Sarajevo 1981.

7.Bg3

a) 7.Bd3 Bxf4 8.exf4 Qb6 9.Qb3 cxd4 10.Qxb6 axb6 11.Nxd4 Nxd4 12.cxd4 Bd7 13.Ke2 Draw, Rozentalis–Dreev, Tbilisi 1989.

b) 7.Bxd6 Qxd6 8.Bb5 O-O 9.O-O Bd7 10.Qa4 cxd4 11.cxd4 a6 12.Bxc6 Bxc6 13.Qc2 Nd7 14.Rfc1 f6 15.Nb3 Rac8 16.Na5 Qb4 17.Qd2 Qb6 18.a3 Rc7 19.Nxc6 bxc6 20.b4 Ra8 21.Ne1 e5 is equal, Rubinetti–Morovic, Buenos Aires 1992.

7...O-O

a) 7...Qe7 8.Bb5 Bd7 9.O-O O-O 10.Qa4 Bxg3 11.hxg3 a6 12.Bxc6 Bxc6 13.Qa3 Nd7 14.Rfe1 Rfe8 15.e4 dxe4 16.Nxe4 cxd4 17.Qxe7 Rxe7 18.Nxd4 Bd5 19.Nd2 Nb6 20.b3 Rd7 21.N2f3 Rad8 is equal, Nikolic–Morovic.

b) 7...Bxg3 8.hxg3 Qd6 9.Qa4 cxd4 10.exd4 Bd7 11.Bb5 Nb8 12.Ne5 a6 13.Bxd7+ Nfxd7 14.f4

Nc6 15.Qc2 h6 16.Ndf3 Ndxe5
17.fxe5 Qe7 18.O-O-O O-O-O unclear, Hulak–Kuijf, Wijk aan Zee
1986.

8.Bd3

8.Ne5 cxd4 9.exd4 Bxe5 10.dxe5
Nd7 11.Nf3 Nc5 12.Be2 b6 13.Nd4
Bd7 14.O-O f5 15.exf6 Qxf6
16.Bd6 Rf7 17.f4 Ne4 18.Nxc6
Bxc6 19.Be5 Qh6 20.Rf3 g6 21.Bd3
Qf8 22.Qe2 is slightly better for
White, Meduna–Inkiov, Gausdal
1988.

8...Qe7

a) 8...b6 9.Ne5 Bb7 10.f4 Ne7
11.Qf3 Ne8 12.Bh4 f5 13.g4 Nf6
14.gxf5 Nxf5 15.Qh3 Nxh4 16.Qxh4
Bxe5 17.fxe5 Ne4 unclear,
Schumacher–Hoen, Lucerne
Olympiad 1982.

b) 8...Re8 9.Ne5 Bxe5 10.dxe5
Nd7 11.f4 Qb6 (White also has a
powerful attack after 11...c4
12.Bc2 Qb6 13.Kf2 Qxb2 14.Rc1
Qxa2 15.Qe2 f5 16.exf6 Nxf6
17.Bh4 Rf8 18.Bxf6 Rxf6 19.Nf3
Qa3 20.Bxh7+ in Burn–Marshall,
Ostend 1906) 12.Qb1 Nf8 13.Bf2
c4 14.Bc2 Qc7 15.Nf3 b5 16.a3 a5
17.O-O Bd7 18.Ng5 h6? (18...g6)
19.Bh7+ 1-0, Maroczy–Mar-
tinolich, Vienna 1907.

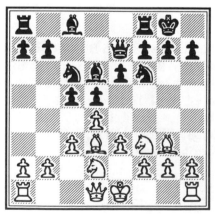

9.Ne5 Rd8 10.f4

Bisguier–Frias, Lone Pine 1981
continued 10...Nd7 11.O-O Nf8
12.Qe2 f6 13.Bh4 Bd7 14.Nxd7
Rxd7 15.Kh1 Re8 16.Rae1 Kh8
17.Nf3 cxd4 18.Nxd4 Qf7 19.Nxc6
bxc6 20.e4 and is slightly better for
White.

Illustrative Game 44

FM Aaron Summerscale
GM Loek van Wely

London 1992

**1.Nf3 d5 2.d4 Nf6 3.Bf4 c5 4.e3
Nc6 5.c3 Qb6 6.Qb3 c4 7.Qxb6
axb6 8.Na3 e5?!**

Better is 8...e6 or 8...Ra5.

**9.Nb5 Ra5 10.Nc7+ Kd7
11.Nxe5+**

Also possible is 11.dxe5 Nh5
12.Nxd5 Rxd5 13.Bxc4 Ra5 14.Bxf7
Nxf4 15.exf4 with a large advantage to White.

11...Nxe5 12.Bxe5 Ng4

If 12...Bd6, then 13.Bxf6! gxf6
14.Nxd5 Rxd5 15.Bxc4 gives White
a large advantage.

**13.Bg3 Bd6 14.Bxd6 Kxd6
15.Nb5! Rxb5 16.b4**

Trapping the Rook and threatening to win it with 17.a4.

16...Bd7

To meet 17.a4 with 17...Ra8.

17.Be2 Nf6 18.f3 Ra8 19.Kd2?

Carelessly allowing Black's next
move. Correct is 19.a4. Then the
only move is 19...Ne4. After
20.fxe4 dxe4 21.O-O Rf5 White
has a slight advantage.

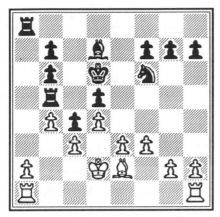

19...Ra3 20.Kc2 Rxb4! 21.cxb4 Rxe3

Black has a very large advantage due to the weaknesses in White's position.

22.Kd2 Ra3 23.Rhc1 Ng8!

Repositioning the Knight to f5 or c6.

24.Rc3 Ra8 25.a3 Ne7 26.Rc2 Ba4 27.Rcc1 Nf5 28.Kc3 Re8 29.Ra2 Re3+ 30.Kd2 Rb3 31.Ke1 b5 32.Bd1 Rd3 33.Be2 Rxd4 34.g3 g5 35.Kf2 Ne7 36.Ke3 Nc6 37.Re1 f5 38.Kf2 f4 39.Bf1 Ne5 40.Kg2 c3 41.Rae2 Rd2 42.Rc1 d4 0-1

Illustrative Game 45

GM Predrag Nikolic
IM Jeroen Piket

Wijk aan Zee 1988

1.d4 d5 2.Nf3 Nf6 3.Bf4 Bf5 4.c4 c6 5.e3 e6 6.Nc3 Nbd7 7.Qb3 Qb6 8.c5 Qxb3 9.axb3 a6 10.b4 Rc8

As mentioned earlier, 10...Rd8 is perhaps better.

11.h3

If immediately 11.Nd2, then

11...Nh5.

11...h6?

Allowing the Bishop to retreat to h7, but actually carelessly losing a valuable tempo. Kovacevic–Byrne, Wijk aan Zee 1980, continued 11...Be7 12.Nd2 O-O 13.g4 Bg6 14.Nb3 Ra8?! (Better is 14...Bd8. White's best then would be 15.Bd6 and later Na5. Black could meet an immediate 15.Na5 with 15...Bxa5 16.bxa5 Ne8 17.Ra4 Nc7 18.Rb4 Nb5.) 15.Na5 Ra7 16.f3 Rc8 17.Kd2 b6 18.Bxa6! Rxa6 19.Nxc6 Rxc6 20.Rxa6 Rc8 21.Rha1 bxc5 22.Ra8 Rf8 23.bxc5 and White's passed pawns brought him victory.

12.Nd2 Be7 13.Nb3 Bd8

To defend against Na5.

14.Bd6!

This move would have had much less effect had Black played 11...Be7.

14...Ne4

If 14...Bc7, then 15.Bxc7 Rxc7 16.b5! cxb5 17.Nxb5 or if 14...Be7, then 15.Bh2 Bd8 16.Na5.

15.Nxe4 Bxe4 16.f3 Bg6 17.Na5 Bxa5 18.bxa5 Kd8

The King must be used to defend the b-pawn.

19.Ra4 Ra8 20.Rb4 Kc8 21.h4!

While Black is tied down on the Queenside, White begins play on the other wing. Nikolic conducts the endgame quite nicely.

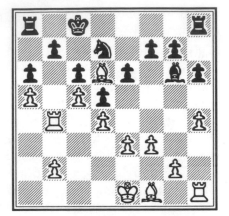

21...h5 22.Rh3 Bf5 23.Rg3 g6 24.Kd2 Re8

A much better defense is 24...Rg8 followed by ...Nf6-e8-c7-b5.

25.Rg5 f6?

Seriously weakening the g6-pawn. Correct is 25...Rg8.

26.Rg3 g5 27.Bd3!

Not 27.hxg5? h4.

27...g4

If 27...gxh4, then 28.Rg7 h3 29.gxh3 Bxh3 30.Rh7 is winning for White.

28.e4 dxe4

If 28...Bg6, then 29.exd5 Bxd3 30.dxc6 wins.

29.fxe4 Bg6 30.Bc2 f5 31.e5 Rg8 32.Rgb3 Ra7 33.Bd3

Threatening 34.Rxb7 Rxb7 35.Bxa6.

33...Nb8 34.Ke3!

The King's entrance into the action is decisive.

34...Rg7 35.Kf4 Bf7 36.Rb6

Threatening 37.Bxb8 Kxb8 38.Rxc6.

36...Be8

If 36...Nd7, then 37.Rxb7.

37.d5 cxd5 38.Bxb8 Kxb8 39.Rxe6 Ba4 40.Rb4 g3 41.Bxf5

1-0

GM Vlado Kovacevic
FM Tom O'Donnell

Toronto 1990

1.d4 d5 2.Nf3 e6 3.Bf4 Nf6 4.e3 Be7?!

Black needs to be contesting the e5-square and therefore the Bishop is better placed on d6.

5.Nbd2 O-O?!

Black is going to regret committing his King so early.

6.Bd3 b6?!

Better is 6...c5 7.c3 Nc6 8.Ne5 Nd7 9.Qh5 f5.

7.Ne5 Bb7 8.Qf3 Nbd7 9.h4

Black will have trouble defending against the coming Kingside attack.

9...Nxe5 10.dxe5 Nd7 11.O-O-O Nc5

Better is 11...f5. Perhaps Black thought that this stops White's attack, but likely he was surprised by...

12.Bxh7+! Kxh7 13.Qh5+ Kg8 14.Nf3

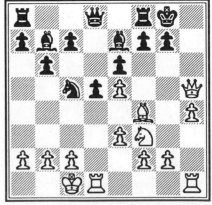

White's sacrifice is very original as he is a tempo down from the well-known Bxh7+ sacrifices. It would be difficult to calculate all the consequences over the board, but compare this with the following game, Kovacevic–Ree, Maribor 1980: 1.d4 Nf6 2.Nf3 d5 3.Bf4 e6 4.Nbd2 c5 5.e3 Be7 6.c3 O-O 7.Bd3 Nbd7 8.h4 b6 9.Ne5 Nxe5 10.dxe5 Nd7 11.Bxh7+ Kxh7 12.Qh5+ Kg8 13.Nf3 f6 14.Ng5 fxg5 15.hxg5 Rf5 16.Qh7+ Kf7 17.g6+ Ke8 18.Qxg7 Bf8 19.Qh8 Rg5 20.Qg8 Nxe5 21.Bxe5 Kd7 22.Rh8 Bb7 23.Qh7+ 1-0. When one becomes experienced with an opening, a deep understanding of the important positions results!

14...f6

If 14...Re8, then 15.Ng5 Bxg5 16.hxg5 Kf8 17.g6 is strong.

15.Ng5 fxg5 16.hxg5

17.g6 is threatened.

16...Rf5

Black must give back material to save his King.

17.g4

17.Qh7+ is not effective as the King can escape to d7.

17...Rxg5 18.Bxg5 Bxg5 19.f4 Bh6

If 19...Ne4, then 20.Qg6. If 19...Be7, then 20.g5 threatening 21.g6.

20.g5 Qe8 21.Qh4 Kh7 22.Rdg1 Ne4

If 22...d4, then 23.gxh6 Bxh1 24.Rxg7+ Kh8 25.Qf6 or if 23...g6 24.Qf6.

23.Rg4 d4 24.gxh6 g5 25.fxg5 Qg6

Black has succeeded in blockading the Kingside but White has won all his material back.

26.exd4

White sacrifices the Exchange, as his pawns will decide.

26...Nf2 27.Rf1 Nxg4 28.Qxg4 Rg8 29.Rf6

Transposing into a superior endgame.

29...Qxg5+ 30.Qxg5 Rxg5 31.Rxe6 Be4 32.Re7+ Kxh6 33.Rxc7 a5 34.c4 Rg2 35.b3 Kg6

Black's best chance is 35...Rc2+ 36.Kd1 Rxa2 37.d5 Bc2+ 38.Ke1 Bxb3.

36.e6 Kf6 37.d5 Rg8

If 37...Rxa2, then 38.Rf7+ Kg6 39.d6 and 40.d7.

38.Rb7 Ke5 39.Rxb6 Kd4 40.e7 Kc3 41.Kd1 Kd3 42.Ke1 Ke3 43.Rf6 a4 44.b4 a3 45.b5 Rc8 46.Ra6 Rh8 47.Rxa3+ Bd3 48.Rxd3+ Kxd3 49.Kf2 1-0

Illustrative Game 47

GM Osip Bernstein

GM Gideon Stahlberg

Zürich 1934

1.Nf3 d5 2.d4 Nf6 3.Bf4 e6 4.e3 Be7 5.Nbd2 O-O 6.Bd3 b6 7.Ne5 Bb7 8.Qf3

Preventing ...Ne4 and preparing a Kingside attack.

8...c5 9.c3 Nbd7 10.Qh3 Re8

Preparing to defend h7 by moving the Knight to f8. However, this move leaves f7 vulnerable.

11.Ndf3

Threatening 12.Ng5.

11...Nxe5 12.Nxe5 c4

Seeking counterchances on the Queenside.

13.Bc2 b5 14.g4 g6

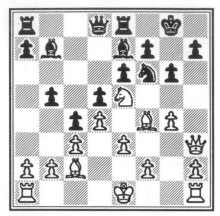

15.Bd1

Threatening 16.g5 Ne4 17.Nxf7 Kxf7 18.Qxh7+ Kf8 19.Be5. If immediately 15.g5, then 15...Nh5.

15...Bf8 16.Bg5 Be7

If 16...Bg7, then 17.Qh4.

17.Qf3 b4

Not 17...Rf8 18.Bh6 Re8 19.g5 winning.

18.cxb4 Bxb4+ 19.Kf1 Be7 20.Kg2

Not 20.Nxc4? Ba6, but now this move is threatened.

20...Rb8 21.Ba4

Winning the Exchange.

21...Rf8 22.Bh6 Qc7 23.h4 Ne4 24.Nd7 Bc6 25.Bxc6 Qxc6 26.Bxf8 Qxd7 27.Bxe7 Rxb2

White is winning easily after 27...Qxe7 28.Qe2.

28.Bf6 Qb7

If 28...Rxf2+, then 29.Qxf2 Nxf2 30.Kxf2 e5 31.Rab1 Qc8 32.Bxe5 winning.

29.Raf1 c3 30.g5 Qb5 31.h5 Nd2 32.hxg6 fxg6 33.Qg4 Qd7 34.Rxh7 Qxh7 35.Rh1 Qxh1+ 36.Kxh1 Kf7 37.Qh3 Rb1+ 38.Kg2 1-0

GM David Janowski
GM Siegbert Tarrasch
Ostende 1905

1.d4 d5 2.Nf3 c5 3.c3 e6 4.Bf4 Qb6 5. Qb3 Nf6

If 5...c4, then 6.Qc2 is best.

6.e3 Nc6 7.h3

A move often played in this type of position to avoid losing the Bishop-pair after ...Nh5.

7...Be7 8.Nbd2 Bd7 9.Be2 O-O 10.O-O Rfc8 11.Ne5 Be8 12.Bg3 Nd7

If 12...Bd6, then 13.Nd7.

13.Ndf3 Nf8 14.Rfd1 Na5 15.Qc2 c4 16.Nd2

Black was planning 16...f6 17.Ng4 h5 18.Ngh2 g5.

16...f6 17.Nef3 Bg6 18.Qc1 h6

Anticipating Nh4, but weakening the Kingside.

19.Nh2 Qd8

Preparing to advance the Queenside pawns.

20.Bf3

Preparing e3-e4.

20...b5 21.e4 Nc6 22.exd5 exd5 23.Re1 b4 24.Ndf1 bxc3

Opening the b-file turns out to favor White. Better is 24...a5.

25.bxc3 Qa5

Better is the cautious 25...Qd7.

26.Ne3 Bf7 27.Qd2

Threatening 28.Nxc4 dxc4 29.Bxc6 Rxc6 30.Rxe7.

26...Ba3

Better is 27...Bd8 28.Rab1 Bb6 or 28.Nf5 Bc7.

28.Rab1 Nd7

If 28...a6, then 29.Rb7 Ra7 30.Rxf7 Kxf7 31.Bxd5+ or if

28...Ne7, then 29.Rb7 Qa6 30.Rxe7 Bxe7 31.Nxd5.

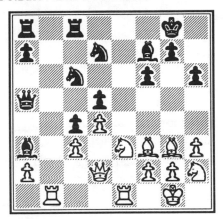

29.Rb7!
The start of a deeply calculated combination.

29...Nb6
Shutting in the Rook and over-protecting d5.

30.Nf5 Qa6?
31...Bf8 was necessary.

31.Nxh6+! gxh6 32.Rxf7 Kxf7 33.Qxh6
Threatening both 34.Bh5+ Kg8 35.Qg6+ Kh8 36.Qxf6+ and 34.Qh7+ Kf8 35.Bh5.

33...Kg8
A defense is not easy to find:

a) If 33...Rf8, then 34.Qh7#.

b) If 33...Bf8, then 34.Qh7+ Bg7 35.Bh5+ Kf8 36.Bd6+ Ne7 37.Bxe7#.

c) If 33...Ne7, then 34.Qh7+ Ke8 35.Bg4 Nd7 36.Qh5+ Kd8 37.Qh8+ Ng8 38.Qxg8+ Nf8 39.Qxd5+ winning.

34.Qg6+ Kh8 35.Qxf6+ Kg8 36. Qg6+ Kh8
If 36...Kf8, then 37.Bf4.

37.Re5! 1-0

Before we look at the Torre Attack, lets look at unusual first moves for Black.

Illustrative Game 49

IM Jon Tisdall
GM Julian Hodgson

London 1990

1.d4 b5
Against 1...b6, White should also get an advantage by playing the same way: 2.e4 Bb7 3.Nd2 followed by Ngf3 and Bd3.

2.e4 Bb7 3.Nd2 a6 4.Ngf3 Nf6 5.Bd3 e6 6.O-O c5 7.c3 Be7 8.dxc5 Bxc5 9.e5 Nd5 10.Ne4 Be7 11.a4 Nc6 12.Nd6+
12.axb5 axb5 13.Rxa8 Qxa8 14.Bxb5 also seems possible, although Black has some compensation for the pawn.

12...Bxd6 13.exd6 Qb8 14.Re1 O-O 15.axb5 axb5 16.Rxa8 Bxa8 17.Qe2 Qxd6 18.Bxb5 f5 19.Rd1 Qc7 20.c4 Nf6 21.Be3 h6 22.Bc5 Rf7
This is a very bad spot for the Rook, although Black's position

was already difficult.

23.Bd6 Qb7 24.Qf1

Defending the vulnerable g2-square.

24...Ne4 25.Bxc6 dxc6

Completely shutting in his Bishop. Of course 25...Qxc6 26.Ne5 is also bad.

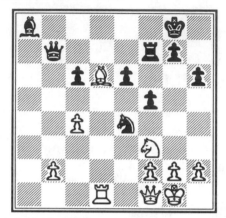

26.Ne5 Rf6 27.c5 Kh7 28.f3 Ng5 29.Qc4 Qxb2

Giving up the Exchange is as good as anything else in this lost position.

30.h4 Nf7 31.Nd7 Bb7 32.Be7 Bc8 33.Bxf6 gxf6 34.Qxe6 Kg7 35.Qxc6 Bxd7 36.Qxd7 1-0

Illustrative Game 50
GM Tony Miles
IM Zvonimir Mestrovic
Baden-Baden 1990

1.d4 Nc6 2.Nf3 d6 3.d5 Ne5

This leaves Black with an awkward pawn formation and he soon falls behind in development. Black's entire opening idea is dubious.

4.Nxe5 dxe5 5.e4 Nf6 6.Nc3 a6 7.f4 Qd6

Bringing the Queen out so early can never be good, but Black must hold the e5-square. Otherwise White's center pawns roll forward.

8.Qf3

Threatening 9.fxe5 Qxe5 10.Bf4.

8...Nd7 9.f5 g6 10.Be3 gxf5

This gives White the e4-square for his pieces.

11.exf5 Bh6

Exchanging pieces is a good idea in a cramped position.

12.O-O-O Bxe3+ 13.Qxe3 Nf6 14.Bd3 Rg8

14...Nxd5 15.Bb5+ axb5 16.Rxd5 is crushing.

15.Kb1 b6

15...Rxg2 is risky when Black is so far behind in development. However, in such a bad position, it was worth a try.

16.g3 Bb7 17.Rhe1 Ng4 18.Qe2 Qh6 19.f6! Qxf6

If 19...exf6 (or 19...Nxf6), then 20.Bf5 is also bad for Black.

20.Bxh7 Rg7 21.Ne4 Qh6 22.Bf5

Now Black's King is stuck in the center

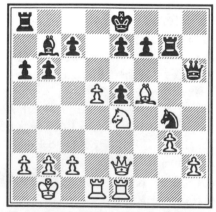

22...Bc8 23.Bxc8 Rxc8 24.Qxa6 Rd8 25.Qa4+ Kf8 26.Qa7 f5 27.Qxc7 Re8 28.d6 exd6 29.Qxd6+ Kg8 30.Qxh6 1-0

Conclusion:

After 1.d4 d5 2.Nf3 c5 3.dxc5 e6 4.e4 Bxc5, Black will get an isolated pawn, but should have enough piece activity to ensure equality.

After 1.d4 d5 2.Nf3, 2...Bf5 has been seen seldomly. Black appears to get a playable although slightly worse position.

1.d4 d5 2.Nf3 Nc6 3.g3 should be slightly better for White.

After 1.d4 d5 2.Nf3 Nf6 3.Bf4, 3...c5 is a strong move. The solid 3...Bg4 is also worth consideration.

Chapter 5
How to Play the Torre Attack

In this chapter the basics of the Torre Attack will be explained. Starting in Chapter 6 we will go through the theory of this opening in more detail.

The Torre Attack is named after its inventor, the Mexican Grandmaster Carlos Torre. He employed it to defeat a very famous opponent:

Illustrative Game 51

GM Carlos Torre
GM Emanual Lasker

Moscow 1925

1.d4 Nf6 2.Nf3 e6 3.Bg5

This first three moves of White characterize the Torre Attack.

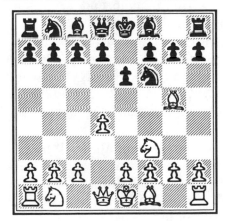

3...c5 4.e3 cxd4

This exchange might have been delayed. 4...Be7 and 4...Qb6 are the most commonly played moves here.

5.exd4 Be7 6.Nbd2 d6 7.c3 Nbd7 8.Bd3 b6 9.Nc4

This may not be a good square for the Knight. Later Black will gain a tempo for a Queenside minority attack when he plays ...b6-b5. Simple and good is 9.O-O.

9...Bb7 10.Qe2 Qc7 11.O-O O-O 12.Rfe1 Rfe8 13.Rad1 Nf8 14.Bc1 Nd5 15.Ng5

Starting a Kingside attack, but White might have first thought defensively by playing 15.Na3 a6 16.Nc2.

15...b5 16.Na3 b4 17.cxb4 Nxb4 18.Qh5 Bxg5 19.Bxg5 Nxd3 20.Rxd3 Qa5

Threatening the King Rook and threatening to win a piece with 21...f6 or 21...h6.

21.b4 Qf5

Black prefers to maintain the horizontal pin instead of winning a pawn. Worth considering is 21...Qd5. If 22.Rg3, then 22...h6 23.Bf6 Ng6 24.Qxd5 Bxd5 winning the Bishop on f6 and 22.Qg4 e5 gives Black the initiative.

22.Rg3 h6 23.Nc4 Qd5

Better is 23...hxg5 24.Nxd6 Qg6 25.Qxg6 Nxg6 26.Nxb7 Reb8 27.Nc5 Rxb4 28.Rxg5 Rxd4 leads to an approximately equal position.

24.Ne3 Qb5?

A mistake that allows White to execute what later became a very famous combination. Correct is 24...Qxd4 25.Bxh6 Ng6 26.Bg5 threatening 27.Rh3 gives White the initiative.

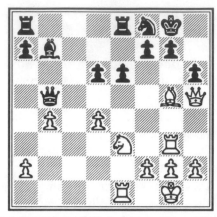

25.Bf6! Qxh5 26.Rxg7+ Kh8 27.Rxf7+ Kg8 28.Rg7+

White recovers more than enough material with this swinging movement. This is known as a windmill combination.

28...Kh8 29.Rxb7+ Kg8 30.Rg7+ Kh8 31.Rg5+ Kh7 32.Rxh5 Kg6 33.Rh3 Kxf6 34.Rxh6+ Kg5 35.Rh3 Reb8 36.Rg3+ Kf6 37.Rf3+ Kg6 38.a3 a5 39.bxa5 Rxa5 40.Nc4 Rd5 41.Rf4 Nd7 42.Rxe6+ Kg5 43.g3 1-0

Although this was not a convincing win because Black made a few mistakes and allowed the windmill combination, it has become very popular among top Grandmasters as well as non-professional players.

Here is another game from the same tournament:

Illustrative Game 52

GM Carlos Torre
GM Fritz Sämisch

Moscow 1925

1.d4 Nf6 2.Nf3 e6 3.Bg5 c5 4.e3 Nc6 5.Nbd2 b6 6.c3 Bb7 7.Bd3 cxd4 8.exd4 Be7 9.Nc4

The Knight is again moved to

this square, although now it makes more sense as 10.Bxf6 is threatened.

9...Qc7 10.Qd2 Rc8 11.O-O h6 12.Bf4 d6 13.Rfe1 Nd8

Protecting the f7- and e6-squares and opening the c-file and a8-h1 diagonal.

14.Qd1 Nd5 15.Bg3 O-O 16.Nh4

In order to meet 16...f5 with Ng6.

16...g5?!

Black probably thought that White would have to retreat the Knight to f3, after which 17...f5 would be strong. However, Torre has other ideas.

17.Qh5! Kg7?

Better is 17...gxh4.

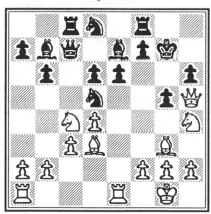

18.Rxe6! Nxe6 19.Nf5+ Kg8 20.Nxh6+ 1-0

If 20...Kg7, then 21.Nf5+ Kg8 22.Nxe7+ Kg7 23.Nxc8 Rxc8 24.Nxd6.

From these games, we see that White can obtain a strong Kingside attack by playing the Torre. This is not always the case. We will see other games in which White will have other plans. For example, see

the Petrosian games in this chapter.

There are a number of reasons for its popularity:

1) It's very solid.

2) One does not need to memorize a bunch of theoretical lines.

3) It leads to interesting middlegame positions.

4) It's very easy to learn.

White can usually play the first three moves no matter how Black replies: **1.d4, 2.Nf3, 3.Bg5.**

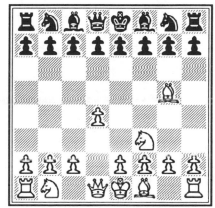

His next few moves will depend on how Black plays, but usually White will strive for this set-up:

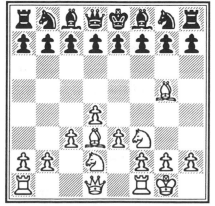

In this opening White is always able to develop his minor pieces and occupy the center. The Torre

Attack also exposes White to very little risk because of the solid central pawns on c3, d4, and e3. Hence White will have little trouble reaching a playable middlegame with a variety of reasonable plans at his disposal.

Many of the top players in the past and present have employed the Torre Attack. This list includes former World Champions Alekhine, Smyslov, Petrosian, Spassky, Kasparov. Other top Grandmasters are Kortchnoi, Timman, Yusupov, Keres, and Bronstein. Because of its versatility, it is employed by both positional and aggressive, tactical players.

In was particularly a favorite of Petrosian, as it was a natural for his solid maneuvering style.

Illustrative Game 52
GM Tigran Petrosian
IM Julius Kozma

Munich 1958

1.d4 Nf6 2.Nf3 e6 3.Bg5 c5 4.e3 b6?!

This move is a mistake because of White's next move. We will discuss this more in Chapter 6.

5.d5 exd5 6.Nc3 Bb7 7.Nxd5 Bxd5 8.Bxf6 Qxf6 9.Qxd5 Nc6

9...Qxb2 10.Rd1 is also good for White. See Chapter 6.

10.Bc4 Be7 11.O-O-O Rd8 12.Rd2

White is better because of his control of the d5-square. Watch how Petrosian slowly improves his position.

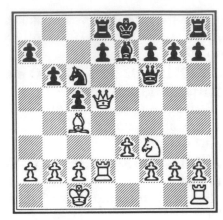

12...O-O 13.c3

Black was threatening 13...b5.

13...Na5 14.Be2 Qe6 15.Rhd1 Qxd5 16.Rxd5 d6 17.Nd2

Threatening 18.Ne4, inducing Black to further weaken his position.

17...f5 18.f4 g6 19.g3 Rf6 20.e4 fxe4 21.Nxe4 Re6 22.Bf3 Kg7

Better is 22...Nc4.

23.b3 Nc6 24.R5d3 Nb8 25.Nf2

Threatening 26.Bg4.

25...h5 26.Kd2 Bf8 27.Bd5 Re7 28.Ne4 Na6 29.Ke3 Nc7?

29...c4 offered more chances of resistance.

30.Kf3 Nxd5?!

Opposite colored Bishops offered better chances. Now its good Knight versus bad Bishop.

31.Rxd5 Rde8 32.Re1 Re6 33.Re2 b5 34.h3 a5 35.g4 hxg4+ 36.hxg4 Be7 37.f5 Re5 38.Rxe5 dxe5 39.Rd2 Rf8 40.Rd7 Rf7 41.Rxe7 1-0

Illustrative Game 53
GM Tigran Petrosian
GM Mark Taimanov

Leningrad 1960

1.d4 Nf6 2.Nf3 e6 3.Bg5 c5 4.e3

Nc6 5.Nbd2 b6 6.c3 Be7 7.Bd3 O-O 8.O-O cxd4 9.exd4 Nd5 10.Bxe7 Ncxe7 11.Re1 Bb7 12.Bf1 f5

This is commonly played here with the idea of starting a Kingside attack, although it is weakening.

13.Ne5 Qc7 14.Rc1 Rae8 15.c4 Nf6 16.Qb3 d6 17.Nef3 Ng6 18.c5 Bd5 19.Qa3 dxc5 20.dxc5 Ne4

If 20...e5, then 21.cxb6 Qxb6 22.Nc4 Bxc4 23.Bxc4+ Kh8 24.Qa6 with advantage to White.

21.Nxe4 fxe4?!

Black does not get enough counterplay on the f-file for his weakened pawn structure.

22.Nd2 Qf4 23.Qe3 bxc5 24.Rxc5 Qf6 25.Rc2 Ne5 26.Qg3

26.Nxe4 Qg6 is unclear.

26...Qf5 27.Rc7 Rf7 28.Rxf7 Nxf7 29.b3 Ne5 30.f3

Winning a pawn.

30...e3 31.Rxe3 Nc6 32.Ne4 Rf8 33.Ng5 Qf6 34.Nxe6 Re8

Of course if 34...Bxe6, then 35.Rxe6 Qxe6 36.Bc4.

35.Nxg7 Rxe3 36.Nf5+ Kf8 37.Nxe3 Qd4 38.Qf2 Bf7 39.h3

Nb4 40.a3 Na2 41.Nc4 Qxf2+ 42.Kxf2 Nc1 43.b4 Na2 44.Ke3 1-0

Illustrative Game 54

GM Tigran Petrosian
GM Mark Taimanov

Moscow 1960

1.d4 Nf6 2.Nf3 e6 3.Bg5 h6

This variation is discussed in Chapter 7. Black gains the Bishop pair, but White gets the center and a lead in development.

4.Bxf6 Qxf6 5.e4 d6 6.Nc3 c6?!

With the idea of playing ...e5 without having to worry about Nd5, but it is too slow and weakens the d6-square. Better is 6...Nd7 or 6...g6.

7.e5 dxe5 8.dxe5 Qf4 9.g3 Qb4 10.a3 Qa5

Not 10...Qxb2 11.Na4.

11.b4 Qc7 12.Ne4 a5 13.Rb1 axb4 14.axb4 Nd7 15.Nd6+ Bxd6 16.exd6

Black is quite cramped.

16...Qb6 17.Bg2 O-O 18.O-O Rd8 19.Qd2 c5 20.Rfd1 Ra2 21.b5 c4

Black is trying to gain counterplay but he is too far behind in development.

22.Qc3 Qc5 23.Nd2 Nb6 24.Ne4 Na4

If 24...Qa3, then 25.Qd4.

25.Qa5 Qb6 26.Qb4 e5 27.Ra1 Qd4 28.Rab1 Qb6 29.Qxc4 Be6 30.Qc7 Rc8

If 30...Qxc7, then 31.dxc7 Rxd1+ 32.Rxd1 Rxc2 33.Rd8+ Kh7 34.Nf6+ followed by 35.Be4+ wins.

31.Qe7 Nc5 32.Nxc5 Qxc5 33.Be4 b6 34.Rd2 Ra4 35.Bc6 Bh3 36.Re1 Kh7 37.Qxf7 Qb4 38.Qd5 Qc3 39.Qd3+ Qxd3 40.Rxd3 Rd8 41.d7 Kg6 42.f3 Kf6 43.g4 1-0

Spassky was more agressive when he played the Torre Attack, as illustrated in the following games:

Illustrative Game 55
GM Boris Spassky
GM Milan Matanovic

Havana 1962

1.d4 Nf6 2.Nf3 e6 3.Bg5 c5 4.e3 d5 5.Nbd2 Be7 6.c3 Nc6 7.Bd3 h6 8.Bh4 cxd4 9.exd4 Nh5?!

This Knight does not have a very good future with this maneuver.

10.Bxe7 Qxe7 11.O-O Nf4 12.Bc2 Qf6 13.Re1 O-O

One of the problems that Black has with this pawn structure is that his Queen Bishop gets shut in.

14.g3 Ng6 15.Qe2 b6 16.h4 Re8 17.Ne5 Ncxe5 18.dxe5 Qe7 19.Nf3 a5 20.Nd4 Bd7 21.Bd3 Rab8 22.a4

Preventing 22...b5. Black's position is very constricted.

22...Nf8 23.f4 Rec8 24.Kh2

White slowly prepares a Kingside attack. There is little that Black can do in the meantime.

24...Qe8 25.g4 Ng6 26.Qf2 Qe7 27.h5 Nf8 28.Rg1 f6 29.Rae1 Bxa4

Spassky does not care about mere pawns when he is concentrating his forces for the final breakthrough.

30.Qg3 Be8 31.exf6 Qxf6 32.Re5 Qf7 33.g5! Qxh5+ 34.Kg2 hxg5 35.fxg5 Qf7 36.Rf1 Qe7 37.g6 Rc4 38.Rh5 Rxd4 39.Rxf8+ 1-0

If 39...Qxf8, then 40.Rh8+ Kxh8 41.Qh3+ followed by mate.

GM Boris Spassky
IM Viacheslav Osnos
USSR Championship 1963/64

1.d4 Nf6 2.Nf3 e6 3.Bg5 c5 4.e3 Qb6

Trying to force White to awkwardly defend his b-pawn.

5.Nbd2

White decides to sacrifice the b-pawn instead in exchange for a lead in development. The move 5.Qc1 is also possible. These variations are discussed in Chapter 6.

5...Qxb2 6.Bd3 cxd4 7.exd4 Qc3 8.O-O d5 9.Re1 Be7 10.Re3 Qc7 11.Ne5 Nc6 12.c3

For the pawn White has a lead in development and attacking chances against Black's King.

12...Nxe5

With this move Black's King Knight gets forced to the back rank and he falls even further behind in development. Worth considering is 12...Bd7 followed by 13...Rc8.

13.dxe5 Ng8 14.Nf3 h6 15.Bf4 Bd7 16.Nd4 Bg5

Not 16...Qxc3? 17.Nxe6.

17.Bxg5 hxg5 18.Qg4 Qxc3 19.Nb3 Nh6 20.Qxg5 Qb4 21.Rg3

Preventing an exchange of Queens with 21...Qg4. Black is fine after 21.Qxg7 O-O-O.

21...Qf8?

Black should have returned the pawn with 21...Qe7 22.Qxg7 O-O-O. With Black's King stuck in the center, Spassky is in his element.

22.Rc1 f6 23.Qe3 f5

Threatening 24...f4, but this does not concern Spassky.

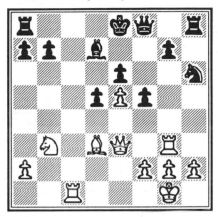

24.Nc5! f4 25.Bg6+ Ke7 26.Qa3 1-0

Many other top players regularly employ the Torre attack. The Croatian Grandmaster Vladimir Kovacevic is one of its most enthusiastic practitioners.

GM Vladimir Kovacevic
GM Bent Larsen
Bugojno 1984

1.d4 Nf6 2.Nf3 g6 3.Bg5

The Torre Attack can also be employed against the King's Indian. We examine this starting in Chapter 11.

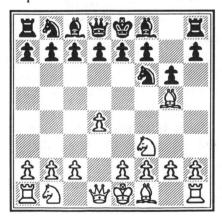

3...Bg7 4.e3

Another plan is 4.Nbd2 with the idea of 5.e4. White chooses a more restrained approach.

4...c5 5.Nbd2 b6 6.c3 Bb7 7.Qa4!?

Bringing out the Queen so early is a bit unusual. White hopes to generate pressure on the Queenside.

7...O-O 8.Be2 d6

If 8...d5, then White will play 9.O-O followed by Rfd1, Rac1 and c4.

9.O-O Nbd7 10.b4 Qc7 11.bxc5 bxc5 12.Rab1 Rfc8 13.Qa3 Nb6 14.Bd3 e6 15.Rfe1 h6 16.Bh4 Nh5 17.Nf1 cxd4

Worth considering is 17...g5 18.Bg3 Nxg3 winning the Bishop pair.

18.cxd4 Bxf3?!

The weakening of White's Kingside is not enough compensation for giving up this important Bishop. Better is 18...g5.

19.gxf3 Qc3 20.Qa6 Bf6 21.Bxf6 Nxf6 22.Kg2?!

Better is 22.Ng3 followed by Ne2 and Rec1.

22...Ne8

Threatening 23...Nc7.

23.Be2 d5 24.Red1 Nd6 25.Nd2 Nf5

This Knight puts pressure on White's Kingside. White should now try to get rid of it with 26.Bd3.

26.Nb3?! Qc7

Black is intending to bring the Queen over to the Kingside with ...Qe7.

27.Nd2 Qe7 28.Bd3 Nh4+ 29.Kf1

The King runs to safety at e2, where it will be safe.

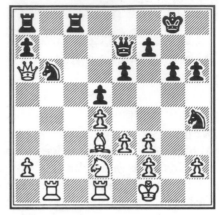

29...Rc6

If 29...Qg5, then White starts an attack on the Queenside with 30.a4 followed by a5.

30.Rdc1 Rac8 31.Rxc6 Rxc6 32.Ke2 Kg7 33.f4 Qc7 34.Qa5 Rc3!

Black should have tried to continue his Kingside initiative with 34...g5.

35.Rb5

With the idea of 36.Rc5.

35...Nd7

If 35...Nf5, then 36.Rc5 Rxc5 37.dxc5 Na8 38.Qxc7 Nxc7 39.Bxf5 gxf5 40.Nb3 followed by Nd4 gives White a large advantage.

36. Qb4 Nf5?

This loses a piece. Better is 36...Qc8. Then White would play 37.a4 followed by a5-a6 and Rb7 with advantage.

37.Bxf5 gxf5 38.Rb7 Qc6 39.Rxd7 1-0

Chapter 6

1.d4 Nf6 2.Nf3 e6 3.Bg5 c5

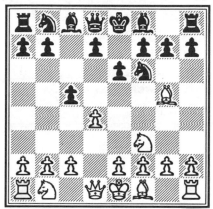

4.e3

We examine four possiblilites for Black:

**A) 4...b6?! B) 4...Qb6 C) 4...h6
D) 4...Be7**

A) 4...b6?!

A common mistake here, after which White often gains a dominating position with **5.d5!**

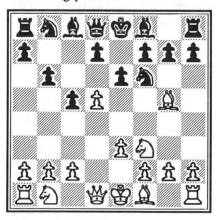

Black has tried the following:

a) 5...exd5 6.Nc3

a1) 6...Bb7 7.Nxd5 Bxd5 8.Bxf6 Qxf6 9.Qxd5 Nc6 (if 9...Qxb2, then

10.Rd1 Qb4+ 11.c3 Qxc3+ 12.Rd2) 10.Bc4 Be7 11.O-O-O Rd8 12.Rd2 O-O 13.c3 is better for White. See Illustrative Game 52.

a2) 6...Be7 7.Nxd5 Bb7 (7...O-O 8.Bxf6 Bxf6 9.c3 Na6 10.Qd2 Rb8 11.Rd1 b5 12.Be2 Nc7 13.Nxf6+ Qxf6 14.O-O Rb6 15.b4 with advantage to White, Chernin–Salov, USSR 1983.) 8.Bxf6 Bxf6 9.c3 O-O (9...Nc6 10.Qc2 Ne5? 11.Nxe5 Bxd5 12.O-O-O Be6 13.Nxd7 Bxd7 14.Qe4+ Be7 15.Rxd7 Qxd7 16.Qxa8+ Bd8 17.Qe4+ Be7 18.Bd3 with a winning advantage to White, Barlov–Ostermeyer, Biel 1985) 10.Bc4. See Illustrative Game 58.

b) 5...d6 6.dxe6 (6.Bxf6 Qxf6 7.Nc3 a6 8.Nd2 Qd8 9.a4 Be7 10.Be2 O-O 11.O-O Nd7 12.Nc4 Nf6 13.e4 Rb8 14.dxe6 fxe6 15.e5 dxe5 16.Qxd8 Rxd8 17.Nxe5 Bb7 18.Rfe1 with advantage to White, Barlov–Andersson, Haninge 1988) 6...Bxe6 7.Bb5+ Nbd7 8.Nc3 a6 9.Bxd7+ Bxd7 10.Nd5 Be7 11.Bxf6 Bxf6 12.Nxf6+ Qxf6 13.Qd5 Ke7 14.O-O-O with a winning advantage to White, Yusupov–Fries-Nielsen, Skien 1979.

c) 5...h6 6.Bxf6 Qxf6 7.Nc3 Bb7 (if 7...a6, then 8.Na4! exd5 [8...Qd8 9.dxe6 fxe6 10.Ne5 or 8...e5 9.d6] 9.Qxd5 Ra7 10.O-O-O Bb7 11.Qd2 Be7 12.Nc3 O-O 13.Bc4 b5 14.Bd5 with advantage to White, Zaichik–Gipslis, USSR 1988. If 7...d6, then 8.Nd2 e5 9.Bb5+ Bd7 10.O-O Bxb5 11.Nxb5 Qd8 12.f4! a6 [12...exf4 13.Qg4] 13.Nc3 Nd7 14.f5 Be7 15.Nce4 Nf6 16.Nxf6+ Bxf6 17.Qh5 Ke7 18.Ne4with advantage to White, Chernin–Kudrin, Mendoza 1985) 8.e4. See Il-

71

lustrative Game 59.

d) 5...b5!? 6.Nc3 a6 7.a4 b4 8.Ne4 d6 9.Bc4 e5 10.Qd3 Be7 11.Bxf6 Bxf6 12.Nxf6+ Qxf6 13.e4 O-O 14.Qe3 Nd7 15.Nd2 Qe7 16.O-O-O a5 17.b3 Nb6 18.f3 Qc7 19.g4 Ba6 20.Qd3 Bxc4 21.Nxc4 Nxc4 22.Qxc4 Qb7 Draw, Cifuentes–Speelman, Malta Olympiad 1980.

Illustrative Game 58

GM Artur Yusupov
GM Anatoly Karpov
London match 1989

1.d4 Nf6 2.Nf3 e6 3.Bg5 c5 4.e3 b6?!

This is probably the most common opening trap. Even Karpov fell into it!

5.d5! exd5 6.Nc3 Be7 7.Nxd5 Bb7 8.Bxf6 Bxf6 9.c3 O-O 10.Bc4

Also good for White is 10.Be2 d6 11.O-O Na6 12.a4 Nc7 13.Bc4 Rb8 14.Qd3 Bxd5 15.Bxd5 a6 16.Rfd1 g6 17.Bc6 Be7 18.Qe4 f6 19.b4 Piket–Farago, Wijk aan Zee 1988.

10...a6 11.O-O b5 12.Bb3

Better is 12.Nxf6+ Qxf6 13.Bd5 Nc6 14.Qd2 d6 15.Rfd1 Rfd8 16.a4 with a large advantage to White.

12...d6 13.Qd2 Nd7 14.Rfd1 Bxd5 15.Bxd5 Rb8 16.Qc2 Nb6 17.Rd2 g6 18.Rad1 Qc7?!

Better is 18...Qe7.

19.Qe4

Worth considering is 19.h4, because 19...h5 would not be possible. After 19...Kg7 20.h5 Qe7 21.g3 followed by Kg2, White has the initiative.

19...Kg7 20.h4 Qe7 21.Qf4 Be5 22.Nxe5 dxe5 23.Qg3 Rbd8 24.h5 Rd7

Not 24...Rd6 because of 25.hxg6 and if 25...hxg6, then 26.Bxf7!

25.b3 Rfd8 26.e4 g5 27.Qe3 h6 28.c4 Rc7

Black wants to play ...Nb6-d7-f6 to hit the weakness at h5.

29.Rd3 Nd7

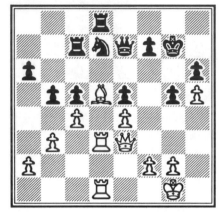

30.Bxf7!

With both players short on time, White complicates the position with a spectacular Bishop sacrifice.

30...Kxf7!

Not 30...Qxf7? because of 31.Qh3 tying Black down.

31.Qd2

White's compensation for the piece is that Black's pieces are pinned to the Knight, he has weak pawns, and the King has little protection.

31...Ke8 32.Qa5 bxc4

If 32...Rc6, then 33.cxb5 axb5 34.Qxb5 Qe6 35.Rd5 with a strong attack.

33.bxc4 Rcc8?

The decisive error. Black wants to play 33...Nf8.

34.Qa4

Threatening 35.Rd6.

34...Rc7 35.Qxa6 Rb8 36.Qg6 + Kf8?

36...Kd8 would have held out longer, although 37.Rd6 Kc8 (or 37...Qe8 38.Qxh6) 38.Re6 Nf8 39.Rxe7 Nxg6 40.Re8+ Kb7 41.Rb1 + is winning.

37.Rf3 + 1-0

Illustrative Game 59
GM Lubomir Kavalek
IM Lucas Brunner

Solingen 1986

1.d4 Nf6 2.Nf3 e6 3.Bg5 c5 4.e3 b6?! 5.d5! h6 6.Bxf6 Qxf6 7.Nc3 Bb7 8.e4

Also good is 8.Bc4 a6 9.a4 d6 10.Qd3 e5 11.a5! bxa5 12.O-O Qd8 13.Nd2 Be7 14.Nb3 O-O 15.Nxa5 with advantage to White, Cifuentes–Tarjan, Malta Olympiad 1980.

8...Qd8 9.e5

White's control of the center gives him the advantage.

9...exd5 10.Nxd5 Nc6 11.Bc4 Na5 12.Qd3 Nxc4 13.Qxc4 Be7 14.O-O-O O-O 15.Rhe1 Bc6 16.Qg4

As Black has been prevented from obtaining any counterplay, White now directs his attention to the Kingside.

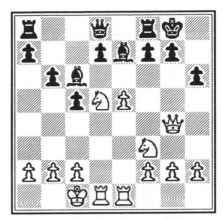

16...a6 17.Kb1 Ra7

If 17...f5, then 18.Qg6 is very strong.

18.Ne3

Threatening 19.Nf5.

18...Kh7 19.h4 Bxf3?

This just opens up the g-file for White.

20.gxf3 g6

Not 20...Bxh4 because of 21.Nf5 Bg5 22.f4 with a winning advantage to White.

21.h5 Rg8 22.f4 Qe8 23.Nd5 Bd8 24.hxg6 + Rxg6

If 24...fxg6, then 25.Nf6 + Bxf6 26.exf6 followed by Re7 + is decisive.

25.Qh3 Qg8 26.Rh1 Qg7 27.f5 Rg4 28.f6 Qg6 29.Ne3 Rg5 30.Qh2 1-0

There is no defense to f4 followed by Rdg1.

B) 4...Qb6

The poisoned pawn variation has been successful for Black and its practitioners include Karpov. However, it is risky. Black will lose time with his Queen and fall behind in development. He will also have trouble finding a safe place for his King.

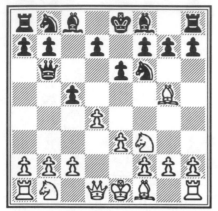

White now has the choice between sacrificing **B1) 5.Nbd2** or protecting **B2) 5.Qc1** the b-pawn.

B1) 5.Nbd2

An alternative is 5.Bxf6.

a) 5...gxf6 6.Qc1 (6.Nbd2 Qxb2 7.Be2 cxd4 8.Nxd4 a6 9.O-O Qb6 10.Rb1 Qc7 with advantage to Black, G. Garcia–Karpov, Leningrad 1977) 6...Nc6 7.c3 d5 8.Nbd2 Bd7 9.Be2 Rc8 10.O-O cxd4 11.exd4 Bd6 12.Qb1 Ne7 13.Re1 with advantage to Black, Holmov–Anikaev, USSR 1976.

b) 5...Qxb2 6.Bxg7 Bxg7 7.Nbd2 cxd4 8.exd4 Nc6 9.Rb1 Qxa2 10.Bd3 Nxd4 11.Nxd4 Bxd4 12.O-O d5 13.Qg4 Bc3 14.Qf4 with compensation for the sacrificed material, Hodgson–Schulz, Benidorm 1988.

5...Qxb2

Black has also declined or postponed the pawn capture:

a) 5...d5 6.Bxf6 gxf6

a1) 7.Qb1 Nc6 8.c3 cxd4 9.Nxd4 e5 10.N4b3 Be6 11.a4 a6 12.a5 (Taimanov–Gipslis, Tallinn 1980) 12...Qc7 13.e4 O-O-O is unclear, according to Taimanov.

a2) 7.Rb1 cxd4 8.Nxd4 Nc6 9.Ne2 e5 10.Ng3 Be6 11.Bd3 e4 12.Be2 f5 13.O-O h5 14.Nxh5 O-O-O 15.c3 Bd6 16.Re1 f4 17.exf4 Bc5 with compensation for the sacrificed material, Torre–Lobron, Lucerne Olympiad 1984.

a3) 7.Be2 cxd4 8.exd4 Nc6 9.Nb3 Bd6 10.O-O O-O 11.Re1 Bd7 12.c3 Ne7 13.Bd3 Bb5 14.g3 Bxd3 15.Qxd3 a5 16.Nc5 Qc6 with equality, Hug–Keller, Zurich 1984.

a4) 7.c4 cxd4 8.exd4 Nc6 (8...dxc4 9.Bxc4 Nc6 10.O-O Bd7 11.d5 exd5 12.Qe2+ Ne7 13.Bxd5 O-O-O 14.Bxf7 with advantage to White, Spassky–Zaitsev, USSR Championship 1962) 9.cxd5 exd5 10.Bd3 Be6 (9...Nxd4 11.Qa4+ Nc6 12.O-O Be6 13.Rac1 Rc8 14.Qh4 Be7 15.Qh5 with advantage to White, Rodriguez–Sunye Neto, Lucerne Olympiad 1984) 11.O-O Bd6 12.Rc1 O-O-O 13.Qa4 Kb8 14.Nb3 Rhg8 15.Rfe1 Rg4 16.Qb5 Rdg8 17.g3 h5 with advantage to Black, Plachetka–Hardicsay, Stary Smokovec 1982.

b) 5...cxd4 6.exd4 Qxb2 7.Bd3 d5 8.O-O.

b1) 8...Qc3 9.Re1 (9.Rb1 Be7 10.Rb3 Qc7 11.Ne5?! Nc6 12.Ndf3 Nxd4 with advantage to Black, Hoi–Shamkovich, Esbjerg 1982; 11.Qb1!? Nc6 12.c4 is unclear, according to Shamkovich) 9...Be7 10.Re3 Qc7 11.Ne5 Nc6 12.c3 Nd7 13.Bxe7 Ndxe5 14.dxe5 Nxe7 15.Qg4 g6 16.c4 Bd7 17.Qg5 unclear, Marovic–Muco, Malta Olympiad 1980.

b2) 8...Nc6 9.c4 Qc3 (if 9...Nxd4, then 10.cxd5 followed by Rb1) 10.Qe2 Nxd4 11.Nxd4 Qxd4 12.Nf3 Qc5 13.cxd5 Qxd5 14.Bc4 Qa5

15.Bxf6 gxf6 16.Bb5+ with a strong attack, Yermolinsky–Garma, Manila Olympiad 1992.

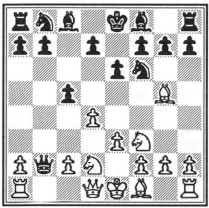

6.Bd3

a) 6.Rb1 Qc3 7.Rb3 Qa5 8.Rb5 Qxa2 9.Bxf6 gxf6 10.Ne4 a6 11.Rxc5 Bxc5 12.dxc5 Qa5+ 13.Nfd2 f5 14.Nd6+ Ke7 15.Qh5 with compensation for the exchange, Kopec–deFirmian, USA 1986.

b) 6.Bxf6 gxf6

b1) 7.Be2

b11) 7...cxd4 8.Rb1 Qc3 9.O-O Qc7 10.Nxd4 a6 11.c4 Nc6 12.Ne4 Be7 13.c5 O-O 14.Bd3 f5 15.Ng3 Ne5 16.Rc1 d6 17.cxd6 Qxd6 18.Bb1 Nc6 19.Nxc6 bxc6 20.Qxd6 Bxd6 21.Rxc6 Be5 22.Rc5 Bd6 23.Rc6 Be5 24.Rc5 Bd6 Draw, Matlak–Bandza, Katowice 1993.

b12) 7...Qb6 8.O-O Be7 9.c4 Nc6 10.d5 Ne5 11.Ne1 f5 12.f4 Ng6 13.Bd3 d6 14.Rb1 Qa5 unclear, Malaniuk–Oll, Novosibirsk 1986.

b13) 7...Nc6 8.O-O cxd4 9.Nc4 Qb4 10.Rb1 Qe7 11.exd4 d5 12.Ne3 Bh6 13.c4 dxc4 14.Bxc4 O-O 15.Qe2 Rd8 16.Rfd1 f5 17.Bb5 Bxe3 18.Qxe3 with compensation, Hug–Torre, Zurich 1984.

b2) For 7.Rb1, see Illustrative Game 60.

Now we examine two moves for Black:
B11) 6...Qc3
B12) 6...d5

Alternatives:
a) 6...Qb6 7.O-O

a1) 7...cxd4 8.exd4 Be7 9.Re1 Qc7 10.c4 b6 11.Rc1 d6 12.Bb1 Nbd7 13.Nf1 h6 14.Bh4 Bb7 15.Ne3 O-O 16.Nd5 Qd8 17.Nxe7+ Qxe7 18.d5 Rfe8 19.Nd4 with a winning advantage to White, Nei–Mikenas, Moscow 1967.

a2) 7...d6 8.dxc5 dxc5 9.e4 h6 10.Bh4 Nc6 11.Nc4 Qc7 12.Qb1 Nh5 13.Qb2 Be7 14.Bxe7 Qxe7 15.Nfe5 O-O 16.Nxc6 bxc6 17.Qe5 Qg5 18.f4 Qxe5 19.Nxe5 Nf6 20.Rab1 with a winning advantage to White, Bondarevsky–Antoshin, Sochi 1964.

a3) 7...Nc6 8.Rb1 Qc7 (8...Qd8 9.e4 cxd4 10.e5 h6 11.Bh4 g5 12.Bg3 Nd5 13.Ne4 b6?! [13...Nc3] 14.Nfd2 with advantage to White, Knezevic–Stean, Cirella di Diamante 1976/77) 9.Bxf6 gxf6 10.Ne4 (Kirpichnikov–Vitolinsh, Yurmala 1978) 10...Be7 equal.

b) 6...Nc6 7.O-O d5 (not 7...Be7? 8.Nc4 Qb4 9.c3! Qxc3 10.Rc1 Qb4 11.a3 Qb5 12.Nd6+ winning the Queen) 8.Bxf6 gxf6 9.c4 Nb4 10.Be2 Qa3 11.e4 dxe4 12.Nxe4 Be7 13.Qd2 Bd7 14.Qf4 O-O-O 15.Nxf6 cxd4 16.Nxd4 Bc6 17.Nb5 Qa5 18.Ne4 Bxe4 19.Qxf7 Rd7 20.Qxe6 Bc6 21.Bg4 h5 22.Bh3 Bd8 23.Rad1 Rh7 24.a3 Nc2 25.Qg6 Rhe7 26.Qxc2 a6 27.Na7+ 1-0, I.

75

Sokolov–Georgiev, Palma de Mallorca 1989.

c) 6...cxd4, see Illustrative Game 56.

B11) 6...Qc3
7.Bxf6

7.O-O d5 8.Re1 (8.dxc5 Qxc5? 9.c4 with a strong position for White, Nun–Sjoberg, Hradec Kralove 1985. Better is 8...Nbd7.) 8...cxd4 (8...c4 9.Bf1 Nc6 10.Bxf6 gxf6 11.e4 with advantage to White, Alexejev–Balashov, USSR 1972) 9.Nxd4 a6 10.N4f3 Nc6 11.e4 Be7 12.exd5 Nxd5 13.Ne4 Qa3 14.c4 Nc3 15.Qd2 Nxe4 16.Bxe4 f6 17.Bf4 e5 18.Rad1 Bg4 19.Re3 Qc5 20.Bg3 O-O 21.Qc2 f5 22.Bd5+ Kh8 23.Bxc6 Qxc6 24.Bxe5 with equality, Salov–Psakhis, Irkutsk 1986.

7...gxf6 8.O-O d5 9.e4

9.dxc5 Qxc5 10.c4 Bg7 11.cxd5 Qxd5 12.Qc2 Nc6 13.Rab1 Qd7 14.Nc4 h6 15.Rfd1 Qc7 Rodriguez–deFirmian, New York 1988. Now White blundered a piece with 16.Bh7? f5 17.Nd6+ Kf8 18.Bxf5 exf5 with a winning advantage to Black. Perhaps the best way for White to continue is with the transfer of the Knight from c4 to h5 via d2, e4, and g3. Nevertheless, the position is good for Black. Later in Kamsky–deFirmian, Reykjavik 1990, Black varied with 9...f5 10.Rb1 Nc6 11.Rb3 Qg7 12.c4 d4 and should again have a fine position. For 9...Bg7, see Illustrative Game 61. For 9...Nd7, see Illustrative Game 62.

9...c4 10.Be2 Be7 11.Re1 Nc6 12.exd5 exd5 13.Bxc4 dxc4 14.Ne4

Qa5 15.d5 Ne5

With two examples:

a) 16.Nxe5 fxe5 17.Qf3 Kf8 18.Rad1 Bd7 19.Qh5 Rg8 20.Qxh7 Bg4 21.Qh6+ Rg7 22.d6 Bd8 23.Qh8+ unclear, Balashov–Oll, Sverdlovsk 1987.

b) 16.d6 Bd8 17.Nxe5 fxe5 18.d7+ Bxd7 19.Nd6+ Kf8 20.Nxf7 Qc7 21.Qf3 Kg7 22.Nxd8 Raxd8 23.Qg3+ Kf6 24.Qh4+ Kg6 25.Qg3+ Kf6 26.Qh4+ Kg6 27.Qg3+ Draw, Shabalov–Oll, Vilnius 1988.

B12) 6...d5

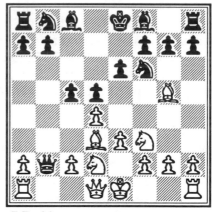

7.Bxf6

A major alternative is 7.c4 Qc3 8.Ne5 Nc6 (8...Nfd7 9.Rc1 Qa3 10.Nxd7 Bxd7 11.Bb1 h6 12.Bf4 cxd4 13.O-O unclear, Karner–Karpov, USSR 1972) 9.Rc1 Qa3 10.Nxc6 bxc6 11.Qc2 Rb8 12.Rb1 Rxb1 13.Qxb1 Be7 14.O-O cxd4 15.exd4 h6 16.Bxf6 Bxf6 17.cxd5 cxd5 18.Bb5+ Ke7 19.Rc1?! (19.Nf3! unclear) 19...Qa5?! (19...Bxd4! 20.Rc7+ Kf6! with advantage to Black) 20.Nf3 Rd8 21.Rc5! unclear, Spassky–Miles, Tilburg 1978.

Dubious is 7.O-O?! c4 8.Be2 Be7

9.Ne5 Nc6 10.Rb1 Qa3 11.Nxc6 bxc6 12.e4 O-O 13.Re1 c3 14.Rb3 cxd2 15.Rxa3 dxe1=Q+ 16.Qxe1 Bxa3 with a winning advantage to Black, Kristenson–Sher, Hastings 1989–90.

7...gxf6 8.c4

8.Rb1 Qc3 9.O-O c4 10.Bxc4 dxc4 11.Ne4 Qa5 12.Nxf6+ Ke7 13.Ne5 Nc6 14.Qh5 Nxe5 15.dxe5 Bg7 16.Rfd1 h6? 17.Rxb7+ 1-0, Pira–Michalet, France 1990.

8...Qc3

8...b5 9.0-0 Qa3 10.Qb1 bxc4 11.Nxc4 Qa6 12.Nce5 c4 13.Nxc4 dxc4 14.Be4 Nc6 15.d5 Rb8 16.Qc2 Nb4 17.Qb2 exd5 18.Bxd5 Rb6 0-1, Klinger–Granda Zuniga, Novi Sad Olympiad 1990. 9.Rb1 would have better tested Black's novelty.

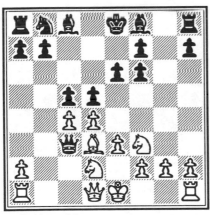

9.Be2 cxd4

9...dxc4 10.O-O Qa5 11.Nxc4 Qc7 12.Rc1 Nc6 13.Ncd2 Be7 gives White the opportunity to seize the advantage by 14.dxc5, Vaganian–Razuvaev, USSR Championship 1983. Vaganian also gives a big advantage for White after 13.e4 cxd4 14.Nxd4 a6 15.Nxc6 bxc6 16.e5.

After the text, Salov–de la Villa Garcia, Szirak Interzonal 1987, continued 10.Rc1 Qa5 11.cxd5 Na6

12.Nxd4 Qxd5 13.O-O Be7 14.Bf3 Qd7 (14...Qd8 15.Qb3 O-O 16.Bxb7 Rb8 17.Rxc8 with advantage to White, Salov) 15.Nc6! O-O 16.Qe2! Nb4 17.Nxb4 Bxb4 18.Ne4 Be7 19.Rfd1 Qe8 20.Rc7 e5 21.Ng3 Bd8 22.Rxc8 Rxc8 23.Be4 f5 24.Nxf5 Kh8 25.Nd6 Qe6 26.Bf5 1-0.

B2) 5.Qc1

5...Ne4

5...Nc6

a) 6.c3 d5 7.Nbd2 Bd7 (7...Be7 8.Be2 Qc7 9.dxc5 Bxc5 10.c4 Be7 11.O-O O-O 12.a3 Bd7 13.cxd5 Nxd5 14.Bxe7 Ndxe7 15.Qc5 e5 12.Rac1 b6? 17.Qxe7 1-0, Kovacevic–Podlesnik, Ljubljana 1989).

a1) 8.Bd3 Rc8 9.O-O h6 10.Bf4 cxd4 11.exd4 Nb4 12.Be2 Bb5 with equality, Prokesh–Capablanca, Budapest 1929.

a2) 8.Be2 Rc8 9.Qb1 Bd6 10.O-O O-O 11.Bxf6 gxf6 12.dxc5 Bxc5 13.e4! dxe4 14.Qxe4 Be7 (14...Qxb2 15.Qh4!) 15.Rad1 Kh8 16.Nc4 Qc7 17.Qh4 Rg8 18.Qh5! Rg7 19.Rd2! Rcg8 20.g3 b5 21.Rfd1 Be8 22.Nd6 a6 23.Qc5 with a winning advantage to White, Larsen–Popel, USA 1972.

b) 6.Bxf6 gxf6 7.c3 d5

b1) 8.Nbd2 Bd7 9.Be2 Rc8 10.O-O cxd4 11.exd4 Bh6 12.Qb1 O-O 13.Nb3 Ne7 14.Nc5 Bc6 15.g3 Kh8 16.a4 Rg8 17.Nh4 Qc7 18.Bd3 Ng6 19.Nxg6+ hxg6 20.Re1 e5 unclear, Kogan–deFirmian, USA 1984.

b2) 8.Bd3?! cxd4 9.cxd4 e5 10.Be2 Rg8 11.g3 Bh3 12.Nc3 O-O-O 13.a3 Kb8 14.b4 Bh6

15.Na4 Qc7 16.Qb2 Rge8 with advantage to Black, Sideif-Zade–Yudasin, USSR 1989.

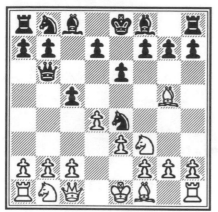

After 5...Ne4, White has two ways of retreating: **B21) 6.Bf4** and **B22) 6.Bh4**

B21) 6.Bf4

6...Nc6

6...d5

a) 7.c3 Bd7 8.Nbd2 Nxd2 9.Qxd2 Bb5 10.Bxb5 Qxb5 11.Qe2 Qxe2+ 12.Kxe2 with equality, Morovic–Miles, Malta Olympiad 1980.

b) 7.Bd3

b1) Dubious is 7...Bd6?! 8.Bxd6 Qxd6 9.c4!

b2) 7...Nd7 8.O-O Bd6 9.Bxd6 Qxd6 10.c4 O-O 11.Qc2 Nef6 with equality, Alekhine–Spielmann, Semmering 1926.

b3) 7...f5 8.c3 Be7 9.Nbd2 Nc6 10.h4 O-O 11.Ne5 Nxe5 12.Bxe5 Bd7 13.f3 Nd6 14.dxc5 Qxc5 15.Bd4 Qc7 16.f4 with advantage to White, Petrosian–Tscherepkov, USSR 1961.

b4) For 7...Nc6, see Illustrative Game 63

7.c3 Be7

7...d5

a) 8.Nbd2 Nxd2 9.Qxd2 Be7

10.Bd3 Bd7 11.O-O O-O 12.dxc5 Bxc5 13.e4 dxe4 14.Bxe4 Rfd8 with equality, Alburt–Sosonko, Lucerne Olympiad 1982.

b) 8.Bd3 Be7 (8...Bd7 9.O-O Rc8 10.Nbd2 f5, Hort–Sosonko, Amsterdam 1979. Now White could obtain an advantage with 11.Ne5.) 9.h3 Bd7 10.O-O f5 11.Ne5 Nxe5 12.Bxe5 Bf6 13.Bxf6 gxf6 14.Bxe4 fxe4 15.f3 Bb5 16.Rf2 with advantage to White, Dreev–Agzamov, Sevastopol 1986.

8.Nbd2 f5 9.Be2 O-O 10.O-O d5 11.Ne5 cxd4 12.exd4 Nxe5 13.Bxe5 Bd7 14.Qc2 Bb5 15.Bxb5 Qxb5 16.Nf3 Rac8 17.Ne1 Qc4 18.Nd3 b5 19.f3

With advantage to White, Spassky–Chandler, London 1985.

B22) 6.Bh4

6...d5

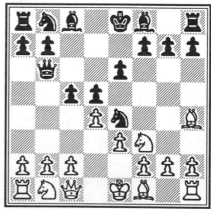

If 6...cxd4 7.exd4 g5 8.Bd3 Qa5+, Kovacevic recommends 9.c3 Nxc3 10.Nxc3 gxh4 11.Nxh4 with advantage to White.

7.c3 Nc6 8.Bd3

a) 8.Nbd2 f5 9.Nxe4?! fxe4 10.Nd2 cxd4 11.exd4 Bd6 12.Be2 O-O 13.O-O Bf4 14.Bg3 e5 15.dxe5 Bxg3 16.hxg3 Nxe5 with

78

advantage to Black, Petrosian–Olafsson, Stockholm 1962.

b) 8.Nfd2 f5 9.Nxe4 fxe4 10.Bg3 Bd7 11.Be2 Rc8 12.Qd2 Be7 13.O-O O-O 14.f4 exf3 15.Bxf3 Bg5 with advantage to Black, Quinteros–Ljubojevic, Las Palmas 1974.

8...Bd7

8...Bd6 9.Bxe4 dxe4 10.Nfd2 f5 11.Nc4 Qc7 12.Nba3 Be7 13.Nb5 Qd7 14.Bxe7 Kxe7 15.dxc5 Qd5 16.Nbd6 Qxc5 17.b4 (17.O-O Ne5 with equality) 17...Qd5 18.f4 b5 (18...exf3?! 19.e4 fxe4 20.Qf4! and Rd1 with advantage to White, Saidy) 19.Qa3! (19.Nxc8 Rhxc8 20.Nd2 Qd3 with a winning advantage to Black) 19...bxc4 20.Rd1 Qxd1+ 21.Kxd1 Rd8 22.b5 Rxd6+ 23.Kc2 Nd8 24.Rd1 Nb7 25.Rd4 Bd7 26.Rxc4 Ke8 with equality, Shirazi–Saidy, USA 1982.

9.Nbd2 f5

Lobron–Kortchnoi, Biel 1984, continued 10.Bg3 Nxg3 11.hxg3 g6?! (better is 11...Be7) 12.g4! and White stands somewhat better.

Illustrative Game 60
GM Rongguang Ye
GM Murray Chandler
Manila Interzonal 1990

1.d4 Nf6 2.Nf3 e6 3.Bg5 c5 4.e3 Qb6 5.Nbd2 Qxb2 6.Bxf6 gxf6 7.Rb1

Sacrificing another pawn to keep the Queen sidelined longer and hence gaining more time.

7...Qxa2

If 7...Qc3, then 8.Bd3 cxd4 9.O-O dxe3 10.Ne4 exf2+ 11.Rxf2 Qc7 12.Nxf6+ with an unclear position.

8.Nc4

Threatening to trap the Queen. For example, if 8...cxd4, then 9.Ra1 Bb4+ 10.Nfd2.

8...Qa4

The only move. If 8...Qa6, then 9.d5! exd5 10.Qxd5 Qc6 11.Qh5 with a large advantage to White.

9.d5 b5!

If 9...exd5, then 10.Qxd5 Qxc2 11.Bd3 Qc3+ 12.Nfd2 is strong.

10.Ncd2

Not 10.Rxb5 Ba6! 11.Nb2 Qe4 12.Rb3 Qxd5 with a large advantage to Black.

10...a6 11.Ra1 Qb4 12.c4! Bb7

Black is finally able to start developing some of his pieces. But his Queen is still in a bad position.

13.e4 Bg7 14.Rb1 Qa5 15.Bd3 Qc7

The Queen is finally able to return, but Black's problem now is finding a safe home for his King.

16.O-O b4 17.Nh4 a5 18.Bc2

It is important to blockade the passed pawns. Not 18.f4 a4 19.Qg4 Bh6 with a winning advantage to Black.

18...Bh6 19.Ba4 Qf4 20.dxe6

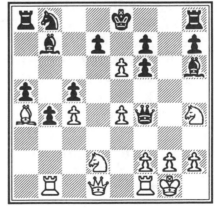

20...fxe6?!

Also bad is 20...Qxd2 21.Qh5 O-O 22.e7 Re8 23.Nf5 Bg7 24.Rfe1 Qg5 25.Qh3 followed by Rb3-g3 with a large advantage to White. Better is 20...Qxh4 21.exd7+ Kd8 22.Nb3 Qxe4 23.f3! Be3+ 24.Kh1 Qe7 25.Re1 with an unclear position.

21.Qh5+ Kd8 22.Ndf3! Bf8?!

Better is 22...Rg8 23.Rbd1 Rg7! 24.Qxc5 Bxe4 with an unclear position. After the text Black's pieces are disorganized and his position falls apart.

23.Rbd1!

23.Ng6 hxg6 24.Qxh8 Ke7 (24...Ke8 25.Qg8) 25.Qh7+ Kd8 is less clear.

23...Bxe4 24.Qf7 Ra7

There is no defense. If 24...Bd6, then 25.g3. Or if 24...Be7 25.Qxe6. Or if 24...Kc7 25.Bxd7.

25.g3!

Once again forcing the Queen into an awkward position on the side of the board.

25...Qh6 26.Qxe6 Bxf3 27.Nxf3 Rc7 28.Rfe1 Bg7 29.Qb6 Kc8 30.Re7 Rd8 31.Nh4 f5 32.Qxa5 Bf8 33.Nxf5! Qa6 34.Nd6+ Qxd6 35.Rxd6 Bxe7 36.Rb6 Rb7 37.Rh6 b3 38.Rb6 b2 39.Rxb7 Kxb7 40.Qb5+ Kc7 41.Qxb2 Nc6 42.Qg7 Bf8 43.Qxh7 Ne5 44.Bb5 Bd6 45.f4 Nf3+ 46.Kg2 Nd4 47.Ba4 Ne6 48.h4 Nf8 49.Qe4 Ne6 50.f5 Nd4 51.h5 Rb8 52.Bb5 Nxb5 53.cxb5 Rxb5 54.h6 Rb2+ 55.Kh3 Rb4 56.Qe8 Rb8 57.Qxb8 Kxb8 58.f6 1-0

Illustrative Game 61

GM Joel Benjamin
GM Leonid Yudasin

New York 1990

1.d4 Nf6 2.Nf3 e6 3.Bg5 c5 4.e3 Qb6 5.Nbd2 Qxb2 6.Bd3 Qc3 7.O-O d5 8.Bxf6 gxf6 9.dxc5 Bg7 10.Rb1 Qxc5 11.e4

White must open up the position before Black completes his development.

11...dxe4 12.Nxe4 Qc7 13.Bb5+ Kf8

If 13...Nc6, then 14.Qd4 is strong.

14.Qd2 a6 15.Be2 Nc6 16.Rfd1 h5

Black is having trouble developing his pieces. Therefore he advances his h-pawn to free his King's Rook and also tries to create a weakness on White's Kingside.

17.Nd6 h4 18.Rb3

Better is 18.h3. White will have trouble with the Black pawn on h3 later on.

18...h3 19.g3 Rh5 20.Rd3 Qa5 21.c3

Exchanging Queens would ease the pressure on Black.

21...Rb8 22.Qb2 Rc5 23.Nxc8

If 23.Bf1, then 23...f5.

23...Rb5??

With this zwischenzug Black seems to stay a pawn ahead. However, there is a simple reply. Better is 23...Rxc8, although after 24.Qxb7 Rb8 25.Qd7 Rxc3 26.Rxc3 Qxc3 27.Nd4 White has the advantage.

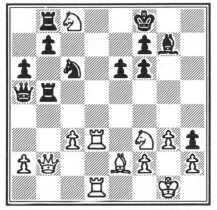

24.Qc2??

But White also misses it: 24.Qa3+! Then of course not 24...Qxa3? 25.Rd8+ mating. However, White is just a piece up after other moves.

24...Rxc8

Now White has inadequate compensation for the sacrificed pawn.

25.Rd7 Rb6 26.Qh7?!

White tries to get the h3 thorn, but now his Queen is out of play.

26...Rb2 27.Kf1 Rd8 28.Rxd8+ Nxd8 29.Qd3 Nc6 30.Qd7

Threatening 31.Qc8+ Ke7 32.Rd7 mate.

30...Bh6 31.Nd4 Nxd4 32.Qxd4 Qe5 33.Bf3 Rxa2 34.Qb4+ Kg7 35.Qg4+ Bg5 36.Qxh3 f5

Shutting off White's Queen.

37.Qg2 Qxc3 38.Be2

Not 38.Bxb7 Be3.

38...Qb3 39.h4 Bd2 40.Kg1 Qd5 41.Bf3 Qc5 42.Bxb7 Be3 43.Rf1 Bd4 44.Qf3 a5

While White is tied to the defense of f2, the passed a-pawn decides.

45.Qf4 Qb6 46.Bg2 a4 47.Kh2 Bf6 48.Qc4 Qb2 49.Bc6 a3 50.Be8 Qc2 51.Qa6 Qc5 0-1

Illustrative Game 62
GM Vladimir Malaniuk
GM Konstatin Aseev

Cattolica 1994

1.d4 Nf6 2.Nf3 e6 3.Bg5 c5 4.e3 Qb6 5.Nbd2 Qxb2 6.Bd3 Qc3 7.O-O d5 8.Bxf6 gxf6 9.dxc5 Nd7 10.e4 Qxc5 11.Rb1 a6

Preventing 12.Rb5.

12.Qe2 dxe4 13.Nxe4 Qa5 14.Nd4

Threatening 15.Nf5.

14...Be7 15.Rfe1

Again threatening 16.Nf5.

15...Kf8

As usual in this variation, Black is having trouble finding a safe spot for his King.

16.Nb3 Qc7 17.Qh5 h6

Preventing 18.Qh6+.

18.Ng3 Ne5 19.Nd4 Rb8

This looks like a waste of time. An immediate 19...Bd7 is worth considering.

20.Bf1 f5?!

Black will later regret this weakening of the a1-h8 diagonal.

21.Qe2 Ng4 22.h3 Nf6 23.Qd2 Bd7 24.Rb3 Rc8?!

Preventing 25.Rc3, but better is 24...Rd8. Black does not see the trap that White is setting up. Black should play ...h6-h5 but he will never find the time.

25.c4 Rd8

In order to defend the b7-pawn with ...Bc8, but White's next move contains a double threat.

26.Qb2 Bc8

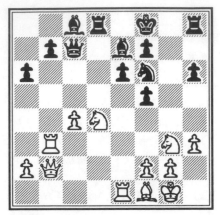

27.Nh5 Nxh5

The only move.

28.Nxe6+ fxe6 29.Qxh8+ Kf7 30.Qxh6 Nf6

White has a Rook and pawn for the two pieces, but more importantly Black is having trouble coordinating his pieces to defend his King.

31.Rg3 Rg8

The only move.

32.Rxg8 Nxg8 33.Qh7+ Kf8 34.Re3

Threatening to bring the other Rook to g3. Black's next move is forced.

34...Bd6 35.Qh5 Nf6?

Bringing the Queen over to the defense of the King with 35...Qf7 would make more sense.

36.Qh8+ Kf7 37.Be2 b5 38.g4

Threatening 39.g5, to which there is no defense.

38...Bf4 39.g5

Trying to force Black to give up control of the g3-square.

39...Bxg5

Black does not defend well in time pressure. But if 39...Ne4, then 40.Rd3 threatening 41.Rd8 and 41.Bh5+ is decisive.

40.Rg3 Ne4

Loses immediately, but there was no defense in any case.

41.Qh7+ 1-0

Illustrative Game 63

GM Alexey Dreev
GM Vadim Ruban

St. Petersburg 1993

1.d4 Nf6 2.Nf3 e6 3.Bg5 c5 4.e3 Qb6 5.Qc1 Ne4 6.Bf4 d5 7.Bd3 Nc6 8.c3 Be7

Hort–Sosonko, Amsterdam 1979 continued 8...Bd7 9.O-O Rc8 10.Nbd2 f5 11.Be5 (better is 11.Ne5) 11...Nxe5 12.Nxe5 Nf6 equal.

9.h4

To meet the threat of 9...g5, but 9.h3 was better.

9...O-O 10.Nbd2 f5 11.Ne5 Nxe5 12.Bxe5 Bd7 13.f3 Nd6 14.f4! Bb5 15.Bc2 Rac8

Now White is able to exchange his Bishop for Black's Knight. Better was 15...Nf7 16.Nf3 Nh6 followed by ...Ng4. Knights are better than Bishops in closed positions.

16.Bxd6 Bxd6 17.Nf3 Ba6?!

Better is 17...Be8.

18.Kf2 Qc7

If 18...cxd4 19.exd4 Bxf4?, then 20.Qxf4 Qxb2 21.Qc1.

19.g3 b5 20.a3 Bb7 21.Bd3 Qb6 22.Qd2

Not 22.Qd1 b4!

22...a5?!

It was necessary to close the Kingside with 22...h5.

23.Ng5 Be7 24.Qe2 h6

Not 24...b4? 25.Qh5 h6 26.Qg6 winning.

25.Nf3 Bc6

Better is 25...b4 with an unclear position.

26.Ne5 Be8 27.g4 Bd6 28.gxf5 Bxe5 29.fxe5 exf5

Not 29...Bg6? 30.f6 winning.

30.h5!

To prevent 30...g6.

30...c4 31.Bc2 b4 32.axb4 axb4 33.Kg3!

The White King is well placed strategically on f4. White has a large advantage. If now 33...Qd8, then 34.Qf3.

33...Bd7 34.Kf4! Be6 35.Qg2 Rb8 36.Rhg1 Rf7 37.Qg6?!

Correct was 37.Qh1 followed by Rg6 and Bd1-f3. The players were getting short on time here.

37...Kh8 38.cxb4?

It was better to try the plan given in the last note. 38.Qg2 followed by Qh1 and Rg6. Now the tables are turned. White will have trouble because the position of his King becomes bad.

38...Qxb4! 39.Qxe6

If 39.Rg2, then 39...Qe7.

39...Qd2 40.Kf3?

Not 40.Qxd5? Qf2+ 41.Qf3 Qh4+ with a winning advantage to Black. However, White could force Black to take a perpetual check with 40.Bxf5 Qf2+ 41.Kg4 Qe2+ 42.Kh4 Qf2+ 43.Kg4 equal. Now Black gets a large advantage.

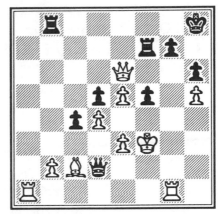

40...Qxc2 41.b4!

The only move. 41.Qxf7? Qe4+, 41.Ra8 Rb7!, and 41.Qxd5 Rxb2 all lose.

41...Qe4+ 42.Ke2 Rfb7?

Losing his advantage. Correct is 42...Rbf8! 43.Qg6 c3.

43.Qg6 Qd3+ 44.Kf3 c3

Black could have forced a perpetual check with 44...Qe4+ 45.Ke2 Qc2+.

45.Ra6! Qe4+

Unclear is 45...c2 46.Rc6 (46.Re6 Qd1+ 47.Kf4 Rg8 48.Re8 immediately forces a draw) 46...Ra8! 47.Re6! Qe4+ 48.Kf2 (not 48.Ke2? c1=N+! with a winning advantage to Black) 48...Qh4+ 49.Kf3.

46.Ke2 Qh4?!

This was Black's last chance to force a perpetual check with 46...Qc2+.

47.Re6 Qd8?

A time trouble error. Now White once again has a large advantage.

48.Rc6 Rc8 49.b5! Rcc7?!
50.Qd6! Rd7 51.Qc5 Rb8

If 51...Qh4, then 52.Qf8+ Kh7 53.Rxh6+ winning.

52.Qxc3 Qe8

If 51...Qh4, then 53.Rc8+ Rd8 54.Qc7! Qh2+ 55.Kd3 winning.

53.Rgg6 Rxb5 54.Rc8 Rd8 55.Qc7! 1-0

C) 4...h6

5.Bh4

5.Bxf6 Qxf6 6.c4!? cxd4 7.exd4 Bb4+ 8.Nbd2 b6 9.Be2 Bb7 10.O-O O-O 11.Ne5 Bxd2 12.Qxd2 d6 13.Ng4 Qg6 14.Ne3 Nc6 15.f4 Ne7 16.d5?! (16.Bd3 with advantage to White) 16...exd5 17.f5 Qg5 with equality, Torre–Cebalo, Novi Sad 1984.

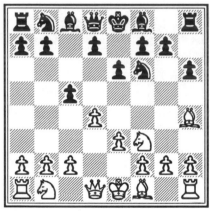

5...Be7

a) 5...b6 6.c3 Be7 7.Nbd2 O-O 8.e4 cxd4 9.cxd4 d5 10.Bxf6 Bxf6 11.e5 Be7 12.Bb5 Ba6 13.a4 Bb7 14.O-O a6 15.Bd3 Nc6 16.Re1 Bb4 17.Re3 Na5 with equality, Yusupov–Beliavsky, Linares 1993.

b) 5...Qb6 6.Qc1 cxd4 7.Bxf6 gxf6 8.exd4 d5 9.Be2 Nc6 10.c3 e5 11.O-O Bf5 12.Na3 Rc8 13.Nc2 h5 with advantage to Black, Spassky–Schmittdiel, German League 1989.

6.Nbd2

6.Bd3 b6 7.O-O Bb7 8.c4 cxd4 9.Nxd4 d6 10.Nc3 Nbd7 11.Re1 a6 12.Bf1 Rc8 with equality, Larsen–Andersson, Buenos Aires 1980.

6...cxd4

6...b6 7.Bd3 Bb7 8.O-O O-O 9.c3 d6 10.Re1 a6 11.Qe2 Nbd7 12.Rad1 Nh5 13.Bxe7 Qxe7 14.Be4 Bxe4 15.Nxe4 Nhf6 with equality, Balashov–Lerner, Kiev 1986

7.exd4 b6

7...Nc6 8.c3 d5 9.Bb5 Bd6 10.O-O a6 11.Bxc6+ bxc6 12.c4 O-O 13.c5 Bf4 14.Re1 Qe7 15.Qc2 unclear, Sideif-Zade–Dautov, Budapest 1989.

8.c3 Bb7 9.Bd3 d6

9...O-O 10.Qe2 d6 11.O-O-O Nbd7 12.Rhe1 a6 13.Kb1 b5 14.Ka1 Re8 15.Bb1 Nf8 16.h3 Nd5 17.Bxe7 Rxe7 18.g3 Rc7 19.Rc1 Rac8 unclear, Hulak–Seirawan, New York 1989.

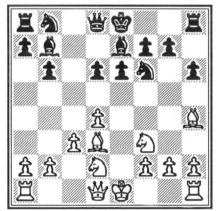

10.Qe2 Nh5?!

Better is 10...Nbd7 11.O-O-O Nd5 12.Bxe7 Qxe7 13.g3 Rc8 with equality.

11.Bxe7 Qxe7 12.g3! Nf6 13.O-O-O Nbd7 14.Rhe1 O-O 15.Kb1 a6 16.Ka1 b5 17.Bb1 Rfc8 18.Nh4 d5 19.f4 b4 20.c4 dxc4 21.Nxc4 Bd5 22.Ne3 Qd6 23.Nxd5 Qxd5 24.f5

with advantage to White, Kovacevic–Henley, New York 1989.

D) 4...Be7

4...cxd4 and 4...Nc6 will usually transpose to variations resulting after 4...Be7. For example, 4...Nc6 5.Nbd2 b6 6.c3 Bb7 7.Bd3 cxd4 8.exd4 Be7 9.Nc4 Qc7 10.Qd2. See Illustrative Game 51. For 4...d5, see Chapter 8, 3...d5.

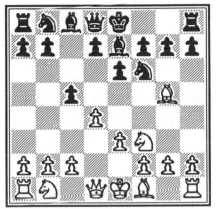

5.Nbd2

Another idea is 5.dxc5.

a) 5...Bxc5

a1) 6.Be2 Be7 7.c4 b6 8.Nc3 Bb7 9.O-O O-O 10.Qc2 Na6 11.Rad1 Nc5 12.Rd4 with advantage to White, Hort–Adorjan, Reggio Emilia 1984/85.

a2) 6.c4 Bb4+ 7.Nbd2 b6 8.Bd3 Nc6 9.O-O Be7 10.Rc1 Bb7 11.Qe2 O-O 12.Rfd1 Qc7 13.Bf4 d6 14.h3 Rac8 15.a3 Rfd8 with equality, Yusupov–Karpov, London 1989.

b) 5...Na6 6.Bxa6 Qa5+ 7.Nbd2 bxa6 8.c6 d6 9.c4 Qc7 10.Qa4 Rb8 11.c5 dxc5 12.Bf4 Bd6 13.Bxd6 Qxd6 14.Nc4 Qc7 15.Nfe5 Draw, Yusupov–Hübner, Baden-Baden 1992.

c) A new move is 5...Qa5+. See Illustrative Game 64.

5...b6

a) For 5...O-O, see Illustrative Game 65.

b) For 5...Nc6, see Illustrative Game 66.

c) 5...cxd4 6.exd4 b6 7.a4 Nc6 8.c3 O-O 9.Bd3 Nd5 10.Bxe7 Qxe7 11.O-O Nf4 12.Bb5 a6 13.Bxc6 dxc6 14.Ne5 f6 15.Nec4 Bb7 16.Qg4 g5 17.Nxb6 Rad8 18.Rfe1 c5 19.d5 h5 unclear, Hodgson–Motwani, London 1988.

6.Bd3

6.dxc5 bxc5 7.e4 Nc6 8.Bb5 Bb7 9.O-O O-O 10.e5 Nd5 11.Bxe7 Ncxe7 12.c4 Nb6 13.Ba4 Nxa4 14.Qxa4 Ng6 with a good position for Black, Utasi–Adorjan, Sarajevo 1984.

6...Bb7

a) Attempting to exchange Bishops with 6...Ba6 is worth considering. Beliavsky–Dolmatov, USSR Championship 1986, continued 7.c4 cxd4 8.Nxd4 Bb7 9.O-O O-O 10.Qe2 d6 11.Rac1 Nbd7 12.Rfd1 a6 with equality.

b) After 6...cxd4, Salov–Cebalo, Leningrad 1984, continued 7.exd4 Ba6 8.Bxf6 Bxf6 9.Ne4 Be7 10.d5 exd5 11.Bxa6 Nxa6 12.Qxd5 Nc7 13.Nd6+ Bxd6 14.Qxd6 Qe7+ 15.Qxe7+ Kxe7 16.O-O-O with advantage to White.

7.c3

7.O-O

a) 7...cxd4 8.exd4 Nd5 9.Bxe7 Qxe7 10.Re1 O-O 11.a4 Nc6 12.c3 f5 13.Nc4 Na5 14.Ne3 Qf6 15.Nxd5 Bxd5 16.b4 Nc6 17.Bf1 d6 18.a5 Draw, Walther–Siklos, 8th World Correspondence Championship.

b) 7...h6 8.Bh4 d6 9.c3 Nbd7 10.e4 g5?! 11.Bg3 Nh5 12.Bb5 Nxg3 13.fxg3 a6 14.Bxd7+ Qxd7 15.Nc4 Qb5?! 16.a4 Qc6 17.d5 with a large advantage to White, Ye–Hracek, Jakarta 1994.

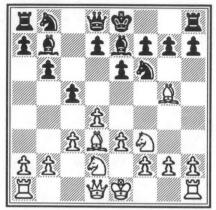

We will now break the line into variations with ...h6, **D1) 7...h6**, and without ...h6, **D2) 7...Nc6** and **D3) 7...cxd4**.

D1) 7...h6
8.Bh4 Nc6

a) 8...d6

a1) 9.Qe2 Nbd7 10.e4 (10.O-O O-O 11.Rad1 Qc7 12.Rfe1 Rfe8 13.h3 e5 unclear, Janowsky–Alekhine, Mannheim 1914) 10...Nh5 11.Bxe7 Qxe7 12.g3 O-O 13.Nh4?! Nf4! 14.gxf4 Qxh4 with advantage to Black, Petrosian–Reschko, Leningrad 1967.

a2) 9.O-O O-O 10.Re1 cxd4 11.exd4 Nbd7 12.a4 a6 13.b4 Nd5 14.Bxe7 Qxe7 15.Qb3 a5 16.b5 Rac8 17.Rac1 Rc7 18.Be4 N7f6 19.Bb1 Rfc8 20.c4 with advantage to White, Larsen–Andersson, Biel Interzonal 1976.

b) For 8...O-O, see Illustrative Game 66.

9.dxc5 bxc5 10.e4

Hort–Makarichev, Oslo 1984 continued 10...d6 11.O-O O-O 12.a3 Rc8 13.h3 Nh5 14.Bxe7 Qxe7 15.Re1 Nf4 16.Bf1 Rfd8 17.b4 with

advantage to White.

D2) 7...Nc6
8.O-O

For 8.a3, see Illustrative Game 68.

8...O-O

8...h6 9.Bh4 g5!? 10.Bg3 h5!? 11.Nxg5 h4 12.Be5 unclear, Krasenkov–Velimirovic, Kusadasi 1990.

9.Qe2

a) Ineffective was 9.e4 cxd4 in the following games:

a1) 10.cxd4 h6! 11.Bxf6? (11.Bh4 Nh5 with equality) 11...Bxf6 12.e5 Be7 13.a3 d6 14.Be4 b5 with advantage to Black, Barlov–Adorjan, New York 1985.

a2) 10.Nxd4 d5 11.Nxc6 Bxc6 12.e5 Ne4 13.Bxe7 Qxe7 14.Nf3 f6 15.Qe2 Bb7 16.exf6 Qxf6 17.Rae1 Rfd8 with equality, Yusupov–Hmadi, Tunis Interzonal 1985.

b) 9.a3

b1) 9...cxd4 10.exd4 Nd5 11.Bxe7 Ncxe7 12.Re1 f5 13.c4 Nf4 14.Bf1 Rf6 15.Qb3 Rh6 16.Rad1 g5 17.d5 g4 18.Nd4 Neg6 19.dxe6 dxe6 20.Nxe6 Nxe6 21.Rxe6 Qh4 22.h3 Rd8 23.c5 Bd5 24.Bc4 Bxe6 25.Bxe6+ Kg7 26.c6 and White

86

prevailed in the complications in Hodgson–Kosten, London 1988.

b2) 9...h6 10.Bh4 cxd4 11.exd4 Nh5 (11...Nd5 12.Bg3 d6 unclear) 12.Bg3 f5 13.d5 exd5 14.Nb3 f4 15.Bg6 Nxg3 16.fxg3 fxg3 17.Bc2 gxh2+ 18.Kh1 Rf6 19.Qd3 g6 20.Qxd5+ with advantage to White, Epishin–Smirin, Vilnius 1988.

c) 9.Re1 Rc8 10.Rc1 Nh5 11.Ne4 f6 12.Bh4 g6 13.a3 c4 14.Bc2 Na5 15.Ned2 f5 with equality, Balashov–Miles, Novi Sad 1975.

d) 9.dxc5 bxc5 10.e4 d6 11.Qe2 Rb8 12.Rad1 Nh5 13.Be3 g6 with equality, Kan–Keres, USSR Championship 1952.

9...Nd5

a) 9...d6 10.e4 cxd4 11.Nxd4 Ne5 12.Ba6 Bxa6 13.Qxa6 Qc8 with equality, Petrosian–Averbakh, Moscow 1950.

b) 9...cxd4 10.exd4 Nd5 11.Bxe7 Ncxe7 12.g3 Nf6 13.Ba6 Qc8 14.Bxb7 Qxb7 with equality, Spassky–Andersson, Clermont-Ferrand 1989.

10.Bxe7 Qxe7

10...Ncxe7 11.g3 f5 12.e4 fxe4 13.Bxe4 Rb8 14.Rae1 unclear, Rechlis–D. Gurevich, Jerusalem 1986.

11.Ba6 Bxa6 12.Qxa6 Nc7 13.Qe2 d5

With equality, Marshall–Capablanca, Bad Kissingen 1928.

D3) 7...cxd4

7...O-O will usually transpose into the other lines examined, although White could try to take advantage of early castling:

a) 8.h4!? d6 9.Bxf6 Bxf6 10.Ne4

cxd4 11.cxd4 Nc6 12.Nfg5 g6 13.a3 Bg7 14.Nxh7 with a winning advantage to White, Z. Nikolic–P. Nikolic, Yugoslavia Championship 1981.

b) 8.Qc2 h6 9.h4!? cxd4 10.cxd4 Nc6 11.Bxf6 Bxf6 12.Ne4 Be7 13.Qe2 f5 14.Ned2 Rc8 15.Ba6 Bxa6 16.Qxa6 Bf6 17.Nb3 Qc7 18.Qe2 Rce8 with equality, Hulak–Spassov, Plovdiv 1983.

8.exd4

8.cxd4

a) 8...Nc6 9.a3 O-O 10.O-O Nd5 11.Bxe7

a1) 11...Qxe7 12.Qe2 Rac8 13.Rac1 Nb8 14.Rfe1 f5 15.Qf1 Nf6 16.Rxc8+ Rxc8 17.Rc1 Qf8 with equality, Hort–Larsen, Linares 1983.

a2) 11...Ncxe7 12.Rc1 Rc8 13.Qe2 Rxc1 14.Rxc1 Qb8 15.Ne5 Nf6 16.Ng4 Nxg4 17.Qxg4 f5 18.Qg3 Qxg3 19.hxg3 with advantage to White, Estevez–Lebredo, Cuba 1984.

b) 8...Nd5

b1) 9.Nc4 O-O (9...Bxg5 10.Nd6+) 10.h4 f5 (10...f6 11.Qb1) 11.a3 Nf6 with equality, Spassky–Portisch, Geneva match 1977.

b2) 9.Bxe7 Qxe7 10.O-O f5 11.Re1 O-O 12.e4 Nf4 13.Bf1 fxe4 14.Nxe4 Nc6 15.g3 Nd5 16.Bg2 with advantage to White, Timman–Andersson, 1984.

8...d6

a) Again, castling could be premature: 8...O-O

a1) For 9.h4, see Illustrative Game 69.

a2) Less aggressive is 9.O-O Nc6 10.Re1 Nd5 11.Bxe7 Ncxe7 12.a4 a6 13.g3 Nf6 14.Qe2 Qc7 15.Ne4

Nxe4 16.Bxe4 Nd5 17.Ne5 Nf6 18.Bf3 d6 19.Nd3 Bxf3 20.Qxf3 d5 21.Ra3 Ne4 22.Qe2 Nd6 23.Ne5 Draw, Kovacevic–Lalic, Sarajevo 1988.

b) 8...Nc6 9.O-O O-O 10.Re1 Nd5 11.Bxe7 Ncxe7 12.Bf1 f5? (better are 12...d6, 12...Ng6, or 12...Rc8) 13.c4 Nf6 14.b4 Ne4 15.Qb3 Kh8?! 16.Rad1 Ng8 17.d5 with a winning advantage to White, Balashov–Lebredo, Cienfuegos 1975.

c) 8...Nd5

c1) 9.Bxe7 Qxe7 10.g3 Ba6 11.Bxa6 Nxa6 12.Qe2 Nac7 13.Ne5 d6 14.Nd3 O-O 15.f4 b5 with equality, Kamsky–Sax, Manila Interzonal 1990.

c2) 9.Ne4 O-O 10.Bxe7 Qxe7 11.Qd2 f5 12.Ng3 Qd6 13.Ne5 Nc6 14.Nc4?! Qc7 15.Ne2 Rf6 with advantage to Black, Klaric–Rashkovsky, Sochi 1977.

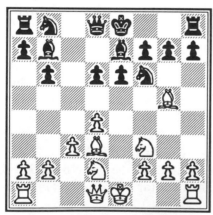

9.O-O

9.Nc4 Qc7 10.Qe2 Nbd7 11.O-O O-O 12.Rfe1 Rfe8 13.Rad1 Nf8 14.Bc1 Nd5 16.Ng5?! b5 17.Na3 b4 18.cxb4 Nxb4 with advantage to Black. See Illustrative Game 50.

9...Nbd7

9...O-O 10.Re1 Nc6 11.a4 Nd5

12.Bxe7 Ncxe7 13.a5 bxa5 14.Qa4 Nf4 15.Be4 d5 16.Bb1 Nc6 17.Qc2 g6 18.Nb3 Rb8 19.Nc5 Bc8 20.Qd2 Nh5 21.Ra2 with advantage to White with the idea Qh6, Ng5, g4, h4, Spassky–Beliavsky, Montpellier 1985.

10.Re1 O-O 11.a4 a6

11...Nd5 12.Bxe7 Qxe7 13.a5 N7f6 14.Qb3 Qc7 15.Qa3 Rab8 16.Bf1 b5 17.Bxb5 Nxc3 led to a simplified position, Timman–Andersson, Brussels 1988.

12.Nf1

a) Less aggressive is 12.h3 Re8 13.Bf4 Qc7 14.Bh2 Bf8 15.Nc4 Bd5 with equality, Spassky–Portisch, Geneva Match 1977.

b) 12.Nc4 b5 13.axb5 axb5 14.Rxa8 Qxa8 15.Na3 b4 16.cxb4 h6 17.Bf4 Nb6 18.b5 Rc8 19.Qe2 Qa4 with compensation, Z. Polgar–Petursson, Reykjavik 1988.

c) DeFirmian–Wedberg, Reykjavik 1990, continued 12.Qe2 Re8 13.Nf1 Qc8 14.Bc2 Bc6 15.Ne3 Qb7 16.Nd2 Nf8 17.h4 b5.

After 12.Nf1 we have two examples, in both of which White gets a dangerous attack:

a) 12...Re8 13.Ng3 Qc7 14.h4 Bf8 15.h5 e5?! 16.Nh4 e4 17.Bc2 d5 18.Nhf5. See Illustrative Game 70.

b) 12...h6 13.Bh4 Re8 14.Ne3 Qb8 15.Nd2 Bc6 16.Bg3 Qb7 17.Ndc4 Qc7 18.Nc2 Rad8 19.Nb4 Bb7 20.Ne3 Nb8 21.Qe2 a5 22.Nbc2 Ne4 23.Na3 Nxg3 24.hxg3 Bc6 25.Nb5 Qb7 26.d5! Tangborn–L. B. Hansen, Berlin 1988.

Illustrative Game 64

GM Roberto Cifuentes Parada
IM Arkadij Rotstein

Wijk aan Zee 1993

1.d4 Nf6 2.Nf3 e6 3.Bg5 c5 4.e3 Be7 5.dxc5 Qa5+ 6.Nbd2 Qxc5 7.c4 b6 8.Bd3 Bb7 9.O-O Qc7 10.Rc1 d6 11.Nd4 Nbd7 12.b4 O-O 13.Nb5 Qc6 14.e4 Ne5 15.Bb1 Qd7 16.Qe2 Nc6 17.a3 a5 18.bxa5 Nxa5 19.Qd3 Rfd8 20.Rfd1 g6 21.Qd4?

This allows Black to play a strong combination. Better is 21.Be3.

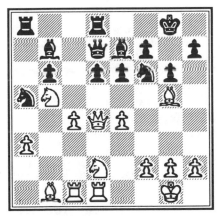

21...e5 22.Qb2 Nxe4! 23.Nxe4

If 23.Bxe7, then 23...Nxd2 24.Bxd8 Qg4 25.f3 Nxf3+ with a very strong attack.

23...Bxg5 24.Nxg5 Qg4 25.f4 Nxc4 26.Qf2 Ne3 27.h3 Nxd1 28.hxg4 Nxf2 29.Kxf2 Ra5 30.a4 Rxa4

The smoke has cleared. Black is winning due to his extra pawns.

31.fxe5 dxe5 32.Rc7 Rf4+ 33.Kg3 Ba6 34.Nc3 Rc8 35.Rxc8+ Bxc8 36.Nf3 Rxg4+ 37.Kf2 Bb7 38.Ba2 Bxf3 39.gxf3 Rd4 40.Ke3 Kg7 41.Ne4 f5

Illustrative Game 65

IM Konstantin Lerner
GM Valery Chekhov

USSR Championship 1984

1.d4 Nf6 2.Nf3 e6 3.Bg5 c5 4.e3 Be7 5.Nbd2 O-O 6.Bd3 b6 7.Qe2

To prevent Black from exchanging Bishops with 7...Ba6.

7...cxd4 8.exd4 Nd5?!

A common move in this type of position, but here it leads to difficulties. Better is 8...Bb7 9.O-O d6 10.Rfe1 Nbd7.

9.h4!

This move is possible as White has not castled. To Black's advantage would be 9.Bxe7? Qxc7 10.O-O Nf4 11.Qe4 Nxd3 12.Qxa8 Nc6 13.cxd3 Ba6 14.Qxf8+ Kxf8.

9...f5

Controlling the e4 square and closing the b1-h7 diagonal. White would have a large advantage after either 9...h6 10.c4 Nb4 11.Bb1 hxg5 12.hxg5 g6 13.Bxg6 fxg6 14.Qe4 or 9...Bb7 10.c4 Nb4 11.Bb1.

10.c4 Bxg5

The h-file is opened, which will later play a decisive role.

11.hxg5 Nf4 12.Qf1 Nc6 13.O-O-O

The position would be unclear after 13.Bb1 g6 (but not 13...d5 14.g3 Ng6 15.Qh3 dxc4 16.Qxh7+ Kf7 17.Rh6 Nce7 18.Nxc4 with a winning advantage to White) 14.g3 Nh5.

13...b5 14.c5

Correctly keeping the Queenside closed.

14...Ba6

White has a large advantage after 14...Qa5 15.Bb1 Ba6 16.g3 b4 17.Nc4.

15.g3 Nxd3+ 16.Qxd3 Qa5 17.Qb3

Not 17.Kb1 Qxa2+.

17...Qa4

Exchanging Queens does not lessen White's attack along the h-file.

18.Rh4 Qxb3 19.Nxb3 Bb7 20.d5!

This move closes the a8-h1 diagonal. Not 20.Rdh1 Ne7.

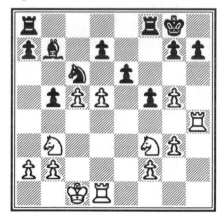

20...Nd8

White also has a great advantage after either 20...exd5 21.Rdh1 or 20...Ne7 21.c6 dxc6 22.Nc5.

21.c6! Rc8 22.Kb1

Not 22.Rdh1 Nxc6!

22...dxc6 23.Rdh1 cxd5

Or 23...h6 24.gxh6 g6 25.h7+ Kh8 26.Ne5 Rf6 27.Rh6 with a winning advantage to White.

24.Rxh7

Black is in a mating net. If 24...Kf7, then 25.Ne5+ Ke7 26.Rxg7+ Kd6 27.Rd7+ Kxe5 28.Re1 mate.

24...Nf7 25.g6 Nh6 26.R1xh6

gxh6 27.Rxb7 f4 28.Ne5 Rf5 29.Ng4 1-0

Illustrative Game 66

GM Ye Rongguang

GM Ye Jiangchuan

Jakarta 1994

1.d4 Nf6 2.Bg5 e6 3.Nf3 c5 4.e3 Be7 5.Nbd2 Nc6 6.c3 cxd4 7.exd4 O-O 8.Bd3 b6 9.O-O Bb7 10.Re1 h6 11.Bxf6 Bxf6 12.Ne4 Be7 13.Bb1

Preparing to line up the Queen and Bishop on the b1-h7 diagonal. 13.Bc2 seems to make more sense, not blocking in the Queen Rook. However, then White could not use the c2 square for his Queen nor the d3-square if Black plays ...Ba6.

13...d5 14.Ng3 Bc8

The e6-square needs to be defended because 15.Qd3 g6 16.Rxe6 was threatened.

15.Nh5 g6 16.Qd3

Threatening 17.Nf4 and 18.Nxg6.

16...Bd6 17.Qd2 Kh7 18.Ne5?!

Black will later open the a8-h1 diagonal because of this move. Worth considering is 18.Nf4 Qc7 19.Nd3. The text also allows Black's next strong move.

18...Qh4 19.Nf4

Of course not 19.Nxc6 Qxh2+.

19...Bxe5 20.dxe5 Qg5 21.Qe3 Bb7 22.g3

Weakening the Kingside, but a better move is hard to find.

22...Rad8

And now ...d5-d4 is in the air.

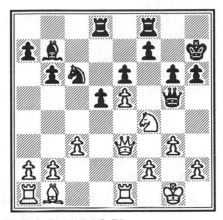

23.h4 Qg4 24.h5?

This looks strong, but Black's coming attack will be even stronger and this pawn will end up being a weakness.

24...Kg7 25.Qd3

25.hxg6 is also met by 25...d4.

25...d4

Opening up the positon for his pieces, especially the a8-h1 diagonal.

26.Kh2

If White tries to keep the position closed with 26.c4, then 26...Nb4 is strong.

26...dxc3 27.Qxc3 Nd4 28.Be4 g5

White's position has fallen apart.

29.Bxb7 gxf4 30.Rad1 Rd7 31.Kg2

Of course 31.Rxd4 is met by 31...Rxd4 32.Qxd4 fxg3+.

31...Rfd8 32.Be4 f3+ 33.Bxf3 Qxf3+ 0-1

White loses material after 34.Qxf3 Nxf3 35.Rxd7 Nxe1+.

Illustrative Game 67

GM Curt Hansen
GM Mikhail Gurevich

Munich 1992

1.d4 Nf6 2.Nf3 e6 3.Bg5 c5 4.e3 Be7 5.Bd3 O-O 6.O-O h6 7.Bh4 b6 8.Nbd2 Bb7 9.c3 cxd4 10.cxd4 Nc6 11.a3 d6 12.e4 Nh5 13.d5!?

An unclear position would result after 13.Bxe7 Nxe7 14.Re1 Nf4 15.Bf1 Qd7.

13...Nb8

Not 13...Bxh4? 14.dxc6 Bxc6 15.Nd4 Nf4 16.Nxc6 Qg5 17.g3 Nxd3 18.Nf3 winning.

14.Bxe7 Qxe7 15.dxe6 fxe6 16.e5 Nd7!?

Black accepts a weakened pawn structure in exchange for active pieces. White would have a slight advantage after 16...Bxf3 17.Nxf3 d5 18.Rc1.

17.exd6 Qxd6 18.Be4 Bd5 19.Nc4 Qc5 20.Bxd5 exd5 21.Ne3 Ndf6 22.Rc1?!

Better is 22.Qd4 Rae8 23.Rad1.

22...Qd6 23.Nd4

It was still better to play 23.Qd4.

23...Rae8 24.g3 Qd7 25.Kg2 Re5 26.Qd3 Ng4 27.Nxg4

Not 27.Rce1? Nxh2! 28.Kxh2 Nf4! 28.gxf4 Rh5+ 30.Kg1 Qh3 winning.

27...Qxg4 28.Kh1 Nf6 29.Nc6! Re6

Not 29...Rh5 30.Ne7+ Kf7 31.Rc7.

30.f4?!

Better is 30.f3 Qh5 31.Nd4 Re5 with an unclear position. Now Black is able to get into an endgame which is favorable because he gets a Rook on the second rank.

30...Qe2! 31.Qxe2 Rxe2 32.Rfe1 Rfe8 33.Rxe2 Rxe2 34.Ne5

Rxb2 35.Rc8+ Kh7 36.f5 Rf2 37.g4 Re2 38.Ng6 Re8 39.Rxe8 Nxe8 40.Kg2 Nd6 41.Ne7 Nc4 42.a4 d4 43.Kf2 d3 44.h4 a5! 45.g5 b5 46.axb5 a4 47.Nd5 a3 48.Nb4 h5!

Black needs to avoid exchanging pawns. This h-pawn will later play a decisive role. Black now plans to march his King to e5.

49.Ke1

According to Gurevich, also losing are 49.b6 Nxb6 50.Ke3 Nd5!+ 51.Nxd5 a2 and 49.Na2 Kg8 50.b6 Nxb6 51.Ke3 Nc4+ 52.Kxd3 Nd6 53.f6 gxf6 54.gxf6 Nf5 55.Kc3 Nxh4 56.Nb4 Nf3 57.Nd5 h4 58.Nf4 Kf7 59.Kb3 Kxf6 60.Kxa3 Kf5 61.Nh3 Kg4 62.Nf2+ Kg3 63.Ne4+ Kg2 64.Nf6 h3 65.Ng4 Ne5.

49...Kg8 50.Kd1

Or 50.b6 Nxb6 51.Kd2 Nd5! 52.Na2 Nf4 winning.

50...Kf7 51.Kc1 Ke7 52.Kb1

52.b6 still does not work due to 52...Nxb6 53.Kd2 Kd6 54.Kxd3 Nd5 55.Na2 Nf4 56.Kc3 Ng2. After the text, 53.Nxd3 is threatened.

52...d2+ 53.Kc2 Kd6 54.b6

Nxb6 55.Kxd2 Nd5 56.Nc2 a2 57.Na1

Or 57.Kc1 Ne3! 58.Na1 Nxf5 winning.

57...Ke5 58.f6 gxf6 59.gxf6 Kxf6 60.Kc2 Kf5 61.Kb3

If 61.Kb2, then 61...Kg4 62.Nb3 Kxh4 63.Nc5 Kg4 64.Ne4 h4 65.Kxa2 Nc3+! 66.Nxc3 h3 67.Ne4 h2 68.Nf2+ Kf3 winning.

61...Kg4 62.Kxa2 Kxh4 63.Nb3 Kg4 64.Nc5 h4 65.Ne4 Nc3+ 66.Nxc3 h3 0-1

GM Yasser Seirawan
GM Ulf Andersson

Skelleftea 1989

1.d4 Nf6 2.Nf3 e6 3.Bg5 c5 4.e3 Be7 5.Nbd2 b6 6.c3 Bb7 7.Bd3 Nc6 8.a3

White wants to play e4 without worrying about ....cxd4 and ...Nb4.

8...O-O?!

Allowing White to create a strong center. Better is 8...Nd5.

9.e4 d6

According to Seirawan, 9...Nh5 can be met with 10.Be3! f5 11.exf5 exf5 12.d5 Na5 (if 12...f4, then 13.dxc6 Bxc6 14.Ne5 with a winning advantage to White or 13...fxe3 14.cxb7 exd2+ 15.Nxd2 with a winning advantage to White) 13.Qc2 f4!? (if 13...g6, then 14.Bh6 Re8 15.O-O Bxd5 16.Bxf5 Bxf3 17.Nxf3 gxf5 18.Qxf5 Ng7 19.Qd5+ with a strong attack) 14.Bxh7+ Kh8 15.Ne5 fxe3 (not 15...Nf6 16.Ng6+ Kxh7 17.Nxe7+ with a winning advantage to White) 16.Ng6+ Kxh7 17.Nxf8+ Kg8 18.Qh7+ Kxf8 19.Qh8+ Kf7

20.Qxh5+ Kg8 21.fxe3 unclear.

10.h3

In order to meet 10...h6 with 11.Be3 and not have to worry about ...Ng4.

10...cxd4 11.cxd4 e5 12.d5 Nb8 13.Be3

Meeting the threat of 13...Nxd5. White's advantage is from his greater control of space and the hole at c6.

13...Nbd7 14.b4 Rc8 15.Rc1?!

With such an advantage in space, it is better not to exchange pieces. Better was 15.O-O Rc3 16.Qe2 Qb8 17.Rfd1 Rfc8 18.Nf1! followed by Bd2.

14...Nh5 16.O-O Rxc1 17.Qxc1 g6

Not 17...Nf4 18.Bxf4 exf4 19.Nd4 eyeing the weakness at c6.

18.Qc2 Qb8 19.Qa4 Rd8 20.Rc1?!

Again it is better not to exchange Rooks. White could have kept a big advantage with 20.Bb5 Nf8 21.Bc6 f5 22.Bh6 Nf6 23.Ng5.

20...Rc8 21.Rxc8+ Bxc8 22.g4

Better is 22.Qc2 followed by Queenside expansion with a3-a4.

22...Ng7

Not 22...Nf4 23.Bxf4 exf4 24.Nd4 and now 24...Ne5 loses a piece to 25.Qe8+ Bf8 26.Ba6.

23.Ba6

This leads to an exchange of Queens. However, White has no advantage in the endgame.

23...Bxa6 24.Qxd7 Qb7 25.Qxb7 Bxb7 26.Ne1

This Knight would like to go to c6. This move also allows White to secure his pawn chain with f3.

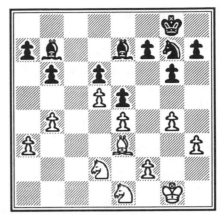

26...f5 27.f3 h5?

A fatal error. Now White is able to maneuver his Knight to c6. Correct is 27...Ba6 28.a4 Be2! threatening ...Bd1.

28.gxf5 gxf5 29.b5

Nc1-c2-b4-c6 will be decisive.

29...Ne8 30.Nc2 Bh4 31.Bf2 Bg5 32.Nc4 Kf7 33.Nb4 fxe4 34.fxe4 Ke7 35.Kg2 Kd7 36.a4 Kc7 37.Nc6 Bxc6 38.dxc6 Nf6 39.a5 bxa5 40.Bxa7 Nxe4 41.Nxa5 1-0

Black cannot stop the b-pawn.

Illustrative Game 69

GM Vlado Kovacevic
IM Dragoljub Minic

Karlovac 1977

1.d4 e6 2.Nf3 Nf6 3.Bg5 c5 4.e3 Be7 5.Nbd2 b6 6.c3 Bb7 7.Bd3 cxd4 8.exd4 O-O?

It is very risky to castle in this variation before White has done so as well. Better is 8...d6.

9.h4! Ne8?

Better is 9...d6, although White has a big advantage after 10.Bxf6! Bxf6 11.Qc2! (not 11.Bxh7+? Kxh7 12.Ng5+ Kh6! 13.Qg4 e5 with a winning advantage to Black)

11...g6 (11...h6 12.g4) 12.h5 Qe8. The idea of the text move is to close the b1-h7 diagonal with ...f5.

10.g4! f5 11.gxf5 exf5 12.Qb3+ Kh8

If 12...d5, then 13.O-O-O Nd6 14.Rde1 Ne4? 15.Bxe4 fxe4 16.Rxe4 with a winning advantage to White.

13.O-O-O Nd6 14.Rde1 Bxg5

Black had no choice but to open the h-file. If 14...Bf6, then 15.Qa3.

15.hxg5 g6

If 15...Nc6, then 16.Nh4.

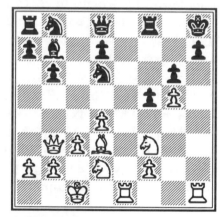

16.d5! Kg8

If 15...Na6, then 16.Bxa6 Bxa6 17.Qa3 wins a piece.

17.Qb4 Nf7

On 17...Qc7, Kovacevic gives the following variation: 18.Qh4 Rf7 19.Ne5 Rg7 20.Nxg6! hxg6 21.Qh8+ Kf7 22.Re7+ Kxe7 23.Qxg7+ Nf7 24.Re1+.

18.Qh4 h6

If 18...h5, then 19.Bxf5!

19.Reg1 Bxd5 20.Qd4 1-0

Illustrative Game 70

FM Matthias Ruf

GM Gerardo Barbero

Germany 1988

1.d4 Nf6 2.Nf3 e6 3.Bg5 c5 4.e3 cxd4 5.exd4 Be7 6.Nbd2 b6 7.c3 Bb7 8.Bd3 d6 9.O-O O-O 10.Re1 Nbd7 11.a4

Restraining Black's Queenside and also threatening to create weaknesses there with 12.a5.

11...a6

In order to meet 12.a5 with 12...b5.

12.Nf1 Re8 13.Ng3 Qc7 14.h4

Starting a Kingside attack. With the text, White will try to induce Black to make weaknesses on his Kingside.

14...Bf8 15.h5 e5?!

Weakening the f5-square.

16.Nh4 e4 17.Bc2 d5 18.Nhf5 g6 19.Nh6+ Kg7 20.Qd2 Re6 21.Bf4 Qc6 22.Bb3 Rae8 23.Re3 b5

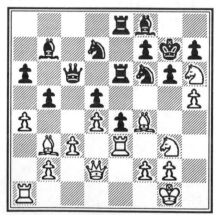

24. Ngf5+! gxf5 25.Rg3+ Ng4

Of course not 25...Kh8 26.Nxf7#.

26.Nxf5+ Kh8

Not 26...Kf6 27.Bg5+ Kxf5 28.Qf4#.

27.Rxg4 Nf6 28.Rh4 Nd7 29.a5 Qc8 30.Re1

This Rook will also enter the front on the Kingside via e3.

30...Qd8 31.Re3 Qf6 32.g4 Be7 33.Rh2 Bd8 34.Rg3 Rf8 35.h6 Rg8 36.Ng7 Bxa5 37.Rh5

Black can not defend d5 and his position falls apart.

37...Qe7 38.Bxd5 Bxd5 39.Rxd5 Nb6 40.Rc5 Rg6 41.b4 Nd7 42.bxa5 Nxc5 43.dxc5 Qxc5 44.Be3 Qc8 45.Bd4 f6 46.Nh5 1-0

Conclusion: After 1.d4 Nf6 2.Nf3 e6 3.Bg5 c5 4.e3, 4...b6 is a mistake often played by those who do not understand the system well or forget about the strong reply 5.d5! 4...Qb6!? is very sharp and both sides need to be well versed in the variations. 4...h6 and 4...Be7 are popular and solid.

Chapter 7

1.d4 Nf6 2.Nf3 e6 3.Bg5 h6

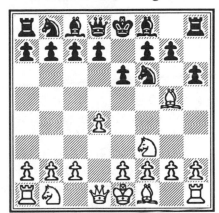

Now White can either retreat **A) 4.Bh4** or exchange **B) 4.Bxf6.**

A) 4.Bh4
4...g5

Other moves should transpose to the other variations we examined in the previous chapter. Here are some exceptions. Examples in which Black postpones ...g5:

a) 4...c5 5.e3 Nc6 6.c3 g5?! 7.Bg3 Ne4 8.d5 exd5 9.Qxd5 Qe7 10.Nbd2 Nxg3 11.hxg3 Rg8 12.Qe4 with advantage to White, Bronstein–Van den Bergh, Beverwijk 1963.

b) 4...d6 5.Nbd2 g5 6.Bg3 Nh5 7.e3 Bg7 8.c3 Nd7 9.Be2 Ndf6 10.O-O Qe7 11.e4 Nxg3 12.hxg3 O-O 13.Bd3 b6 14.Qe2 Bb7 15.Ba6 Bc6 16.Bb5 Bb7 17.Ba6 Bc6 Draw, Seirawan–Ehlvest, Skelleftea 1989.

Here is an example in which ...g5 is not played:

4...b6 5.e3 Bb7 6.Nbd2 d6 7.c3 Nbd7 8.Bc4 Be7 9.O-O O-O 10.Qe2 c5 11.Ba6 Bxa6 12.Qxa6 d5

13.Rfd1 Qc8 14.Qe2 Re8 15.e4
dxe4 16.Nxe4 Nxe4 17.Qxe4 Bxh4
18.Qxh4 e5 19.dxc5 Nxc5 20.Rd5
Qf5 21.Rad1 Qc2 22.R5d2 Qf5
23.Rd5 Qc2 24.R5d2 Qf5 Draw,
Yermolinsky–Romanishin, Sim-
feropol 1988.

5.Bg3 Ne4

a) 5...Nh5 6.Be5 f6 7.Qd3 Kf7
8.g4 Ng7 9.Bg3 h5 10.gxh5 Nxh5
11.e4 d5 unclear, Van Scheltinga–
Portisch, Beverwijk 1965.

b) 5...d6 6.Nbd2 (6.h3) 6...Nh5
7.e3 Bg7 8.c3 f5 9.Bc4 Qe7 10.Ng1
Nf6 11.f4 (11.f3 e5 with advantage
to Black) 11...Nc6 12.Nf3 Bd7
13.Qe2 O-O-O 14.O-O-O Nh5
with advantage to Black, Trifunovic–Kortchnoi, Havana 1963.

6.Nbd2

a) 6.Qd3 Nxg3 7.hxg3 Bg7 8.Nc3
d6 9.O-O-O Nd7 10.e3 a6 11.Nd2
b5 12.f4 Bb7 13.Kb1 Qe7 14.Nb3
O-O-O is equal, Larsen–Byrne,
Las Palmas 1976.

b) 6.Nfd2 Nxg3 7.hxg3 d5 8.e3
Bg7 (8...c5 9.dxc5 Bg7 10.c3 Qc7
11.e4 O-O 12.Be2 Rd8 unclear)
9.c3 Nd7 10.Bd3 c5 11.O-O with
advantage to White, Bohm–
Hamann, Amsterdam 1975.

6...Nxg3 7.hxg3 Bg7 8.e3

For 8.c3, see Illustrative Game 71.

**8...d6 9.Bd3 Nc6 10.c3 Qe7
11.Qc2**

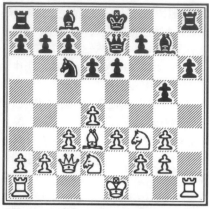

The position is unclear. Some
examples:

a) 11...Bd7

a1) 12.O-O-O O-O-O (12...a5
13.e4 a4 14.a3 Na5 15.Rde1 with
advantage to White, Petrosian–
Botvinnik, USSR Championship
1951) 13.g4 Rdf8 14.Nf1 f5 15.d5
Ne5 16.Nxe5 Bxe5 17.dxe6 Qxe6
18.Bxf5 Qxa2 19.Bxd7+ Kxd7 20.f3
a5 21.Nd2 b5 22.Qb3 Qxb3
23.Nxb3 a4 24.Nd4 Rb8 25.Kc2
Draw, Mih. Tseitlin–Levitt,
Polanica Zdroj 1988.

a2) 12.g4 Qf8 13.O-O-O O-O-O
14.Nc4 Kb8 15.e4 Ne7 16.Ne3 with
advantage to White, Meduna–
Prandstetter, Erevan 1984.

b) 11...f5 12.e4 Bd7 13.O-O-O
fxe4 14.Nxe4 O-O-O 15.Kb1 Qf7
16.Qb3 Kb8 17.Rhe1 Rhf8 18.Bc2
b6 is equal, Hort–Browne, London
1979.

Illustrative Game 71
GM Mikhail Tseitlin
IM Pawel Stempin

Polanica Zdroj 1989

**1.d4 Nf6 2.Nf3 e6 3.Bg5 h6
4.Bh4 g5 5.Bg3 Ne4 6.Nbd2
Nxg3 7.hxg3 Bg7 8.c3 d6 9.e4
Qe7 10.Bd3 Nc6 11.Qb3 a6**

12.O-O-O b5 13.Rhe1 Bd7 14.d5 Ne5

White has a large advantage after 14...Na5 15.Qa3 Nb7 16.dxe6 fxe6 17.e5 Nc5 18.Bg6+.

15.Nxe5 dxe5 16.Nf1 Qc5

Better is 16...O-O

17.Ne3 a5 18.dxe6 fxe6 19.Be2

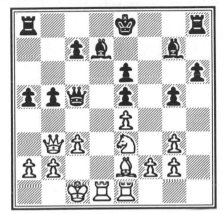

19...h5

Black loses quickly after 19...a4? 20.Bh5+ Ke7 21.Nf5+! Kf6 22.Rxd7 axb3 23.Rf7 mate. However, after the text White has a combination that wins material.

20.Bxh5+! Rxh5 21.Rxd7 Kxd7 22.Qd1+ Kc6 23.Qxh5 Qe7

If 23...b4, 24.Qf7 bxc3 25.Qxe6+.

24.Rd1 a4 25.a3 Bf6 26.Kb1 Kb6 27.Qg6 Rf8 28.Rd3 c6 29.c4 b4 30.axb4 Qxb4 31.Rc3 Ka6 32.Nc2 Qd6 33.c5 Qd2 34.Rc4 Qd3 35.Rxa4+ Kb5 36.Rb4+ Kxc5 37.b3 Qd1+ 38.Kb2 Qd7 39.Qh5 Qd2 40.Qh7 Kd6 41.Rb7 Rd8 42.b4 1-0

B) 4.Bxf6
4...Qxf6

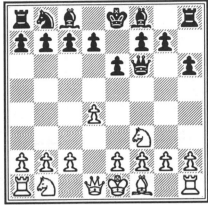

In this variation Black has the two Bishops, but White gets the center and a lead in development. Black has a sound position, but has to play exactly to avoid a quick knockout, as GM Hodgson has demonstrated in many of his games. We examine **B1) 5.e4** and **B2) 5.Nbd2**.

B1) 5.e4

Several moves have been played in this position: **B11) 5...d6, B12) 5...d5, B13) 5...c5, B14) 5...b6, B15) 5...g6, B16) 5...Nc6.**

B11) 5...d6

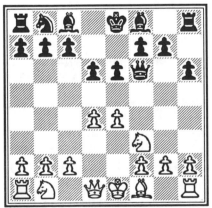

We examine **B111) 6.Nc3** and **B112) 6.Nbd2.**

Seldom seen are:

a) 6.e5 Qe7 7.Nbd2 g6 8.Bd3 Bg7 9.O-O dxe5 10.dxe5 Nc6 11.Qe2 Bd7 12.g3 g5 unclear, Grivas–Luther, Leningrad 1989.

b) 6.c3 Nd7 7.Bd3 b6 8.O-O Bb7 9.a4 a6 10.Nbd2 Qd8 11.Ne1 c5 12.Qg4 cxd4 13.cxd4 e5 14.f4 with advantage to White, Dreev–Kengis, USSR 1988.

c) 6.Bd3

c1) 6...g6 7.O-O Bg7 8.e5 Qe7 9.Qe2 Nd7 10.c4 c5 11.Nc3 (Sideif-Zade–A. Ivanov, USSR 1985) 11...O-O 12.Nb5 dxe5 13.dxe5 a6 14.Nc3 b5 unclear.

c2) 6...e5 7.c3 Be7 8.Nbd2 O-O 9.O-O Nc6 10.dxe5 Nxe5 11.Nxe5 dxe5 12.Qe2 a5 13.a4 Bc5 is equal, Spiridonov–Zaichik, USSR 1984.

c3) 6...Nc6 7.c3 g5 8.Nbd2 g4 9.Ng1 h5 10.Qb3 Bh6 11.Nc4 e5 12.dxe5 Nxe5 13.Nxe5 dxe5 14.Ne2 h4 15.Rd1 c6 16.a4 Bg5 with advantage to Black, I. Ivanov–Browne, U.S. Championship 1989.

c4) 6...Nd7 7.O-O g5 8.c3 Bg7 9.Nbd2 O-O 10.b4 e5 11.d5 h5?! 12.Nc4 Re8 13.Nfd2 g4 14.f3 with a large advantage to White, Sandler–Plaskett, Hastings 1989-90.

B111) 6.Nc3
And now Black has played **B1111) 6...g6** and **B1112) 6...Nd7.**

B1111) 6...g6
a) Worth considering is 6...a6 7.e5 Qd8 8.Bd3 d5 9.Ne2 c5 10.c3.

a1) 10...Nc6 11.O-O Bd7 12.Qd2 Qb6 13.Rad1 (better is 13.dxc5 Bxc5 14.b4) 13...cxd4 14.cxd4 Be7 with a big advantage for Black, Terpugov–Botvinnik, Moscow 1951.

a2) 10...Qb6 11.O-O? (better is

11.Rb1 Bd7 12.O-O Bb5 equal) 11...Qxb2? (better is 11...c4 12.Bc2 Qxb2 with advantage to Black) 12.Rb1 Qa3 13.c4 dxc4 14.Be4 cxd4 15.Qxd4 Bc5 16.Qxc4 O-O unclear, Yap–Sax, Szirak 1985.

b) 6...g5?! 7.e5! Qe7 8.h4 g4 9.Nd2 h5 10.f4 gxf3 11.Nxf3 Nc6 12.Bb5 Bd7 13.Qe2 dxe5 14.Bxc6 Bxc6 15.Nxe5 Qb4 16.O-O-O Bg7 17.Nxf7! Kxf7 18.Rhf1+ Bf6 19.d5! exd5 20.Rxf6+ 1-0, King–Summermatter, Germany 1989.

c) 6...c6 7.Qd2 (if 7.e5, Black should play 7...Qd8 instead of 7...dxe5?! 8.dxe5 Qf4 9.g3 Qb4 10.a3 Qa5 11.b4 Qc7 12.Ne4 with a large advantage, Petrosian–Taimanov, USSR team championship 1960) 7...e5 8.O-O-O Be7 9.Kb1 Nd7 10.h4 exd4?! 11.Nxd4 Ne5 12.f4 Ng4 13.h5 Bd8 14.Ndb5! cxb5 15.Bxb5+ Bd7 (15...Kf8 would have held out longer, although after 16.e5 White has a very strong attack) 16.Bxd7+ Kxd7 17.Qe2 Qxf4 18.Rhf1 Qg5 19.Rf5 Qh4 20.Qb5+ Kc8 21.Rxf7 Be7 22.Nd5 1-0, Hodgson–S. Polgar, Lucerne 1989.

d) For 6...Nc6, see Illustrative Game 72.

7.Qd2
a) 7.Bb5+ Nd7

a1) 8.e5 Qe7 9.d5!? dxe5 10.Qe2 Bg7 11.O-O-O O-O 12.Rhe1 e4 is equal, Shabalov–Ivanov, USSR 1987.

a2) 8.Bxd7+ Bxd7 9.Qd2 Bg7 10.O-O O-O 11.Rfe1 Qe7 12.Rad1 a6 13.e5 Rfd8 14.Qf4 Bc6 15.exd6 Rxd6 16.Ne4 Bxe4 17.Qxe4 c6 is equal, Bany–Levitt, Polanica Zdroj 1988.

98

b) 7.Bd3 Bg7 8.Qe2 Nd7
9.O-O-O a6 10.Rhe1 e5?! (better
is 10...Qe7) 11.Nd5 Qd8 12.dxe5
dxe5 13.h4 c6 14.Ne3 h5 15.Bc4 b5
16.Bb3 Qe7 17.Ng5 O-O 18.Nf5!
gxf5 19.Rxd7! Qxd7 20.Rd1 with a
winning advantage to White,
Velikov–D. Cramling, Reggio
Emilia 1980.

c) For 7.e5, see Illustrative
Game 73.

7...Qe7

7...Bg7 8.O-O-O

a) 8...Qe7 9.e5 dxe5 10.Nxe5
Nd7 11.f4 Nxe5 12.fxe5 Bd7 13.g3
O-O 14.Bg2 c5 15.dxc5 Rfd8 with
advantage to Black, Fernandes–
Wirthensohn, Dubai Olympiad
1986.

b) 8...Nc6 9.Bb5 O-O

b1) 10.e5 dxe5 11.Bxc6 exd4
12.Ne4 Qe7 13.Ba4 c5 with compensation, Hodgson–Eingorn,
Reykjavik 1989.

b2) 10.Bxc6 bxc6 11.e5 Qf5
12.Rhe1 c5 13.Ne4 dxe5 14.dxe5
Bb7 15.Qe3 Bxe5 16.Nxe5 Qxe5
17.Nxc5 Qxe3 18.fxe3 Bxg2 19.Rd7
with compensation, Piket–Nijboer,
Wijk aan Zee 1990.

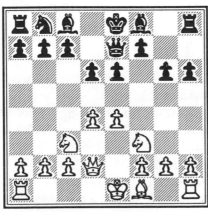

8.O-O-O a6 9.h4 Bg7
See Illustrative Game 74.

B1112) 6...Nd7
7.Qd2

a) 7.d5 exd5 (more solid is 7...e5
and 8...g6 is equal) 8.Nxd5 Qd8
9.Nd4 (stronger is 9.Qd4 c6 10.Ne3
with advantage to White) 9...c6
10.Ne6!? Qa5+ (10...fxe6??
11.Qh5+) 11.b4 Qa3 12.Nec7+?!
(Better is 12.Ndc7+ Ke7 13.Nxf8
Qc3+ [13...Qxb4+ 14.Qd2 Qxd2+
15.Kxd2 Rb8 is equal] 14.Ke2 Nxf8
15.Nxa8 Ne6 16.f3 Nd4+ 17.Kf2
Nxc2 18.Rc1 Qe3+ with advantage
to White, Makarichev) 12...Kd8
13.Rb1 cxd5 14.Rb3 Qxb3
(14...Qxa2 15.Nxa8 dxe4 16.Bc4
Ne5 17.Bd5) 15.axb3 Kxc7 16.Qxd5
Lerner–Makarichev, USSR 1982
and now Black should play 16...Bc7
17.Qxf7 Bf6 with advantage to
Black.

b) 7.Bd3 g6 8.Qe2 Bg7 9.O-O
O-O 10.Rhe1 e5 11.Nd5 Qd8 12.c3
exd4 13.Nxd4 Nc5 14.Bc2 Re8
15.f3 c6 16.Ne3 Qc7 17.Qd2 b5 unclear, Morovic–Browne, Santiago
1981.

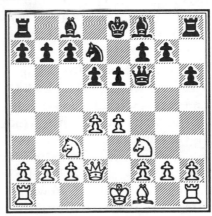

7...c6
a) Not 7...g6? 8.Nb5 Qd8 9.Qc3
c6 10.d5.

b) 7...a6 8.O-O-O.

b1) 8...g6 (8...c5?! 9.dxc5) 9.e5

(for 9.Bd3, see Illustrative Game 75)

b11) 9...Qe7 10.Qf4 dxe5 11.dxe5 Bg7 12.Bd3 g5 13.Qg3 h5 14.Rhe1 Bh6 15.Nd2 Nc5 (15...Bg7 16.h4) 16.Nde4 Nxe4 17.Nxe4 Kf8 18.Nf6 g4+ 19.Kb1 Bg7 20.Qf4 Bh6 21.Qe4 with advantage to White, Hort–Wirthensohn, San Bernardino 1984.

b12) 9...dxe5 10.dxe5 Qe7 11.Ne4 Bg7 12.Qc3 Nb6 13.Nf6+ Kf8 14.Be2 Bd7 15.Qxc7 Bb5 16.Qxb6 Bxe2 17.Rd7 with a winning advantage to White, Hodgson–Ward, Haringey 1988.

b2) 8...Qd8 9.h4 b5 10.Bd3 Bb7 11.Kb1 c5 12.dxc5 Nxc5 13.Qe3 Qc7 14.Nd4 O-O-O!? unclear, Hodgson–Miles, Kuala Lumpur, 1992.

8.O-O-O e5

This move may not be best. Worth considering is:

a) 8...Be7 9.Kb1 e5 and now:

a1) 10.Ne2 exd4 11.Nfxd4 Qxf2 12.Nf5 Bf8 13.Nxd6+ Bxd6 14.Qxd6 Qf6 15.Qc7 O-O 16.Ng3 Nc5 17.Bc4 Be6 18.Rhf1 Qg6 19.Nf5 Kh8 unclear, Morovic–Popovic, Bor 1985.

a2) 10.h4 Nb6 (Not 10...Nf8? 11.dxe5 dxe5 12.Nb5) 11.a4 Bg4 12.a5 Bxf3 13.gxf3 exd4 14.Qxd4 Qxd4 15.Rxd4 Nd7 is equal, Hodgson–Carlier, Stavanger 1990.

b) 8...Qd8 9.Kb1 Be7 10.h4 e5 11.dxe5 dxe5 12.g4 Qc7 13.Be2?! Nf8 14.g5 h5 15.Qd3 Ng6 with advantage to Black, Blatny–Tolnai, Stara Zagora 1990.

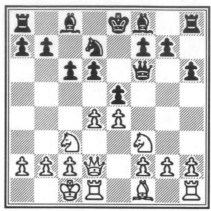

9.dxe5

For 9.h4?! see Illustrative Game 76.

9...Nxe5

A mistake is 9...dxe5? 10.Nb5!

a) 10...cxb5 11.Bxb5 Qe6 12.Nxe5 Qxe5 13.Bxd7+ Ke7 14.Bxc8 with a winning advantage to White.

b) 10...Rb8 11.Nxa7 Nc5 12.Nxc8 Rxc8 13.b4 Qe6 14.bxc5 Bxc5 15.Qc3 with a winning advantage to White, Klinger–King, Lucerne 1989.

c) 10...Kd8 11.Qc3? (correct is 11.Qa5+! b6 12.Qc3 cxb5 13.Bxb5 Bd6 14.Qc6 or 12...a6 13.Nd6 Bxd6 14.Qxc6 with a winning advantage to White) 11...cxb5 12.Bxb5 Bd6 13.Rxd6 Qxd6 14.Rd1 Qc7 with a winning advantage to Black, Hodgson–Mednis, Stavanger 1990.

After 9...Nxe5, strongly worth considering is 10.Nd4. Instead Plaskett–Ward, Hastings 1989-90, continued 10.Nxe5 Qxe5 11.f4 Qa5 12.Bc4 Be7 13.Kb1 b5 unclear.

B112) 6.Nbd2

6...Nd7

a) 6...Nc6 7.c3 g6 8.Bb5 Bd7 9.O-O Bg7 10.e5 dxe5 11.Bxc6 Bxc6 12.Nxe5 Bb5 13.Re1 (Black also has problems after 13.c4 Bc6 14.Nxc6 bxc6 15.Nf3 O-O 16.Ne5) 13...O-O-O 14.a4 Be8 15.b4 with advantage to White, Zlotnik–Andreiev, Burevestnik 1976. An example in which the Knights are superior to the Bishop pair.

b) 6...g6 7.Bd3 Bg7 8.e5 Qe7 9.O-O Nd7 10.Re1 dxe5 11.dxe5 b6 12.Qe2 Bb7 13.Qe3 Rd8 14.Qf4 g5 15.Qg3 Qb4 16.Nc4 Qc5 17.a4 Bd5 18.b3 Qe7 19.a5 Bxf3 20.axb6 axb6 21.gxf3 Nc5 unclear, Giffard–Kosten, Cannes 1988.

c) 6...Qe7 7.Bd3 g6 8.O-O e5 9.c3 Bg7 10.Nc4 O-O 11.Ne3 Nd7 12.Re1 Nf6 13.a4 c6 14.dxe5 dxe5 15.a5 Ng4 16.Nc4 Be6 17.Qe2 Rad8 is equal, Dreev–Romanishin, Lvov 1987.

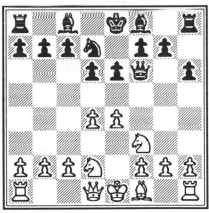

7.c3

7.Bd3 e5 8.c3 g6 9.Nc4 Bg7 10.d5 O-O 11.Ne3 h5 12.Qe2 Bh6 13.O-O-O Nc5 14.Bc2 Bg4 15.Kb1 Bxf3 16.gxf3 a5 with advantage to Black, Hoi–Browne, Reykjavik 1988.

7...g6

a) Interesting is 7...g5!? 8.Nc4 g4 (8...Bg7 9.Bd3 Qe7 10.Qe2 b6 11.O-O-O Bb7 12.Rhe1 O-O-O 13.Kb1 Kb8 14.Na3 Nf6

15.Nd2 Qd7 16.Ba6 Qc8 [16...Ba8!?] 17.Bxb7 Qxb7 18.f3 with advantage to White, Yusupov–Gurgenidze, USSR 1981) 9.Nfd2 (worth considering is 9.e5!? Qe7 10.exd6 cxd6 11.Nfd2 d5 12.Ne3 h5 unclear, according to Browne) 9...h5 10.h3 Bh6 11.Bd3 e5 12.Ne3 Nb6 13.dxe5 Qxe5 with advantage to Black, Silman–Browne, USA 1987.

b) 7...Qd8 8.Bd3 Be7 9.Qe2 c5 10.h4 cxd4 11.cxd4 e5 12.O-O-O Bf6? 13.Nc4 Qc7 14.Bc2 Be7 15.Ne3 with advantage to White, McCambridge–Reshevsky, USA 1988.

8.Bd3 Bg7 9.a4

a) 9.O-O O-O

a1) 10.Re1 e5 11.Qe2 Qe7 12.Nc4 Nb6 13.Ne3 (13.Na5!?) 13...h5 14.h3 a5 with advantage to Black, Gruenfeld–Wirthensohn, Biel 1981.

a2) 10.a4 e5 11.dxe5?! (11.Qc2) 11...dxe5 12.a5 Rd8 13.Qe2 Nc5 14.Bc2 Ne6 with advantage to Black, Ortega–Psakhis, Alma-Ata 1986.

b) 9.Qe2 a6 10.a4 b6 11.O-O O-O 12.b4 Bb7 13.a5 b5 14.c4 bxc4 15.Bxc4 Ra7 is equal, Botterill–Andersson, Hastings 1978-79.

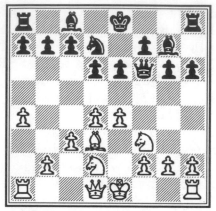

9...Qe7

9...a5 10.O-O and now:

a) 10...O-O 11.Re1 e5 12.Nc4 Qe7 13.Qb3 b6 14.Ne3 Bd7 15.Nd5 Qd8 16.Rad1 with advantage to White, Johanssen–Lawton, London 1984.

b) 10...e5 11.d5 O-O 12.b4 Qe7 13.Qc2 Nf6 14.Nb3 axb4 15.cxb4 Nh5 16.Rfc1 Nf4 17.Bb5?! (17.Bf1) 17...f5 18.Qxc7 Qf6 unclear, Silman–Benjamin, USA 1989.

10.a5 a6 11.O-O O-O 12.Rfe1 e5 13.Qc2

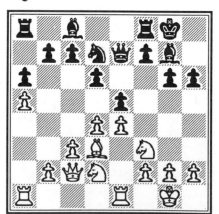

A typical position in this variation. White has the more comfortable position. Black can keep the equilibrium but should not remain passive. In the game Psakhis–

Makarichev, USSR Championship 1983, Black sought chances with an Exchange sacrifice: 13...Nf6 14.Nc4 Nh5 15.Ne3 Be6 16.Bc4 Rae8 17.Bxe6 fxe6 18.dxe5 Rxf3 19.gxf3 Bxe5 20.Ng4 Rf8 unclear.

B12) 5...d5

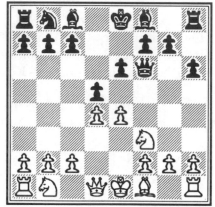

Not a popular move. Black fixes the position too early.

6.Nbd2

A France Defense structure also resulted in Ermenkov–Burger, New York 1980 after 6.e5 Qd8 7.Nbd2 c5 8.c3 Qb6 9.Qb3 Bd7 10.Be2 Nc6 11.O-O Be7 12.dxc5 Bxc5 13.Rae1 with advantage to White.

6...Nc6

a) 6...Qd8 7.Bd3 Be7 8.O-O O-O 9.Qe2 c5 10.dxc5 Bxc5 11.Nb3 Bb6 12.Rad1 with advantage to White, Smith–Flear, Great Britain Championship 1978.

b) 6...dxe4 7.Nxe4 Qd8 8.Bd3 Be7 9.c3 Nd7 10.Qc2 c6 11.O-O-O with advantage to White, Hoi–Hansen, Esbjerg 1982.

7.c3 Bd7 8.Bd3

Risky is 8.Qb3 O-O-O 9.exd5 exd5 10.Qxd5 Bf5 with advantage to Black.

102

8...O-O-O 9.e5

White would also get a large advantage after 9.b4 g5 10.b5 Ne7 11.Qa4 Kb8 12.Ne5.

9...Qe7 10.b4 g5 11.Nb3 g4 12.Nfd2 Qg5 13.O-O f6 14.b5 Nxe5

Practically forced. If 14...Ne7, then 15.f4 gxf3 16.Nxf3. After the text, Vaganian–Psakhis, USSR Championship 1983, continued 15.dxe5 fxe5 16.c4 h5 17.Qe2 e4 18.Nxe4 dxe4 19.Bxe4 with a large advantage to White.

B13) 5...c5?!

A dubious move which allows White to roll his center forward.

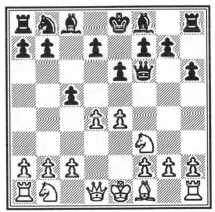

6.e5 Qd8 7.d5!

Harmless is 7.Nc3 cxd4 8.Nxd4 Nc6 9.Nxc6 bxc6 10.Bd3 Rb8 with equality, Torre–Sämisch, Marianske Lazne 1925. After the text move White stands well, as the following examples demonstrate:

a) 7...d6 8.Bb5+ Bd7 9.Bxd7+ Qxd7 10.O-O Na6 (10...dxe5 11.Nxe5 Qxd5 12.Qxd5 exd5 13.Re1 Be7 14.Nc3 O-O 15.Nxd5 Bd8 16.Rad1 with advantage to White) 11.exd6 Bxd6 12.dxe6 fxe6 13.Nbd2 O-O-O 14.Qe2 with advantage to White, Malich–

Grünberg, Leipzig 1973.

b) 7...exd5 8.Qxd5 Be7 9.Nc3 O-O 10.O-O-O Nc6 11.Qe4 d6 12.exd6?! (12.Bd3 g6 13.Bc4 Bf5 14.Qe3 with advantage to White, Uhlmann) 12...Bxd6 13.Nb5 Re8 14.Qa4 Re6 15.Bc4 Rf6 16.Rhe1 Bf5 17.Bd3 Bxd3 18.Rxd3 a6 19.Nxd6 Rxd6 with equality, Malich–Zaitsev, Berlin 1986.

c) Perhaps best is 7...Qb6 8.Nc3 and now:

c1) 8...g5 9.Nd2 Qxb2 10.Nde4 with compensation, Pribyl–Videnkeller, 1983.

c2) 8...a6 9.Nd2 Qxb2 10.Nde4 Qb4 11.Rb1 Qa5 12.a4 Be7 13.Bc4 with compensation, Thai–Sitanggang, Asian Team Championship 1991.

B14) 5...b6
6.Nbd2

a) 6.Nc3 Bb7 7.Bd3 Bb4 (7...d6 8.Qe2 Qd8 9.O-O Nd7 [9...a6!?] 10.d5 e5 11.Ba6 Bxa6 12.Qxa6 with advantage to White, B. Schmidt–Miles, Germany 1981-82 or 7...g5 8.Qe2 Nc6 9.e5 Qg7 10.Ne4 g4 11.Nf6+ Kd8 12.Nd2 Nxd4 13.Qe3 Bc5 14.Qg3 Be7 15.Qf4 Nc6 16.Nde4 unclear, Murshed–Conquest, London 1989) 8.O-O Bxc3 9.bxc3

a1) 9...d6 10.Nd2 e5 11.f4 exf4 12.g3 g5 13.a4 Nc6 14.Qe2 O-O-O 15.a5 Nxa5 16.Ba6 Bxa6 17.Qxa6+ unclear, Spassky–Miles, Niksic 1983.

a2) 9...O-O? 10.Nd2 e5 11.f4 exf4 (11...exd4 12.e5 Qc6 13.Be4) 12.e5 Qh4 13.Ne4 d5 14.g3 Qh3 15.Nf6+ gxf6 18.Rxf4 fxe5 17.Bf5 exf4 18.Bxh3 fxg3 19.Qg4+ Kh7

20.Qf5+ Kg8 21.Qf6 1-0, Cifuentes–Ligterink, Wijk aan Zee 1988.

b) For 6.a3, see Illustrative Game 77.

6...Bb7 7.Bd3

7.c3 g6 8.a4 a6 9.e5 Qe7 10.Nc4 Bg7 11.Bd3 Nc6 12.O-O O-O 13.Re1 f5 14.exf6 Qxf6 15.Qc2 with advantage to White, Christiansen–J. Whitehead, U.S. Championship 1987.

7...Qd8

a) 7...d6 8.c3 g5?! (8...Qd8 transposes back to the main line) 9.Qa4+ Kd8?! (9...Bc6) 10.O-O-O Qe7, Hort–Planinc, Moscow 1975 and now White should play 11.Rhe1 with the idea of d5 with advantage to White.

b)7...a6 8.Qe2 d6 9.O-O-O Nd7 10.Kb1 e5?! 11.c3 Be7 12.Nc4 O-O 13.Bc2 Rfe8 14.d5! c5?! (better is 14...c6 followed by ...b5) 15.Ne3 Bf8 16.g4! with advantage to White, Kortchnoi–Karpov, Hastings 1971/72.

8.Qe2

8.c3 d6 9.O-O Nd7 10.a4 a6 transposes into Dreev–Kengis, Barnaul 1988, which continued 11.Ne1 c5?! 12.Qg4 cxd4 13.cxd4 e5 14.f4 Nf6 15.Qg3 exd4 16.Nc2

with advantage to White.

8...d6

Worth considering is 8...Be7:

a) 9.h4 d6 10.O-O-O Nd7 11.g4 Nf6 12.g5 (12.Rhg1!?) Nh5 13.g6? (better is 13.Qe3 and then g6) 13...fxg6 14.e5 O-O 15.Rhg1 Nf4 16.Qe3 Qe8 17.Rg4 Qf7 with a winning advantage to Black, Palatnik–Tukmakov, USSR 1982.

b) 9.O-O-O d6 10.h4 a6 11.Nc4 Nd7 12.Ne3 Nf6 13.e5 Nd5 (13...Ne4? 14.d5 exd5 15.Nxd5 Bxd5 16.Bxe4 with advantage to White) 14.Nxd5 Bxd5 15.Be4 c6 with only a slight advantage for White, Lerner–Yudasin, USSR 1983.

c) 9.c3 d6 10.O-O-O Nd7 11.Kb1 c5 12.g4 Qc7 13.Rhg1 O-O-O 14.Ba6 Nf8 15.Bxb7+ Kxb7 16.h4 d5? 17.exd5 cxd4 18.cxd4 exd5 19.Rc1 Qd6 20.Ne5 Bxh4 21.Qf3 Nd7 22.Nxf7 Qg6+ 23.Ka1 Nf6 24.Nxh8 Rxh8 25.Nc4 Rd8 26.Nd6+ 1-0, Kavalek–Bösken, German League 1987-88.

9.a4

a) White can advance energetically with 9.h4. Karner–Ornstein, Tallinn 1977, continued 9...a6 10.O-O-O Nd7 11.g4 g6 12.c3 Bg7 13.Kb1 Qe7 14.Nf1 h5 15.gxh5 Rxh5 16.Ng3 Rh8 17.h5 g5 18.Rhg1. Black's King will have problems finding a safe home.

b) 9.O-O-O also gives White a comfortable position: 9...Nd7 10.e5 Qe7 11.Ba6 O-O-O 12.Kb1, Ermenkov–Szekely, Bulgaria 1982.

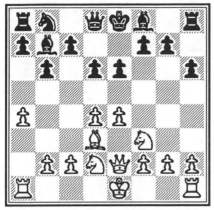

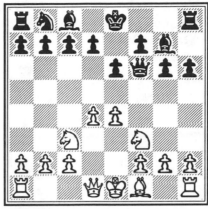

9...a6 10.O-O Be7 11.d5 exd5

If 11...e5, then 12.a5 O-O 13.axb6 cxb6 14.b4 with advantage to White, according to Vaganian.

12.exd5 Bxd5 13.Rfe1 c5 14.Nh4 Ra7

Vaganian–Kengis, USSR 1982 continued 15.Qh5 Bc6 16.Nc4 Kf8 17.Ng6+!? fxg6 18.Bxg6 Nd7 19.Re6 Nf6 20.Qf5 h5! and Black held. Instead White should have played 15.Qg4 Kf8 16.Qf5 Bxh4 17.Qxd5 g6 18.Ne4 to demonstrate an advantage.

B15) 5...g6
6.Nc3 Bg7

6...Qe7 7.Bc4 Bg7 8.O-O d6 9.Qd3 O-O 10.Rae1 a6 11.a4 b6 12.Ne2 c5 with equality, Gregory–Nimzovitch, St. Petersburg 1913.

7.Qd2 a6

7...O-O 8.e5 Qe7 9.O-O-O d6 10.Bc4?! Nd7 11.Qf4 a6 12.Bd3 b5 13.Ne4 Bb7 14.exd6?! cxd6 15.Qxd6 Qxd6 16.Nxd6 Bxf3 17.gxf3 Nb6 18.c3 Ra7 19.Ne4 Nd5 20.Rhe1 Rd8 21.Nc5 b4 22.Kc2 bxc3 23.bxc3 Nxc3! with a winning advantage to Black, Timman–Lobron, TV World Cup, Hamburg 1982.

8.O-O-O b5 9.e5 Qe7 10.Ne4 d5 11.exd6 cxd6 12.Qb4 d5 13.Nd6+ Kd7

If 13...Kf8, then 14.Qc5 would be uncomfortable.

14.Ne5+ Bxe5 15.dxe5 Nc6 16.Qf4 g5! 17.Qe3

If 17.Qxf7, then 17...Qxf7 18.Nxf7 Rh7 19.Nd6 Nxe5.

17...f6

Not 17...Nxe5 18.Nxc8. Hodgson–Lputian, Hastings 1986-87, continued 17...f6 18.c4 d4 19.Qf3 fxe5 20.Nf7 e4 with a very complex position which later ended in a draw.

B16) 5...Nc6
6.c3

6.e5 Qe7 7.Nc3 d6 8.Bb5 Bd7 9.O-O a6 10.Bxc6 Bxc6 11.d5 exd5

105

12.Nxd5 Bxd5 13.Qxd5 O-O-O
with equality, Hodgson–A. Sokolov, Reykjavik 1990.

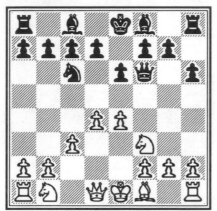

After 6...d5 7.Nbd2 we transpose
into Vaganian–Psakhis, USSR
1983, given in **B12**.

B2) 5.Nbd2
5...d6

Worth considering is 5...c5 and
now:

a) 6.Ne4 Qf5 7.Ng3 Qf6 8.e3
cxd4 9.exd4 b6 10.Be2 (10.Bd3)
10...Bb7 11.O-O h5 with advantage
to Black, Vaganian–Taimanov,
USSR 1983.

b) 6.c3 cxd4 7.cxd4 Nc6 8.e3 g5
9.a3 (9.h3 h5 10.g3 unclear) 9...g4
10.Ng1 h5 11.g3 d5 12.Bg2 Bd7
13.Ne2 h4 with advantage to Black,
Lechtynsky–Velimirovic, Banja
Luka 1985.

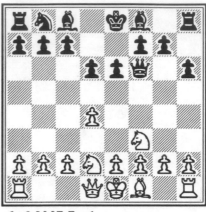

6.c3 Nd7 7.a4

a) 7.g3

a1) 7...g5 8.Bg2 g4 9.Nh4 h5
10.O-O Be7 11.e4 Qh6 12.f4 Nf8
13.e5 d5 14.c4 c6 15.Qe2 Bd7
16.Rac1 Bxh4 17.gxh4 Ng6 18.Qf2
Ne7 with equality, Salov–P.
Nikolic, Belgrade 1987.

a2) 7...g6 8.Bg2 Bg7 9.O-O O-O
10.a4 a5 11.Qb3 e5 12.e4 Nb6
13.Nc4 Nxc4 14.Qxc4 Qe7 15.Rad1
Be6 16.d5 Bc8 17.Nd2 h5 unclear,
Kosten–Adams, London 1990.

b) 7.e4 g5 8.g3 Be7 9.Bd3 Qg7
10.h3 h5 11.Qe2 g4 12.Nh2 c5
13.dxc5 Nxc5 14.Bb5+ Kf8
15.O-O-O a6 16.Bd3 b5 unclear,
Estevez–Ortega, Cuba 1984.

c) 7.e3 Qd8 8.Be2 Be7 9.O-O
O-O 10.Qc2 b6 11.a4 Draw, Benjamin–Hjartarson, Szirak (interzonal) 1987.

7...g5

More constrained is 7...g6 8.g3
Bg7 9.Bg2 O-O 10.a5 Rb8 11.O-O
Qe7 12.e4 e5 13.Nc4 exd4 14.Nxd4
Ne5 15.Ne3 Bd7 16.f4 Nc6 17.Nd5
Qd8 18.Nc2 Ne7 19.Nxe7+ Qxe7
20.Nb4 Qd8 21.Qd2 Re8 22.Qf2 a6
23.Rfd1 Qc8 24.Nd5 Bc6 25.Qd2
Bxd5 Draw, Tangborn–Kosten,
Hastings 1989-90.

8.g3 Bg7

See Illustrative Game 78.

Illustrative Game 72

GM Julian Hodgson

IM James Howell

British Championship 1991

1.d4 Nf6 2.Bg5 e6 3.e4 h6 4.Bxf6 Qxf6 5.Nf3 d6 6.Nc3 Nc6 7.Qd2

Hodgson–Adams, Ireland 1991 continued 7.d5 Ne5 8.Bb5+ Bd7 9.Nxe5 Qxe5 10.Bxd7+ Kxd7 with advantage to White.

7...Bd7 8.O-O-O O-O-O 9.d5 Ne7

If 9...Ne5, then 10.Nd4 and Ncb5 can be played later, attacking the Black King.

10.Qe3 Kb8 11.e5 Qg6

If 11...dxe5, then 12.Ne4 Qf4 13.Qxf4 exf4 14.dxe6 fxe6 15.Ne5 with a winning advantage to White.

12.exd6

Also possible is 12.Bd3, as 12...Qxg2 13.h3 leaves the Queen trapped. White will get a good position after 12...Nf5 13.Qe2.

12...cxd6 13.dxe6 fxe6

Also losing is 13...Bxe6 14.Nb5 Nc6 15.Ne5 Nxe5 (not 15...dxe5 16.Rxd8+ Nxd8 17.Qxe5+ with mate to follow) 16.Qxa7+ Kc8 17.Qa8+ Kd7 18.Qxb7+ Ke8 19.Nc7+ Ke7 20.Nd5+ Ke8 21.Bb5+ Bd7 22.Rhe1. 13...Qxe6 would have put up the most resistance, although White is much better after 14.Qd2.

14.Rxd6!

This does not seem to be possible because of Black's next move.

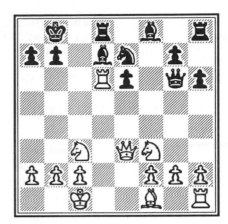

14...Nf5

14...Nd5 would be met with the same response.

15.Rxd7! Rxd7

If 15...Nxe3, then 16.Rxd8+ Kc7 17.Rd7+! Kc8 18.fxe3 and White has a strong attack as well as a material advantage.

16.Ne5 Qe8

If 16...Nxe3, then 17.Nxg6 Nxf1 18.Nxh8 Nd2 19.Rd1 winning the Knight.

17.Nxd7+ Qxd7 18.Qe4 Bc5 19.Bc4 Nd6 20.Qe5 Qc7 21.Bxe6 Nb5

With stubborn resistance, Black is able to enter an endgame just one pawn down. However, White activates his pieces quickly and ends the game with a strong attack.

22.Qxc7+ Nxc7 23.Bg4 Bxf2 24.Rd1 Bh4 25.Rd7 Bg5+ 26.Kb1 Bf6 27.Ne4 Be5 28.h3 a6 29.c3 Ka7 30.Bf3 Kb6 31.Nd6 Bh2 32.Nxb7 Ne6 33.a4 a5 34.Rd5 Ng5 35.Rb5+ Kc7 36.Bd5 1-0

Illustrative Game 73

GM Michael Adams

GM Vladimir Epishin

Dos Hermanas 1993

1.d4 Nf6 2.Bg5 e6 3.e4 h6
4.Bxf6 Qxf6 5.Nf3 d6 6.Nc3 g6
7.e5

Normal and more restrained is 7.Qd2.

7...Qe7 8.Qd2 Bg7 9.O-O-O a6

A common move in this type of position. It is important to prevent White from having access to the b5-square. Also ...b7-b5 may later be played to start a Queenside attack.

10.h4

Also a common move. White gains space on the Kingside and makes Black think twice about castling there.

**10...Bd7 11.Ne4 Bc6 12.Qf4
Bxe4 13.Qxe4 c6 14.Qf4 dxe5
15.Nxe5 Nd7 16.Nc4 Nf6
17.Nd6+ Kf8 18.Nc4**

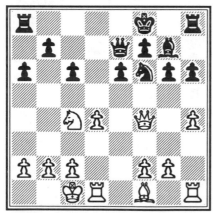

White has prevented Black from castling, but he has lost a lot of time. Black is planning to break with ...c7-c5, after which the h8-a1 diagonal will become very powerful.

**18...h5 19.Kb1 Rd8 20.Be2 Nd5
21.Qg3 c5 22.Ne5 Qf6 23.Qa3**

Worth considering is simplifying the position with 23.dxc5 Qxe5

24.Qxe5 Bxe5 25.c4.

23...Kg8 24.Qxc5 Qxf2

White's position is very difficult. Black is threatening both 25...Qxe2 and 25...Bxe5.

**25.Qa5 Rc8 26.Qe1 Qxg2
27.Bd3 Nf4 28.Be4 Qe2
29.Qxe2 Nxe2 30.Bxb7**

This loses the exchange but White had little hope in any case.

**30...Rb8 31.Bxa6 Nc3+ 32.Ka1
Nxd1 33.Rxd1 Bxe5 34.dxe5
Kg7 35.c4 Rhd8 36.Rc1 g5
37.c5 Rd2 38.Bc4 Rdxb2
39.hxg5 R2b7 40.Bd3 Rc7 41.a4
Rb4 42.Bb5 Ra7 43.Bc6 Ra6
44.Bd7 Rb7 45.Rd1 Ra5 0-1**

Illustrative Game 74

GM Viktor Kortchnoi

GM Anatoly Karpov

Moscow match 1974

**1.d4 Nf6 2.Bg5 e6 3.e4 h6
4.Bxf6 Qxf6 5.Nf3 d6 6.Nc3 g6
7.Qd2 Qe7 8.O-O-O a6 9.h4
Bg7 10.g3 b5 11.Bh3 b4 12.Nd5
exd5 13.Bxc8 O-O 14.Bb7 Ra7
15.Bxd5 c6 16.Bb3 Qxe4
17.Qd3**

Botvinnik suggests instead 17.Qf4 Qxf4 18.gxf4 followed by 19.f5 or 19.h5 with a slight advantage to White. Now the endgame is equal.

**17...Qxd3 18.Rxd3 Nd7 19.Re1
Nb6 20.a4 bxa3 21.bxa3 a5
22.Rde3 Bf6**

Better is 22...a4 23.Ba2 Bf6.

23.a4 c5?!

Black could have maintained equality with 23...Rc7 24.Re4 c5 (or 24...d5 25.R4e3 c5 26.dxc5

Rxc5) 25.dxc5 dxc5 26.Bc4.

24.dxc5 dxc5 25.Nd2 Kg7 26.Rf3 Rc7 27.Nc4 Nxc4 28.Bxc4 Rd8 29.c3 Rcd7 30.Kc2

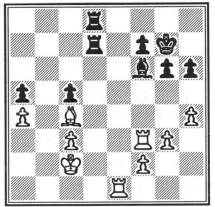

White is planning to attack the Queenside weaknesses with Kc2-b3-c4-b5.

30...Rd2+ 31.Kb3 Rd1 32.Rxd1 Rxd1 33.Bb5 Rd5?!

Correct is 33...Rc1 34.Kc4 Rc2 35.Bc6 Rc1 36.Bd5 Rc2 37.Kb5 Rxc3 38.Kxa5 Rxf3 39.Bxf3 Bd4 40.Bd5 c4! equal, according to Botvinnik. After the text, White should play 34.Kc4.

34.Re3 Re5 35.Rd3 Re2 36.Rf3 Re5?!

As mentioned before, 36...Re1 37.Kc4 Rc1 is correct.

37.Kc4 Rf5 38.Rd3 Rxf2 39.Kxc5 Be5 40.Kb6 Rg2 41.c4 Rxg3

If 41...Bxg3, then 42.Rxg3 Rxg3 43.c5 g5 44.hxg5 hxg5 45.c6 Rc3 46.c7 Rxc7 47.Kxc7 f5 48.Kb6 winning.

42.Rd7 g5 43.hxg5 hxg5 44.c5 Rc3 45.c6 g4 46.c7 g3 47.Bc6 Bxc7+ 48.Rxc7 Kh6

According to Botvinnik, Black draws with 48...Rxc6+! 49.Rxc6 f5.

49.Rc8 f5 50.Rf8

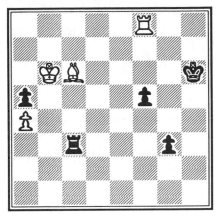

50...Rxc6+?

Now this loses. According to Botvinnik, Black still could have drawn with 50...Kg5! 51.Ba8 f4 52.Kxa5 Rb3! 53.Ka6 (53.Bd5 Rb2) 53...Kg4 54.a5 f3 55.Ka7 g2 56.a6 Kh3.

51.Kxc6 Kg5 52.Rg8+ Kf4 53.Kb5 Kf3 54.Kxa5 f4 55.Kb4 Kg2 56.a5 f3 57.a6 f2 58.a7 f1=Q 59.a8=Q+ Qf3 60.Qa2+ Qf2 61.Qd5+ Qf3 62.Qd2+ Qf2 63.Kc3 Kg1 64.Qd1+ Kg2 65.Qd3 Qc5+ 66.Kb3 Qb6+ 67.Kc2 Qc6+ 68.Kd2 Qh6+ 69.Qe3 Qh4 70.Rb8 Qf6 71.Rb6 Qf5 72.Rb2 Kh2 73.Qh6+ Kg1 74.Qb6+ Kh2 75.Qb8 Kh3 76.Qh8+ Kg4 77.Rb4+ Kf3 78.Qh1+ Kf2 79.Rb2 1-0

Illustrative Game 75

GM Artur Yusupov
GM Klaus Bischoff

Munich 1990

1.d4 Nf6 2.Nf3 e6 3.Bg5 h6 4.Bxf6 Qxf6 5.e4 d6 6.Nc3 Nd7 7.Qd2 a6 8.O-O-O Qe7 9.Bd3

g6 10.Rhe1 Bg7 11.h4 O-O

If 11...c5, then 12.e5 d5 13.dxc5.

12.e5 d5 13.Ne2 c5 14.c3 cxd4 15.Nexd4

If 15.cxd4, then Black can obtain counterplay with 15...Nb6 followed by ...Bd7-b5.

15...Nc5 16.Bb1 Bd7 17.h5

It is important to play this move before Black can play ...Rfc8 followed by ...Be8.

17...g5 18.Re3

Not 18.Nh2 due to 18...f5!

18...Rfc8?!

Better was 18...g4. According to Yusupov, the position is equal after 19.Nh2 Qg5 20.Nxg4 Qxg4 21.Rg3 Qxh5 22.Qf4 Kh8 23.Rh3 Qxe5 24.Rxh6+ Kg8 25.Bh7+.

19.Nh2 b5 20.Qc2 g4?

According to Yusupov, better was either 20...Kf8, although White has a strong position after 21.Ng4! Ke8 22.Qh7 Qf8 23.Rf3, or 20...Ne4, and if 21.f3, then Black has counterplay after 21...f5! 22.fxe4 dxe4.

21.Nxg4!

Not 21.Qh7+? Kf8 22.Nxg4 Qg5 with counterplay.

21...Qg5 22.Nf6+ Bxf6

23.Nf3!

A very strong *Zwischenzug* which gives White control of the e5 square.

23...Qg7 24.exf6 Qxf6 25.Ne5 Kf8

Also losing is 25...Be8 26.Qh7+ Kf8 27.Ng6+.

26.Nxf7! Ke7 27.Ne5 Kd6 28.Qd2 b4 29.Nc4+ Kc7 30.cxb4 Na4 31.Bc2 Kd8 32.Ne5 Nb6? 33.Qd4 1-0

Illustrative Game 76

GM Julian Hodgson
GM Ian Rogers

Wijk aan Zee 1989

1.d4 Nf6 2.Bg5 e6 3.e4 h6 4.Bxf6 Qxf6 5.Nf3 d6 6.Nc3 Nd7 7.Qd2 c6 8.O-O-O e5 9.h4?!

White would like to play g4-g5. But this does not fit in well here. Better is 9.dxe5.

9...Be7 10.Qe3 Nf8! 11.Be2

If 11.d5, then 11...Nd7 followed by ...Nc5 and ...Bd8-b6 is good for Black.

11...Ne6 12.Bc4 Bd8! 13.Bxe6 Bxe6

Black has the better position because of his two Bishops. If now 14.d5, then 14...Bd7.

14.dxe5 dxe5 15.Na4 O-O 16.Kb1

If 16.Nc5, then 16...Bb6 17.Qc3 Bg4.

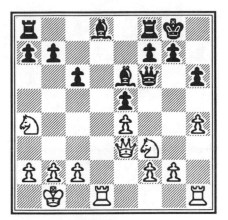

16...Bg4 17.Rd3?

The only move was 17.Qc3. Black would be slightly better after 17...b5 18.Nc5 Bb6.

17...b5! 18.Nc5?!

18.Nc3 Bb6 would have held out longer.

18...Bb6 19.Rc3

Black would get a strong attack after 19.b4 a5 20.c3 Qe7.

19...Qe7

Threatening 20...b4 21.Rc4 Be6.

20.a3 a5 21.b4 0-1

21...axb4 22.axb4 Qa7.

Illustrative Game 77

GM Viktor Kortchnoi

GM Paul Keres

USSR Championship, Tallinn 1965

1.d4 Nf6 2.Nf3 e6 3.Bg5 h6 4.Bxf6 Qxf6 5.e4 b6 6.a3 Bb7 7.Nc3 d6 8.Qd2 Nd7 9.O-O-O g5?!

Better is 9...O-O-O.

10.Nb5 Kd8

Not 10...Qd8 11.Qc3 c6 12.d5.

11.h4 g4 12.e5 Qg7 13.Ne1 a6 14.Nc3 d5 15.f4 f5

With Black's King in the center, it is risky to open up the center. But White was threatening 16.f5

exf5 17.Nd3 followed by Nf4 and Bd3.

16.exf6 Qxf6 17.h5?!

Better is 17.Ne2 to meet 17...c5 with 18.c3 or 18.c4. Now Black obtains counterplay.

17...c5 18.dxc5 bxc5 19.g3 Bc6 20.Rh4 Rg8 21.Nd3 Rb8 22.Nf2 c4 23.Nxg4 Qe7 24.Re1

Correct is 24.Qe3. Now Black has a brilliant combination.

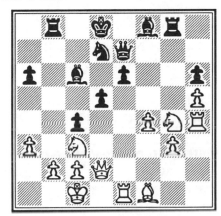

24...Rxb2! 25.Kxb2 Qxa3+ 26.Kb1 Bg7 27.Ne5 Kc7 28.Nb5+ axb5 29.c3 Bxe5 30.fxe5 Rxg3 31.Rh3 Rg5 32.Rhe3 Nc5 33.Rf3 Be8 34.Qa2 Qxa2+ 35.Kxa2 Rxh5 36.Ka3 Ne4 37.Rf8 Bd7 38.Kb4 Rxe5 39.Ra1 Rf5 40.Rh8 Rf2! 0-1

If 41.Ra7+, then 41...Kb6! 42.Rxd7 Rb2+ 43.Ka3 Rb3+ 44.Ka2 Nxc3+ 45.Ka1 Rb1 mate.

Illustrative Game 78

GM Rafael Vaganian

IM Jim Plaskett

Hastings 1982-83

1.d4 Nf6 2.Nf3 e6 3.Bg5 h6 4.Bxf6 Qxf6 5.Nbd2 d6 6.c3 Nd7 7.a4 g5 8.g3 Bg7

Worth considering is 8...g4 9.Nh4 Be7 followed by ...h5, ...Nf8, and ...Qh6.

9.Bg2 O-O 10.a5

Threatening 11.a6.

10...Rb8 11.O-O e5

This severely weakens the f5 square, but Black had little scope for his pieces.

12.e3 Qe7

Better is 12...Re8 followed by 13...Nf8.

13.e4 exd4

13...g4 14.Nh4 exd4 15.Nf5 with advantage to White.

14.Nxd4 Ne5 15.Re1

The White Knight maneuvers to e3 via f1 where it will be very well posted.

15...Re8 16.Nf1 Nc6 17.Nc2

Correctly avoiding exchanging pieces when one has a space advantage.

17...Qe5 18.Nfe3 Qc5

Not 18...Nxa5 19.Nd5 Nb3 20.Ra3 c6 21.Rxb3 with a winning advantage to White or 19...Nc6 20.f4 with a winning advantage to White.

19.Nd5 Ne7 20.b4 Qc6 21.Nd4 Qd7 22.Qd2 Nxd5 23.exd5 Rxe1 +

Better was 23...Re5.

24.Rxe1 Qd8 25.a6!

Creating a fresh weakness at c6.

25...Bxd4

Exchanging off White's active Knight, but now Black's King position is weakened. If 25...Bd7, then 26.axb7 Rxb7 27.Nc6 Bxc6 (27...Qf6 28.Re7 Bxc6 29.dxc6 Qxe7 30.cxb7) 28.dxc6 Rb8 29.Bd5 Qf6 30.Re3.

26.Qxd4 b6

Better was 26...bxa6.

27.h4 Bd7 28.Bf3 gxh4

If 28...Qf8, then 29.hxg5 hxg5 30.Qf6 Qg7 31.Qxg7+ Kxg7 32.Re7 Rd8 33.Bh5 with a winning advantage to White.

29.gxh4 Qf8 30.Kh2 Re8 31.Rg1 + Kh7 32.Qf6 Re5 33.Bd1 Bf5 34.Bh5 Bd3 35.Bxf7 Re8 36.Rg3 Bb1 37.Rf3 Rd8 38.Bg6 + Bxg6 39.Qxf8 Rxf8 40.Rxf8 1-0

Conclusion: After 1.d4 Nf6 2.Nf3 e6 3.Bg5 h6 4.Bh4, Black can win the Bishop pair with 4...g5 5.Bg3 Ne4 or transpose into Chapter 6 with 4...c5. After 4.Bxf6 Qxf6 Black has the two Bishops and a solid position, but must play accurately. After 5.e4 the best move is 5...d6 and if then 6.Nf3, then 6...a6 or 6...Nd7 7.Qd2 c6 followed by ...Be7 and ...e5 are worth considering.

Chapter 8

1.d4 Nf6 2.Nf3 e6 3.Bg5 d5 4.e3

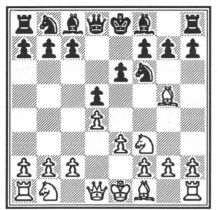

We will classify the variations according to the plan that Black chooses: A) ...Nbd7, ...b6, ...Bb7; B) ...c5, ...Nc6; C) ...b6.

A) Black plays ...Nbd7, ...b6, ...Bb7
4...c5

Black can also play without ...c5:
4...Be7 5.Nbd2

a) 5...O-O 6.Bd3 b6 7.Ne5 Bb7 8.Bxf6 Bxf6 9.f4 Bxe5 10.fxe5 Qh4+ 11.g3 Qh6 12.Qe2 Nc6 13.O-O (not 13.c3 f6) 13...Nb4 14.Rf4 with advantage to White, Timman–Geller, Linares 1983.

b) 5...b6 6.Bd3 Bb7 7.Bxf6 Bxf6 8.c3 O-O 9.h4 (the point of 7.Bxf6: the defensive f6-Knight is exchanged and the g5 square is available to the White Knight) 9...Nd7 10.Ng5 g6 11.Qg4 h5 12.Qg3 Bxg5 13.hxg5 c5 14.O-O-O a5 15.Qd6 c4 16.Bc2 Ra7 17.g4 with advantage to White, Gallego–Al-Othman, World Junior Championship, Kiljava 1984.

c) 5...Nbd7 6.Bd3 O-O 7.c3 b6 8.b4 Bb7 9.Qb1 h6 10.Bh4 Nh5 11.Bg3 Qc8 12.Be5 Nhf6 13.O-O c5 with equality, Petrosian–Andersson, Amsterdam 1973.

5.c3 Be7

5...Nbd7 6.Nbd2

a) 6...Bd6 7.Bd3 h6 8.Bh4 O-O 9.O-O b6 10.e4 dxe4 11.Nxe4 Be7 12.dxc5 Nxc5 13.Nxc5 bxc5 14.Qe2 Bb7 15.Rad1 Qc7 16.Ne5 with advantage to White, Meister–Pigusov, USSR 1985.

b) 6...Qb6 7.Rb1 h6 8.Bh4 Bd6 9.Bd3 Qc7 10.Qe2 cxd4 11.cxd4 O-O 12.O-O a6 13.Rbc1 Qb8 14.Bb1 b6 15.e4 dxe4 16.Nxe4 Nd5 17.Nxd6 Qxd6 18.Qc2 N7f6 19.Ne5 Bb7 unclear, Rongguang Ye–Lukov, Thessaloniki Olympiad 1988.

6.Nbd2

6.Bd3 would be inexact: 6...Qb6 7.Qb3 c4 8.Qxb6 axb6 9.Bc2 b5 followed by ...b4.

6...Nbd7

a) 6...b6 7.Bd3 Bb7 8.Ne5 Nbd7 9.Bb5 O-O 10.Nc6 Bxc6 11.Bxc6 Rc8 12.Bb5 Ne8 13.Bf4 Bd6 with equality, Barlov–Psakhis, Sochi 1984.

b) 6...O-O 7.Bd3 b6

b1) 8.O-O Nbd7 9.Qb1 h6 10.Bh4 Bb7 11.b4 cxb4 12.cxb4 Rc8 13.Bg3 Rc3 14.a3 Nh5 15.Be5 f6 16.Bf4 Nxf4 17.exf4 Bd6 with equality, Kiselov–Gavrikov, Moscow 1983.

b2) 8.Ne5

b21) 8...Nfd7 9.Qh5 g6 10.Bxe7 Qxe7 11.Qh6 Nxe5 12.dxe5 Nc6 13.f4 f6 14.Bb5 Nd8 15.Nf3 fxe5 16.Nxe5 with advantage to White, Kiselev–Ivanenko, Moscow 1984.

b22) 8...Bb7

b221) 9.Qf3 Nbd7 10.Rd1 cxd4

11.exd4 a6 12.O-O Re8 13.Rde1 Nf8 14.Qh3 b5 15.a3 Qb6 16.Re3 a5 17.Qh4 b4 18.Rh3 with a decisive advantage to White, Zs. Polgar–Dive, Wellington 1988.

b222) 9.Bxf6 Bxf6 10.f4 Ba6 11.Bxa6 Nxa6 12.Ndf3 Nc7 13.Qe2 Ne8 with equality, Platonov–Dolmatov, Tashkent 1980.

b223) 9.O-O Nfd7 10.Bxe7 Qxe7 11.f4 Ba6 12.Bxa6 Nxa6 13.Qa4 Nb8 14.b4 with advantage to White, Spassky–Hübner, Montreal 1979.

7.Bd3 b6

a) The moves 7...h6 8.Bh4 have often been inserted here. Yusupov–Speelman, Hastings 1989-90, continued 8...b6 9.Ne5 Nxe5 10.dxe5 Nd7 11.Bxe7 Qxe7 12.f4 Bb7 13.Qe2 O-O-O 14.O-O-O f6 15.exf6 gxf6 16.e4 d4 17.c4 h5 18.g3 Kb8 19.Nf3 b5 20.Rhe1 (20.cxb5 Nb6 21.Nd2 f5) 20...Nb6 with advantage to Black.

b) Dubious is exchanging 7...cxd4 8.exd4. White will obtain a strong position by playing O-O, Qe2, Rae1, Ne5.

c) Also dubious is 7...a6?! 8.O-O b5 9.Ne5 Bb7 10.f4 c4 11.Bc2 Ne4 12.Bxe7 Qxe7 13.Bxe4 dxe4

14.Nxd7 Qxd7 15.b3 O-O 16.bxc4 bxc4 17.Qc2 Qc6 18.Rab1 with advantage to White, Seirawan–Larsen, Linares 1983.

d) Black also has no reason to immediately castle (forfeiting the option of Queenside castling) with 7...O-O 8.Ne5 Nxe5 9.dxe5 Nd7:

d1) For 10.Bf4, see Illustrative Game 79.

d2) Dreev–Ostenstad, World Junior Championship, Kiljara 1984, continued 10.Bxe7 Qxe7 11.f4 f6 12.exf6 Qxf6 13.O-O Qh6 14.Nf3 e5 15.Bb5! with a decisive advantage to White.

e) Another plan here is 7...Qc7 to hinder Ne5. Holmov–Gipslis, USSR team Championship 1962, continued 8.O-O O-O (Dubious is 8...e5 9.dxe5 Nxe5 10.Nxe5 Qxe5 11.Nf3 Qe6 12.Bb5+, Dreyer–Gonzales, Siegen Olympiad 1970) 9.Qe2 b6 (on 9...e5, 10.e4 is strong) 10.e4 dxe4 11.Nxe4 Bb7 12.Rad1 Rfe8 13.dxc5 bxc5 14.Ng3 with advantage to White.

8.O-O

a) 8.Ne5 should also be considered here:

a1) 8...Nxe5 9.dxe5 Nd7

a11) 10.Bf4 Bb7 11.O-O g5 12.Bg3 h5 13.f4 h4 14.Be1 gxf4 15.exf4 Qc7 16.Qg4?! O-O-O with advantage to Black, Klaric–Geller, Sochi 1977.

a12) 10.Bxe7 Qxe7 11.f4 f5 12.exf6 Nxf6 13.O-O O-O 14.e4 dxe4 15.Nxe4 Bb7 16.Qe2 with advantage to White, Machulsky–Fernandez, Manila 1987.

a2) 8...cxd4 9.exd4 Nxe5 10.dxe5 Nd7 11.Bxe7 Qxe7 12.Nf3 O-O 13.O-O Nc5 14.Bc2 a5 15.Re1 with advantage to White, Lein–Seirawan, Lone Pine 1981.

b) Dubious is 8.Qa4?!:

b1) 8...O-O 9.Ne5 Bb7 10.Nc6 Bxc6 11.Qxc6 a6 12.Qa4 b5 13.Qd1 b4 14.c4 cxd4 15.exd4 dxc4 16.Nxc4 Nd5 17.Bd2 a5 with advantage to Black, Slipak–Panno, Buenos Aires 1984.

b2) 8...h6 9.Bxf6 Bxf6 10.e4 Bb7 11.e5 Be7 12.O-O a6 13.bxc5 bxc5 14.Qg4 Rh6 with advantage to Black, Haritonov–Nokikov, USSR Championship 1984.

c) 8.Qb1 a5 9.O-O Ba6 10.Bxf6 Bxf6 11.Bxa6 Rxa6 12.Qd3 c4 13.Qe2 b5 14.e4 O-O 15.Rfe1 Rb6 16.exd5 exd5 17.Nf1 Re6 with equality, Day–Vranesic, Toronto 1989.

d) 8.Qe2 h6 9.Bh4 O-O 10.Ne5 Nxe5 11.dxe5 Nd7 12.Bxe7 Qxe7 13.f4 f6 14.exf6 Qxf6 15.O-O e5 16.fxc5 Qxc5 17.Nf3 Qe7 18.e4 Bb7 19.e5 with advantage to White, Timman–Hartston, The Hague 1967.

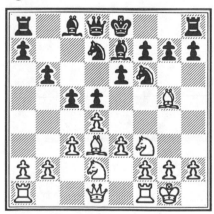

After the text we examine **A1) 8...Bb7** and **A2) 8...O-O.**

An alternative is 8...h6 9.Bh4 O-O 10.Ne5 Nxe5 11.dxe5 Nd7 12.Bg3 Bb7 (12...Bh4? 13.Bxh4

Qxh4 14.f4 Bb7 15.Rf3 Qe7 16.Rg3 Kh8 17.Qh5 with a large advantage to White, Tartakower–Keres, Kemeri 1937) 13.Qg4 c4 (13...Qc8? 14.Bf4 with a decisive advantage to White, Bronstein–Roizman, USSR 1963) 14.Be2 Nc5 15.Rad1 Nd3 16.Bxd3 cxd3 17.Nf3 Ba6 unclear, Kavalek–deFirmian, USA 1985.

A1) 8...Bb7

Black reserves the option of castling Queenside.

9.Ne5

a) 9.Qb1 (a common maneuver in this position, controlling the e4 square and bolstering Queenside play beginning with b2-b4) and now:

a1) 9...Qc7 10.b4

a11) 10...c4 11.Bc2 h6 12.Bh4 O-O 13.a4 a6 14.Re1 Rfc8 15.Re2 b5 16.a5 Re8 17.Qe1 Rad8 18.Rc1 Qb8 19.Bb1 Qc7 20.Qd1 Ba8 21.Qc2 Bb7 22.Rf1 Qb8 23.Bxf6 Nxf6 24.Ne5 Bd6 25.f4 Ne4 with equality, Hodgson–Unzicker, Almada 1988.

a12) 10...Rb8 11.c4 dxc4 12.Bf4 Bd6 13.Bxd6 Qxd6 14.Nxc4 Qe7 15.e4 b5 16.Na5 cxb4, Tukmakov–Schussler, Helsinki 1983. Tukmakov now recommends 17.Nxb7 Qxb7 18.Qc2 with advantage to White.

a2) 9...h6 10.Bh4 Qc7 11.b4 Bd6 and now Damljanovic–Vaiser, Vrnjacka Banja 1986, continued 12.Rfc1 c4 13.Bc2 a6 14.a4 Ng4 15.h3 Ngf6 16.Bxf6 Nxf6 17.Re1 O-O-O with advantage to Black. Instead White should play 12.bxc5 bxc5 13.e4 with equality.

b) 9.a4 a6 10.Qb1 h6

b1) 11.Bf4 Nh5 12.Be5 O-O 13.h3 c4 14.Bh7+ Kh8 15.Bc2 b5 with equality, Hort–Kir. Georgiev, Thessaloniki Olympiad 1984.

b2) 11.Bh4 O-O 12.Re1 Qc7 13.e4 dxe4 14.Nxe4 Rfe8 15.dxc5 bxc5 16.Nxf6+ Bxf6 17.Bg3 Qc8 18.Nd2 Be7 19.Nc4 Bd5 20.Qc2 Qb7 with equality, Hodgson–Razuvaev, Sochi 1987.

c) 9.Qc2 O-O 10.Rae1 c4 11.Be2 b5 12.Ne5 Nxe5 13.dxe5 Ne4 14.Bxe7 Qxe7 15.f4 Qc5 16.Bf3 f5 17.exf6 Nxf6 with equality, Torre–A. Sokolov, Biel 1985.

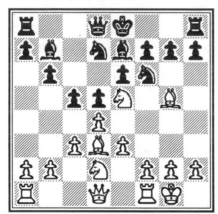

9...Nxe5 10.dxe5 Nd7

10...Ne4? loses a pawn: 11.Bxe7 Qxe7 12.Nxe4 dxe4 13.Bxe4 Bxe4 14.Qa4+.

11.Bxe7

An inaccuracy would be 11.Bf4?! See Illustrative Game 80.

11...Qxe7 12.f4 f6

12...O-O-O

a) 13.a4 f6 14.exf6 gxf6 15.a5 c4 16.Be2 b5 17.a6 Bc6 18.b4 Nb6 unclear, Garcia–Kortchnoi, Las Palmas 1981.

b) 13.Qe2 f6 14.exf6 gxf6 (weak is 14...Nxf6 15.Nf3 c4?! 16.Bc2 Kb8 17.Qd2 Nd7 18.Qd4 Rde8 19.Ba4 Ref8 20.Bxd7 Qxd7 21.a4 Qc7

22.a5 bxa5 23.Ne5 Ka8 24.Ra2 Qb6 25.Rfa1 with advantage to White, Hebert–Ivanov, Montreal 1983) 15.e4 d4 (15...c4 16.Bc2 Kb8 17.b3 with advantage to White; 15...Nb8 16.exd5 Bxd5 17.Be4! with the idea Nc4, a4 with advantage to White) 16.a4, see Spassky–Sokolov below.

13.Qh5+

a) 13.exf6 gxf6 14.e4 O-O-O 15.Qe2 d4 16.a4 e5 (16...a5?! 17.Ra3! with the idea Rb3, Bxa5) 17.f5 Nb8 18.a5 dxc3 (18...Nc6 19.axb6 axb6 20.Ba6 with good attacking prospects, Spassky–A. Sokolov, Bugojno 1986) 19.bxc3 (19.axb6 cxd2 20.bxa7 Nc6 21.a8=Q Bxa8 22.Rxa8+, Kc7) 19...Qd6 20.Rf3 b5 21.Nf1 c4 with advantage to Black, Heyland–Tulfer, correspondence 1989.

b) 13.Nf3 O-O-O (13...fxe5 14.Bb5) 14.Bb5 Kb8 15.a4 Nf8?! (15...a6) 16.b4 a6 17.Bd3 fxe5 18.Nxe5 Nd7 19.Qh5 with advantage to White, Dreev–Novikov, USSR 1984.

13...Qf7 14.Qe2 O-O

a) 14...f5 15.a4 a5 16.Nf3 h6 17.h3 Nb8 18.Bb5 Nc6 19.Rfc1 with advantage to White, Hulak–Polajzer, Portoroz/Ljubljana 1987.

116

b) 14...O-O-O 15.e4 fxe5 16.exd5 exd5 17.fxe5 Qe7 18.Nf3 Kb8 and now 19.e6 would give White a big advantage, Hulak–van der Sterren, Wijk aan Zee 1987.

15.exf6 Nxf6 16.Nf3 Qh5
See Illustrative Game 81.

A2) 8...O-O
9.Ne5
Other possibilities:

a) 9.e4 dxe4 10.Nxe4 Bb7 11.Qe2 (11.Nxf6+ with equality) 11...Nxe4 12.Bxe7 Qxe7 13.Bxe4 Bxe4 14.Qxe4 Nf6 15.Qe5 Rfd8 16.dxc5 Rd5 17.Qe3 Rxc5 18.Rfd1 Rd8 19.h3 h6 20.Rxd8+ Qxd8 21.Qe2 Rd5 with advantage to Black, Shirazi–Browne, Los Angeles 1982.

b) 9.Qe2 Bb7 10.Ne5 Nxe5 11.dxe5 Ne4 12.Bxe7 Qxe7 13.Bxe4?! (better is 13.f3) 13...dxe4 14.Qg4 Qc7 15.Qf4 Qc6 16.Rfd1 Rad8 17.h4 c4 18.h5 h6 19.Nf1 Rd3 with advantage to Black, Diakovsky–Cvetkovic, Yugoslavia Championship 1968.

c) 9.Qb1 Bb7 10.b4 cxd4 11.cxd4 Rc8 12.b5 h6 13.Bh4 Rc3 14.a4 Qc7 15.Rc1 Rc8 16.Nb3 Rxc1+ 17.Qxc1 Qxc1+ 18.Rxc1 Rxc1+ 19.Nxc1 Draw, Hübner–Keene, Hastings 1969/70.

d) 9.Qc2 h6 10.Bh4 Bb7 11.Rae1 c4 12.Be2 Qc7 13.Bg3 Bd6 14.Bxd6 Qxd6 15.e4 with advantage to White, Spassky–Reshevsky, Amsterdam Interzonal 1964.

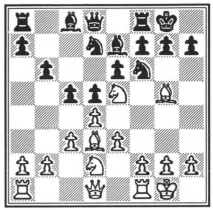

9...Bb7
9...Nxe5 10.dxe5 Nd7 11.Bxe7 Qxe7 12.f4 f5 13.exf6 Rxf6 14.e4 Bb7 15.e5 Rf7 16.Qg4 g6 17.Nf3 Rg7 18.Rad1 with advantage to White, Trifunovic–Filip, Varna Olympiad 1962.

10.f4
Several Queen moves have been tried here:

a) 10.Qa4. Kavalek–Ravi, Dubai Olympiad 1986, continued 10...h6 (very bad is 10...Nxe5?? 11.dxe5 Nd7? 12.Qh4 with a decisive advantage to White) 11.Bh4 Nxe5 12.dxe5 Nd7 13.Qg4 with advantage to White. Recommended instead is 10...a6, as 11.Nc6?! Bxc6 12.Qxc6 b5 is very risky for White.

b) 10.Qf3 h6 (not 10...Nxe5? 11.dxe5 Ne4 12.Bxe7 Nxd2 13.Bxh7+ with a decisive advantage to White) 11.Bf4 Nxe5 12.dxe5 Nh7 13.Qh5 f5 14.Qg6 Rf7 unclear, Trifunovic–Filicic, Yugoslavia 1945.

c) 10.Qb1 (10.Qc2 followed by Rae1 is also worth considering) 10...h6 11.Bxf6 Bxf6 12.Nxd7 Qxd7 13.f4 Bc6 14.Rf3 Bb5 15.Rh3 Bxd3 16.Qxd3 Be7 17.Nf3 Bd6 18.g4 with advantage to White, Sokolov–Pismenny, USSR 1974.

117

10...h6

10...a6 11.Qf3 Nxe5 12.fxe5 Nd7 13.Qh3 g6 14.Bh6 with strong attacking chances, Torre–Verlinski, Moscow 1925. After the text, Dreyer–Ramirez, Tel Aviv Olympiad 1964, continued 11.Bh4 Ne4 12.Bxe7 Qxe7 13.Ndf3 Ndf6 14.Qe1 g5 15.Rd1 c4 16.Bxe4 Nxe4 17.Nd2 Nxd2 18.Rxd2 Kg7 19.g4 f6 20.Nf3 Rae8 21.Rg2 Rh8 22.Qg3 with advantage to White.

B) Black plays ...c5 and ...Nc6.
4...c5 5.c3 Nc6 6.Nbd2

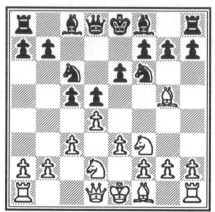

6.Bd3 would be inexact here: 6...Qb6 7.Qb3 c4 8.Qxb6 axb6 9.Bc2 b5 with advantage to Black, Zara–Gheorghiu, Bucharest 1967.

6...Be7

a) 6...cxd4?! 7.exd4

a1) 7...Bd6 8.Bd3 Bd7 9.O-O Rc8 10.Re1 Qc7 11.Qe2 h6 12.Bh4 Nh5 13.Bg3 Nxg3 14.hxg3 O-O 15.Ne5 Nxe5 16.dxe5 Be7 17.Nf3 a6 18.Rad1 b5 19.a3 Rb8 20.Bb1 Rfc8 21.Rd4 and White has a dangerous attack, Tartakover–Sämisch, Vienna 1921.

a2) For 7...Be7, see Illustrative Game 82.

b) 6...Bd6 7.Bd3 h6 8.Bh4 O-O

9.O-O and now:

b1) 9...b6?! 10.Qe2 Bb7 (11...dxe4 12.Nxe4 Be7 13.Bxf6 Bxf6 14.dxc5 wins a pawn) 11.e4 Be7 12.e5 with advantage to White, Kopec–Bauer, USA 1988.

b2) 9...e5?! 10.e4 (also possible is 10.dxe5 Nxe5 11.Nxe5 Bxe5 12.f4 and 13.e4) 10...exd4 11.exd5 dxc3 12.Ne4 cxb2 13.Nxf6+ gxf6 14.Qd2 Kg7 15.Rae1 with advantage to White, Tseitlin–Roguli, Lodz 1980.

b3) Black's best may be 9...Re8. If 10.e4, then 10...cxd4 11.cxd4 dxe4 12.Nxe4 Be7.

c) 6...Qb6 7.Bxf6 (7.Rb1 cxd4 8.exd4 e5!? is Bisguier–I. Ivanov, USA 1986) 7...gxf6 8.Rb1 e5 9.e4 cxd4 10.exd5 Ne7 11.cxd4 Nxd5 12.Bc4 Be6 13.Rc1 exd4 14.O-O Bh6 15.Bxd5 Bxd5 16.Nc4 Qd8 17.Rc2 b5 18.Re1+ Kf8 19.Ncd2 Qd7 20.Ne4 with advantage to White, Yermolinsky–Naumkin, Tashkent 1987.

d) Another idea here is 6...Qc7 to hinder Ne5, in which case White usually plays for e3-e4: 7.Bd3 Be7 8.O-O b6 9.e4 dxe4 10.Nxe4 O-O 11.Qe2 Bb7 12.Rad1 Rfe8 13.dxc5 bxc5 14.Ng3 Rad8 15.Rfe1 Qc8 16.Rd2 with advantage to White, Holmov–Gipslis, USSR 1962.

e) 6...h6 7.Bh4 Be7 8.Bd3 O-O 9.O-O Ne8 10.Bxe7 Qxe7 11.dxc5 Qxc5 12.e4 dxe4 13.Nxe4 Qe7 14.Re1 e5 15.Ng3 Nf6 16.Bb5 Bg4 17.Qe2 with advantage to White, Trifunovic–Velimirovic, Yugoslavia 1963.

7.Bd3 h6

a) 7...Nd7 8.Bxe7 Qxe7 9.O-O O-O (9....e5? 10.e4) 10.Re1!

a1) 10...Qf6 11.Bb5! Qd8

(11...e5?! 12.Bxc6 bxc6 13.dxe5)
12.Rc1 Qb6 13.Bxc6 bxc6 14.Qc2
with advantage to White, Timman–
Beliavsky, Wijk aan Zee 1985.

a2) 10...Rd8 11.Qe2 g6 12.Rad1
c4?! (better is 12...e5 13.e4 dxe4
14.Qxe4 f5 15.Qd5+ Kg7 16.Bb5
unclear) 13.Bc2 f5 14.Ba4! with a
large advantage to White due to
the weakness at e5.

b) 7...O-O 8.Bxf6 Bxf6 9.dxc5
Qe7 10.Qc2 h6 11.Nb3 a5 12.a4 e5
13.e4 Be6 14.Nfd2 Bg5 15.Rd1
Rad8 16.exd5 Bxd5 17.Be4 with ad-
vantage to White, Tihi–
Schoneberg, Prague 1981.

c) 7...b6 8.Qa4 Bd7 9.Qc2 h6
10.Bh4 Qc7 11.O-O O-O 12.a3
Rad8 13.Rfe1 Bc8 14.b4 Bb7 15.b5
Na5 16.Qb1 Ng4 17.Bg3 Bd6 with
equality, Psakhis–Tiviakov, Moscow 1989.

d) 7...Qb6 8.Rb1 h6 9.Bh4 cxd4
10.cxd4 g5 11.Bg3 Nh5 12.Be5?!
(12.O-O) 12...Nxe5 13.Nxe5 Nf4
14.Bf1 Bd6 with advantage to
Black, Pekoveli–G. Garcia,
Havana 1986.

8.Bh4 cxd4

a) 8...O-O 9.Ne5 Nxe5 10.dxe5
Nd7 11.Bg3 f6 12.exf6 Bxf6 13.Qg4
Ne5 14.Bxe5 Bxe5 15.Qg6 Qf6
16.Qh7+ Kf7 17.f4 Bd6 18.e4!
Bxf4 19.O-O with a decisive ad-
vantage to White, Klaric–Majeric,
Yugoslavia 1981.

b) 8...Nd7 9.Bg3 O-O 10.Qe2 c4
11.Bc2 f5 12.h4 b5 13.e4! Nf6
(13...fxe4 14.Nxe4) 14.exf5 exf5
15.Ne5 Nxe5 16.dxe5 Ne4 17.Nxe4
dxe4 18.Rd1 with advantage to
White, Holmov–Tseshkovsky,
USSR Championship 1970.

9.exd4

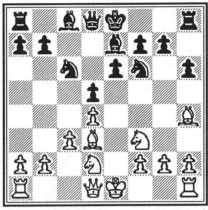

This position is much better for
White. He has the initiative in the
center and on the Kingside. The
following examples demonstrate
this:

a) 9...Qc7 10.O-O O-O 11.Re1
Nh5 12.Bxe7 Qxe7 13.Nf1 f5
14.Bb5 Nf6 15.Bxc6 bxc6 16.Ne5
Qd6 17.Nd2 c5 18.dxc5 Qxc5
19.Nb3 Qd6 20.Qd4 with advantage to White, Polugaevsky–
Padevsky, Budapest 1965.

b) 9...Nh5 10.Bxe7 Qxe7 11.O-O
Nf4 12.Bc2 Qf6 13.Re1 O-O 14.g3
Ng6 15.Qe2 b6 16.h4 Re8 17.Ne5
Ncxe5 18.dxe5 Qe7 19.Nf3 a5
20.Nd4 with advantage to White,
Spassky–Matanovic, Havana 1962.

C) Black plays ...b6
4...Be7 5.Nbd2 b6 6.c3

a) 6.Ne5 Nfd7 7.Bxe7 Qxe7 8.f4
c5 9.c3 O-O 10.Bd3 Ba6 11.Bxa6
Nxa6 12.Qa4 Nxe5 13.fxe5 Qb7
14.O-O b5 15.Qd1 b4 with
equality, Cifuentes–Schüssler,
Lucerne Olympiad 1982.

b) 6.Bd3 O-O 7.h4 Ba6 8.Bxa6
Nxa6 9.Ne5 Qe8 10.Qe2 Nb4
11.Ndf3 c5 12.c3 Nc6 13.h5 h6
14.Nxc6 Qxc6 15.Ne5 Qb7 16.Bxf6
Bxf6 17.f4 Bxe5 18.dxe5 b5 19.O-O

119

Rad8 Draw, Spassky–Taimanov, USSR Championship 1963.

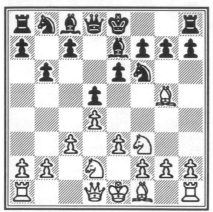

6...c5 7.Bd3

7.Bb5+ Nfd7 8.Bf4 O-O 9.Ne5 Nxe5 10.dxe5 Ba6 11.Bxa6 Nxa6 12.Qg4 Kh8 13.Rd1 Qe8 14.O-O Qa4 15.e4 Nc7 16.a3 with advantage to White, Klaric–Flear, London 1979.

7...O-O 8.Ne5

8.O-O Bb7 transposes into Spassky–Hübner, Montreal 1979, which continued 9.Ne5 Nfd7 10.Bxe7 Qxe7 11.f4 Ba6 12.Bxa6 Nxa6 13.Qa4 Nab8 14.b4 with advantage to White.

8...Bb7 9.f4 Ne4 10.Bxe7 Qxe7 11.O-O f6 12.Nf3 Nd7 13.Qc2 f5 14.Bb5 Ndf6 15.Nxe4 dxe4 16.Ne5 a6 17.Be2 Nd5 with equality, Petrosian–Gligoric, Niksic 1983.

Illustrative Game 79

GM Tigran Petrosian
NM Viktor Liublinsky

USSR Championship, Moscow 1949

1.d4 Nf6 2.Nf3 e6 3.Bg5 c5 4.e3 Be7 5.Nbd2 d5 6.c3 Nbd7 7.Bd3 O-O

This allows White to invade e5 with his Knight. Correct is 7...Qc7.
8.Ne5!

Without this move White can establish no advantage.

8...Nxe5 9.dxe5 Nd7 10.Bf4 f5

If 11...f6, then 11.Qh5 forcing 11...f5, as 11...g6 would be met by 12.Bxg6 hxg6 13.Qxg6+ Kh8 14.h4 followed by Rh3. After the text it seems it will be more difficult to start an attack.

11.h4!

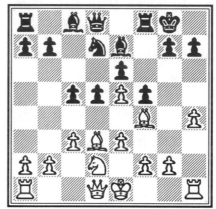

White prevents ...g7-g5 and prepares g2-g4. Not 11...Bxh4? due to 12.Qh5.

11...c4 12.Bc2 b5

Better is 12...Nc5 followed by ...Ne4 closing the b1-h7 diagonal.

13.Nf3

Petrosian gives 13.g4 as even stronger.

13...Nc5 14.g4 b4 15.gxf5

Too hasty according to Petrosian. Better is 15.Nd4.

15...exf5 16.Ng5 g6?

According to Petrosian, correct is 16...h6 17.Qh5 Nd3+ 18.Bxd3 cxd3 19.Qg6 hxg5 20.hxg5 Qe8 21.Qh7+ Kf7 22.Rh6 Rg8 with an unclear position. Now the opening of the h-file will be decisive.

17.h5 Nd3+

If 17...Bxg5, then 18.Bxg5 Qxg5 19.Qxd5+ Be6 20.Qxc5 with a

decisive advantage to White.

18.Bxd3 cxd3 19.hxg6 hxg6 20.Qxd3 bxc3 21.bxc3 Bxg5 22.Bxg5 Qa5 23.Bf6 Re8 24.Qd4 Kf7 25.e6+ Rxe6 26.Bd8 1-0

Illustrative Game 80
GM Boris Spassky
GM Tigran Petrosian
World Championship Match, Moscow 1966

1.d4 Nf6 2.Nf3 e6 3.Bg5 d5 4.Nbd2 Be7 5.e3 Nbd7 6.Bd3 c5 7.c3 b6 8.O-O Bb7 9.Ne5 Nxe5 10.dxe5 Nd7 11.Bf4?!

Correct is 11.Bxe7.

11...Qc7

Even stronger is 11...g5 as in Klaric–Geller, Sochi 1977.

12.Nf3

Not 12.Qg4 due to 12...g5 13.Bxg5 (13.Bg3 h5) 13...Rg8 with a decisive advantage to Black.

12...h6 13.b4

Accepting the pawn would give White a strong position: 13....cxb4 14.cxb4 Bxb4 15.Nd4.

13...g5 14.Bg3 h5 15.h4

If 15.h3, then Black is better after 15...g4 16.hxg4 hxg4 17.Nh2 Nxe5 18.Bb5+ Kf8 19.Nxg4 Bd6 20.f4 Nc4.

15...gxh4 16.Bf4 O-O-O 17.a4

It would have been better to open lines on the Queenside with 17.bxc5.

17...c4!

Giving up the d4-square, but closing the Queenside.

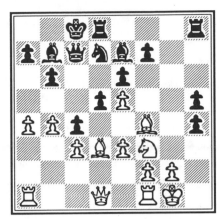

18.Be2

Correct was 18.Bf5 in order to give the Bishop a better defensive role on h3. If 18...exf5, then 19.e6 Bd6 20.Bxd6 Qxd6 21.exd7+ Rxd7 22.Nd4 with an unclear position.

18...a6 19.Kh1 Rdg8 20.Rg1 Rg4 21.Qd2 Rhg8 22.a5 b5 23.Rad1 Bf8

Threatening 24...f6 25.exf6 e5 and 24...Bg7 25.Qd4 Nb8 followed by ...Nc6.

24.Nh2 Nxe5!

Petrosian was well known for his positional Exchange sacrifices.

25.Nxg4 hxg4 26.e4 Bd6 27.Qe3 Nd7

Preparing to push his central pawns.

28.Bxd6 Qxd6 29.Rd4 e5 30.Rd2 f5! 31.exd5

Better is 31.exf5, although Black remains better after 31...Nf6.

31...f4 32.Qe4

If 32.Qa7, then 32...e4.

32...Nf6 33.Qf5+ Kb8 34.f3

If 34.Qe6, then 34...Qxe6 35.dxe6 Ne4.

34...Bc8 35.Qb1 g3 36.Re1 h3 37.Bf1 Rh8 38.gxh3 Bxh3 39.Kg1 Bxf1 40.Kxf1 e4 41.Qd1 Ng4! 42.fxg4 f3 43.Rg2 fxg2+

121

Illustrative Game 81

GM Ivan Sokolov
GM Vassily Ivanchuk

Biel 1989

**1.d4 Nf6 2.Nf3 e6 3.Bg5 c5 4.e3
d5 5.Nbd2 Be7 6.c3 Nbd7
7.Bd3 b6 8.O-O Bb7 9.Ne5
Nxe5 10.dxe5 Nd7 11.Bxe7
Qxe7 12.f4 f6 13.Qh5+ Qf7
14.Qe2 O-O 15.exf6 Nxf6
16.Nf3 Qh5 17.Qe1 Ng4?!**

Loses time. White now gets a very strong position.

18.h3 Nf6 19.Ne5 a6 20.g4 Qe8

Of course not 20...Qxh3? 21.Rf3.

21.g5 Nd7 22.Qh4

22.Bxh7+ Kxh7 23.Qh4+ Kg8 24.Nxd7 (24.g6 Nf6) 24...Qxd7 25.g6 Rf5 26.e4 dxe4 27.Rad1 Rd5 is not enough.

**22...g6 23.Ng4 Qe7 24.Qg3
Rae8 25.h4 Kh8 26.Qh2 e5
27.fxe5**

Better is 27.h5.

27...Rxf1+?!

According to Sokolov, correct is 27...Qe6 28.Qg3 d4! 29.cxd4 cxd4 30.exd4 Qd5 with compensation for the sacrificed pawn.

**28.Rxf1 Nxe5 29.Nxe5 Qxe5
30.Rf8+ Kg7 31.Rxe8 Qxe8
32.Qc7+ Kg8 33.e4 Bc6
34.Qxb6?!**

Now the Queen is out of play. Better is 34.Bxa6.

34...Qe5 35.Qxc6?

Short on time, White allows a perpetual check. He could have won with 35.Kg2 Qe6 36.Qxc5 Qg4+ 37.Kf2 Qxh4+ 38.Ke2.

35...Qg3+ Draw

Illustrative Game 82

GM Tigran Petrosian
GM Henrique Mecking

Wijk aan Zee 1971

**1.d4 Nf6 2.Nf3 e6 3.Bg5 c5 4.e3
d5 5.c3 Nc6 6.Nbd2 cxd4?!
7.exd4 Be7 8.Bd3 h6 9.Bf4 Nh5
10.Be3 Nf6 11.Ne5 Nxe5
12.dxe5 Nd7 13.Bd4 Nc5
14.Bc2 a5 15.Qg4 g6 16.O-O
Bd7 17.Rfe1 Qc7 18.a4 Na6
19.Qe2 Kf8 20.Nf3 Kg7 21.Be3
Nc5 22.Nd4 Ra6 23.Bc1 Raa8**

This game is very typical of Petrosian's style. A position has been reached in which although White can only make progress very slowly, Black can make no progress at all.

**24.g3 b6 25.h4 h5 26.Qf3 Qd8
27.Bd2 Qe8?**

Black attacks the a-pawn, but allows the dark-squared Bishops to be exchanged.

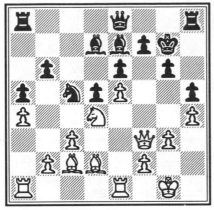

28.Bg5! Qd8

Ivkov gives the following variation: if 28...Bxg5, then 29.hxg5 Bxa4 30.Bxa4 Nxa4 31.Rxa4 Qxa4 32.Nxe6+ fxe6 33.Qf6+ Kg8 34.Qxg6+ Kf8 35.Qf6+ Kg8 36.Qxe6+ Kg7 37.Qf6+ Kg8 38.Qg6+ Kf8 39.Re3.

29.Qf4 Rc8 30.Re3 Bxg5 31.hxg5 Ra8 32.Qf6+ Qxf6 33.exf6+ Kh7 34.Kg2 Rae8 35.f4 Rb8 36.Reel Nb7 37.Rh1 Kg8 38.Nf3 Nd6 39.Ne5 Be8 40.Bd3 Rc8 41.Kf3 Bc6 42.Rh2 Be8 43.Ke3 Rc7 44.Kd4 Nb7 45.b4 Nd8 46.Rh4 Nb7 47.Ra2 Nd6 48.Rh1 Nb7 49.b5 Nc5 50.Bc2 Nd7 51.Ra3 Nc5 52.c4 Nd7 53.Rc3 Nxe5 54.Kxe5 dxc4 55.Be4 Rc8 56.Kd6 Rc5 57.Rhc1 h4 1-0

Ivkov gives the following logical conclusion: 58.Rxc4 Rxc4 59.Rxc4 hxg3 60.Rc8 Kh7 61.Rc3 Kg8 62.Ke7 Kh7 63.Rxg3.

Conclusion: After 1.d4 Nf6 2.Nf3 e6 3.Bg5 d5 4.e3, Black should maintain equality if he fights for control of the e5-square. It is best to play ...Nbd7 followed by ...b6.

Chapter 9

1.d4 Nf6 2.Nf3 e6 3.Bg5 b6

This will likely transpose into one of the other variations. Unusual third moves are:

a) 3...d6 4.Nbd2 Nbd7 5.e4 e5 6.c3 h6 7.Bh4 g6 8.Be2 Bg7 9.O-O O-O 10.Re1 Qe8 11.Bf1 Nh5 12.Nc4 Bf6 13.Bxf6 Nhxf6 14.Qc2 Qe7 15.a4 Re8 16.Rad1 Draw, Morovic–Robatsch, Malta Olympiad 1980.

b) 3...a6 (the actual order of moves was 2...a6 3.Bg5 e6) 4.Nbd2 h6 5.Bh4 d6 6.e4 g5 7.Bg3 Nh5 8.Bd3 Bg7 9.c3 Nd7 10.a4 Nf8 11.O O Ng6 12.e5 Ngf4 13.Be4 f5 14.exf6 Qxf6 unclear, Nemet–Miles, Germany 1989.

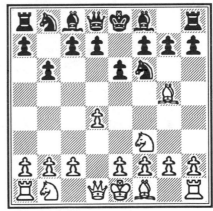

4.Nbd2

a) 4.e3

a1) 4...Bb7 5.Bd3 Be7 6.O-O O-O 7.c4 h6 8.Bxf6 Bxf6 9.Nc3 c5 10.Rc1 Na6 11.Be4 d5 12.cxd5 exd5 13.Bb1 Re8 14.Qd2 Qd7 15.dxc5 bxc5 16.Ne4 Bxb2! 17.Rcd1 Bd4! with advantage to Black, Speelman–Kortchnoi, Wijk aan Zee 1983.

a2) 4...h6 5.Bh4 Bb7 6.Bd3 c5

123

7.O-O Be7 8.c4 cxd4 9.Nxd4 d6
10.Nc3 Nbd7 11.Re1 a6 12.Bf1 Rc8
is equal, Larsen–Andersson,
Buenos Aires 1980.

b) 4.e4 h6 5.Bxf6 Qxf6 transposes to Chapter 2.

4...Bb7 5.e3 Be7

5...c5 transposes to Chapter 1.

**6.Bd3 d6 7.O-O Nbd7 8.e4 e5
9.Re1**

White is better.

Chapter 10

Second Move Alternatives

1.d4 Nf6 2.Nf3

We examine five moves: A)
2...b5, B) 2...d6, C) 2...c6, D) 2...a6,
E) 2...b6.

A) 2...b5
3.Bg5

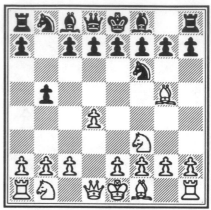

3...Bb7

3...d5 4.e3 c6 5.Nbd2 h6 6.Bh4
Bf5 7.Bd3 Bxd3 8.cxd3 Nbd7 9.Rc1
Qb6 10.O-O e6 11.Bxf6 gxf6
12.Qc2 Rc8 13.e4 with advantage
to White, Wirthensohn–Partos,
Biel 1977.

4.Nbd2

4.e3 a6

a) 5.c3 e6 6.e4 h6 7.Bxf6 Qxf6
8.Bd3 c5 9.e5 Qd8 10.Be4 Qb6
11.O-O cxd4 Draw, Browne–Miles,
London 1980/81.

b) 5.Nbd2 g6 6.c4 bxc4 7.Bxc4 d5
8.Bxf6 exf6 9.Be2 Nd7 10.Nb3
Bb4+ 11.Nfd2 a5 12.O-O O-O
13.Nf3 a4 14.Nc1 Bd6 15.Nd3 Ba6
16.Rc1 with advantage to White,
Ivkov–Ljubojevic, Hilversum 1973.

4...a6 5.a4

5.c3 e6 6.e4 h6 7.Bxf6 Qxf6
8.Bd3 c5 9.O-O Qd8 10.Qe2 cxd4
11.cxd4 Be7 12.Rc1 with advantage
to White, Langeweg–Miles,
Amsterdam 1981.

**5...b4 6.c4 e6 7.e3 c5 8.Bd3 Be7
9.O-O d6 10.Re1 Nbd7 11.Rc1 h6
12.Bxf6 Nxf6 13.Bb1 Qc7 14.Qe2
g5 15.Red1 g4 16.Ne1 h5 17.d5
O-O-O**

Unclear, Ribli–Miles, Bled/Por-
toroz 1979.

B) 2...d6

3.Bg5

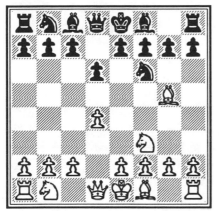

If Black plays an Old Indian setup, the Torre Attack is not effective.

3...Nbd7 4.e3 h6 5.Bh4

5.Bxf6 Nxf6 6.Nbd2 c6 (6...g6) 7.Bd3 Qc7 8.c3 e5 9.Qc2 Be7 10.dxe5 dxe5 11.Nc4 b5 12.Ncd2 O-O 13.O-O Bb7 14.c4 b4 15.Ne4 with advantage to White, Klaman–Karasev, USSR 1976.

5...g5 6.Bg3 Nh5 7.Nbd2

7.Bd3 Nxg3 8.fxg3 Bg7 9.Nbd2 c5 10.c3 Rb8?! 11.Qe2 e6 12.O-O Qe7 13.Kh1?! O-O 14.e5?! and now with 14...cxd4 15.cxd4 g4 16.Nh4 Bxd4 17.Qxg4 Qg5 Black has a big advantage, Xu Jun–Lobron, China 1988.

7...Bg7 8.Bd3

8.Bc4 Ndf6 9.Qe2 Nxg3 10.hxg3 d5 11.Bb3 c6 12.e4 Nxe4 13.Nxe4 dxe4 14.Qxe4 Qa5+ 15.c3 Bf5 16.Qe2 e6 with advantage to Black, Rossetto–Gligoric, Buenos Aires 1960.

8...e6 9.c3 f5 10.Ng1?!

Better is 10.Qe2 followed by O-O-O.

10...Ndf6 11.f3 Nxg3 12.hxg3 d5 13.Ne2 Qd6 14.Qb3 e5

Black is better, Bohm–Ljubojevic, Wijk aan Zee 1976.

C) 2...c6

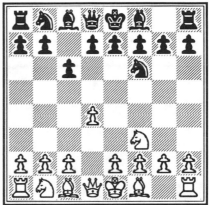

Against this move bringing out the Queen Bishop may be inferior as well. Short–Kasparov, Skelleftea 1989, continued 3.Bf4 d6 4.h3 Qb6 5.b3 (better is 5.Qc1) 5...c5 6.dxc5 Qxc5 7.c4 g6 8.Nc3 Bg7 9.Rc1 Bf5 10.Be3 Qa5 11.Bd2 Qd8 12.Nd4 Bc4 13.e3 Nc6 14.Nde2 Bd3 with advantage to Black.

D) 2...a6

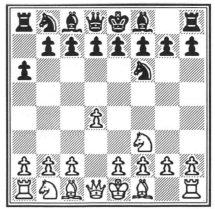

3.Bg5 e6 4.Nbd2 d6 5.h3 Nbd7 6.e4 h6 7.Be3 g6 8.c3 Bg7 9.Bd3 O-O

White is better. Veingold–Mainka, Candas 1992 continued

10.g4!? e5 11.dxe5 Nxe5 12.Bc2 b5
13.Nxe5 dxe5 14.Nb3 Bb7 15.Nb3
Bb7 and was later drawn.

E) 2...b6
3.Bg5

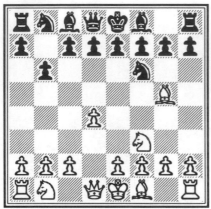

Now we examine two moves for
Black: **E1) 3...Bb7, E2) 3...Ne4.**

E1) 3...Bb7
4.Nc3

a) 4.Bxf6 exf6

a1) 5.g3?! Qe7! 6.Bg2 Qb4+
7.Nbd2 Qxb2 8.O-O Qa3 9.Nc4
Qa4 10.Qd3 Na6 11.Qe3+ Be7
12.c3 d5 with advantage to Black,
Stean–Kortchnoi, Beersheva 1978.

a2) 5.Qd3 d5 6.g3 Bd6 7.Bg2
O-O 8.O-O g6 9.c4 dxc4 10.Qxc4
Nd7 11.Nc3 a6 12.e4 b5 13.Qb3 c5
14.Rad1 cxd4 15.Rxd4 Bc5 16.Rd2
Qe7 17.a4 b4 18.Nd5 Bxd5 19.Rxd5
Ne5 with equality, Hodgson–Mor-
rison, British Championship 1988.

b) 4.Nbd2 c5 (4...d5 has also
been tried. 4...e6 would transpose
back into the normal lines) 5.Bxf6
gxf6 6.e3 e6 7.Bd3 Nc6 8.O-O d5
9.dxc5 (9.c3 c4 10.Bc2 f5) 9...bxc5
10.a3 f5 11.b4 Bd6 12.c4 Ne5 with
equality, Kochiev–Veingold, Tallinn 1985.

4...g6
4...d5?! 5.e3 Nbd7?! 6.Ne5 Nxe5
7.dxe5 Ne4 8.Nxe4 dxe4 9.Qg4 Qc8
10.e6 with a large advantage for
White, Petrosian–Golombek, Bucharest 1953.

5.e3 Bg7
5...d5?! 6.Bb5+ c6 7.Bd3 Bg7
8.e4 O-O 9.e5 Nfd7 10.Ne2 f6
11.exf6 exf6 12.Be3 Na6 13.h4 Nb4
14.h5 Nxd3+ 15.Qxd3 Qe8 16.hxg6
hxg6 17.Nf4 Ne5 18.dxe5 fxe5
19.Qxg6 exf4 20.Qh7+ Kf7 21.Rh6
Qe7 22.Qg6+ Kg8 23.Ng5 1-0,
Petrosian–Nievergelt, Belgrade
1954.

**6.Bd3 c5 7.O-O d6 8.Qe2 O-O
9.Rfd1 a6**
Füster–Csom, Siegen Olympiad
1970 continued 10.dxc5 bxc5 11.e4
Nfd7 12.Nd5 Nc6 13.c3 Re8 with
equality.

E2) 3...Ne4
4.Bh4
4.Bf4 Bb7 5.Nbd2 e6 (better is
5...Nxd2 with equality) 6.Nxe4
Bxe4 7.e3 Nc6 8.c3 Be7 9.Be2 O-O
10.h4 h6 11.Bd3 d5 12.g4 Bd6
13.Bxd6 Qxd6 14.Bxe4 dxe4
15.Nd2 with advantage to White,
Hulak–Miralles, Haifa 1989.

4...Bb7
For 4...d5, see Illustrative Game
83.

5.Nbd2 Nxd2
For 5...g6, see Illustrative Game
84.

6.Qxd2 g6
6...Bxf3? 7.exf3 c6 8.Bd3 Qc7
9.f4! Qd6 (9...d6 10.f5) 10.O-O-O
Qxd4 11.Rfe1 e6 12.c3 Qd6 13.f5
Be7 14.Bg3 Qd5 15.Kb1 Bf6
16.Qe2 Qxg2 17.fxe6 dxe6 18.Qg4

126

Qd5 19.Bxh7 Rxh7 20.Rxd5 cxd5 21.Rxe6+ 1-0, Romanishin–Savon, USSR 1979.

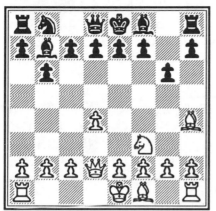

7.Bg5 h6 8.Bf4 d6 9.d5 Bg7 10.c4
With advantage to White, Guimard-Bolbochan, Mar del Plata 1946.

Illustrative Game 83
IM Mikhail Tseitlin
IM Nikolay Popov
USSR 1982

1.d4 Nf6 2.Nf3 b6 3.Bg5 Ne4 4.Bh4 d5?! 5.Nbd2 Bb7 6.e3 Nd7?! 7.c4 Ndf6 8.Rc1 e6 9.cxd5 Qxd5

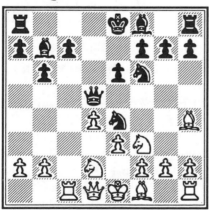

Black is already lost. If 9...Nxd2, then 10.Qa4+. If 9...exd5, then

10.Qa4+ c6 11.Rxc6 Qd7 12.Bb5 a6 13.Rxe6+.

10.Rxc7 Nxd2 11.Nxd2 Bd6 12.Qa4+ Kf8 13.e4 Nxe4
If 13...Qh5, then 14.Rxb7 Qxh4 15.e5 Bxe5 16.Qa3+ with a decisive advantage to White.

14.Bc4 Qxd4 15.Rxf7+ Kg8 16.Nf3 Qxb2 17.O-O Nc5 18.Bxe6 Nxe6 19.Rxb7 b5 20.Qe4 Qxa2 21.Rd7 Bxh2+ 22.Kxh2 Rf8 23.Re1 Nc5 24.Rxg7+ Kxg7 25.Qg4+ 1-0

Illustrative Game 84
NM Khapilin
NM I. Komissarov
Podolsk, Russia 1993

1.d4 Nf6 2.Nf3 b6 3.Bg5 Ne4 4.Bh4 Bb7 5.Nbd2 g6 6.e3
6.Nxe4 Bxe4 7.Nd2 Bb7 8.e4 Bg7 9.c3 O-O 10.Bc4 d5 11.exd5 Bxd5 12.O-O Nc6 13.Re1 Bxc4 14.Nxc4 with advantage to White, Trifunovic–Bolbochan, Mar del Plata 1950.

6...Bg7 7.Bd3 Nxd2 8.Qxd2 c5 9.c3 O-O 10.e4 cxd4 11.cxd4 f5

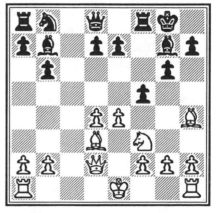

12.exf5
This allows Black to ruin White's pawn structure. Better is 12.Qe2,

127

and if 12...f4 (threatening ...h6 and ...g5), then 13.e5.

12...Bxf3 13.gxf3 Nc6 14.fxg6 Nxd4 15.gxh7+ Kh8

Black is much better because his King is safer and the Knight is very imposing on d4.

16.Be2 Rc8 17.Rc1 Rxc1+ 18.Qxc1 Rf5 19.Bg3 Rc5 20.Qd1 Nxe2 21.Kxe2 Qc8 22.Qd3 Rc2+ 23.Kf1 Qc4 24.Qxc4 Rxc4

Black is winning in the endgame because White's Rook is temporarily out of play and his pawns are weak and scattered.

25.b3 Rc2 26.Kg2 Rxa2 27.Re1 e6 28.Rd1 d5 29.Re1 d4 30.Rxe6 Rb2 31.Re8+ Kxh7 32.Re7 Kg6 33.Rxa7 Rxb3 34.Kh3 Rxf3 35.Kg4 Rf7 36.Ra8 Rb7 37.Ra6 d3 38.Kf2 Bd4 39.Ra2 Bc3 40.Ke3 Rd7 41.Rd2 Bxd2+ 42.Kxd2 Kf5 43.f3 b5 44.Be1 Kf4 45.h4 Kxf3 46.h5 Ke4 47.Bh4 Rh7 0-1

Conclusion: 2...d6 is a very frusterating move for Torre players to have to face. It is probably better for White to transpose into a normal Old-Indian Defense. 2...c6 is an interesting move.

Chapter 11

1.d4 Nf6 2.Nf3 g6 3.Bg5 Bg7

Inferior is 3...c5 4.Bxf6 exf6 5.dxc5 Bxc5 6.e3 Qb6 7.Qc1 d5 8.Be2 O-O 9.O-O Rd8 10.Rd1 is better for White, Holmov–Taimanov, USSR 1963 as is 3...h6 4.Bxf6 exf6 5.e4 Qe7 6.Nc3 Bg7 7.Bc4 O-O 8.O-O d6 9.Nh4 Kh7 10.g3 Nd7 11.f4 Nb6 12.Bd3 c5 13.f5 g5 14.Nf3 cxd4 15.Nxd4 Moiseev–Ageichenko, Moscow 1967.

4.Nbd2

4...O-O

4...h6 5.Bh4 will transpose to lines examined in Chapter 12.

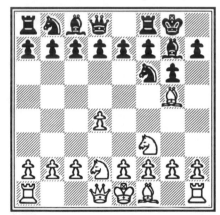

5.c3

This is more precise than 5.e4 as then Black has the option of trying 5...d5:

a) 6.exd5?! Nxd5 7.c3 h6 8.Bh4 Nd7 9.Bc4 (9.Bg3 with equality) 9...N7b6 10.Bb3 f5 11.Qe2 g5 12.Bxg5 hxg5 13.Nxg5 e6 14.Nxe6 Bxe6 15.Qxe6+ Kh7 16.O-O-O Qh4 17.g3 Qh3 18.Qe2 c6 19.Nf3 Qg4 20.Bc2 Rae8 21.Qd3 Ne3 with advantage to Black, Platonov–Gutman, Reykjavik 1978.

128

b) 6.e5 Ne4 7.Bd3 (7.Be3 c5 8.c3 Nc6 9.dxc5?! Qc7 10.Bd3 Bf5 11.Qc2 Nxd2 12.Qxd2 Be4 with advantage to Black, Trifunovic–K. Georgiev, Kragujevac 1984) 7...Nxg5 8.Nxg5 c5 9.h4 c4 10.Be2 Qb6 (10...f6 unclear) 11.c3 Qxb2 12.Rc1 f6 13.Nxc4 dxc4 14.Bxc4+ Kh8 15.Nf7+ Rxf7 16.Bxf7 Bf5 17.h5 with advantage to White, Umansky–Petrushin, Krasnodar 1982.

c) 6.Bd3 dxe4 7.Nxe4 Nxe4 8.Bxe4 c5 9.c3 Qd6 10.dxc5 Qxc5 11.O-O Nc6 12.Qb3 Na5 13.Qc2 Nc4 unclear, Braga–Nunn, Germany 1989.

Also worth considering after 5.e4 is 5...c5. Rozentalis–Glek, Odessa 1988, continued 6.e5 (not 6.c3?! cxd4 7.cxd4 d5) 6...Nd5 7.dxc5 h6 8.Nc4 hxg5 9.Qxd5 g4 10.Nfd2 Nc6 11.c3 Qc7 12.f4 gxf3 13.Nxf3 b5 14.cxb6 axb6 unclear.

5...d6 6.e4

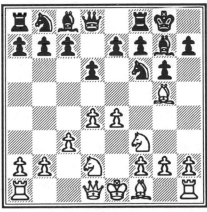

Now we examine **A) 6...Nc6, B) 6...h6, C) 6...c5, D) 6...Nbd7.**

Alternatives are:

a) 6...Na6 7.Be2 c5 8.O-O Nc7 9.dxc5 dxc5 10.Qc2 Ne6 11.Bh4 Nf4 12.Bc4 Qd7 13.a4 N6h5 14.Rfe1 Qg4 15.Bg3 e5 16.Rad1 Qd7 17.Nf1 Qc7 18.Ne3 with advantage to White, Kasparov–McNab, World Junior Championship, Dortmund 1980.

b) 6...Nfd7 7.Be2 c5 8.d5 Nf6 9.O-O Nbd7 10.a4 b6 11.Qc2 a6 12.Rfe1 Rb8 13.c4 with advantage to White, Levitina–Abhyankar, Thessaloniki Olympiad 1988.

c) 6...c6 7.Bd3 Nbd7 8.O-O e5 9.Re1 Qc7 10.a4 Re8 11.Nc4 Nf8 12.dxe5 dxe5 13.Bf1 Bg4 14.h3 Rad8 15.Qe2 Bc8 16.a5 with advantage to White, Bottema–Van Wely, Dieren 1988.

d) 6...b6 7.Bc4 Bb7 8.Qe2 c5 9.dxc5 bxc5 10.O-O Nc6 11.Ba6 Qb6 12.Bxb7 Qxb7 13.Nc4 Nd7 14 Rfe1 Rab8 15.Rac1 Qa6 16.b3 Qb7 17.h4 with advantage to White, Szily–Liptay, Hungarian Championship 1965.

e) 6...e5 7.dxe5 dxe5 8.Nxe5 Qe8 9.Bxf6 Bxf6 10.Nef3 Nd7 11.Bc4 Nc5 12.Qe2 Rb8 13.Qe3 Qe7 14.O-O b5 15.Bd5 Bd7 16.Rfe1 with advantage to White, Petrosian–Bronstein, Moscow 1983.

f) 6...Qe8

f1) 7.Bd3 Nc6 8.O-O e5 9.Re1 h6 10.Bh4 Nh5 11.dxe5 Nxe5 12.Nxe5 dxe5 with advantage to White, Torre–Romanishin, Leningrad 1987.

f2) 7.Bc4

f21) 7...e5 8.dxe5 dxe5 9.a4 Nh5 10.O-O Nd7 11.Re1 Nc5 12.Be3 Qe7 13.b4 Ne6 14.a5 a6 15.Qc2 with advantage to White, Kortchnoi–Gutman, Wijk aan Zee 1987.

f22) 7...Nc6 8.e5 dxe5 9.dxe5 Ng4 10.e6 f6 11.Bf4 Na5 12.Be2 Bxe6 13.Nd4 Bd7 14.Bxc7 e5

129

15.Nc2 Nc6 16.Bd6 Rf7 17.Bxg4 Rd8 18.Ba3 and White is a piece ahead, Miles–Glek, London 1993.

f3) 7.Be2

f31) 7...Nc6 8.O-O e5 9.dxe5 dxe5 10.Qc2 Nd8 11.Bh4 Nh5 12.Rfe1 Ne6 13.Nc4 Nf4 14.Bf1 with advantage to White, Salov–Romanishin, Leningrad 1987.

f32) 7...h6 8.Bh4 Nh5 9.O-O Nf4 10.Bc4 e5 11.Re1 Nc6 12.dxe5 dxe5 13.Qc2 Kh8 14.Rad1 f5 15.Bg3 g5 16.Bxf4 exf4 17.exf5 Bxf5 18.Bd3 Bxd3 19.Qxd3 Qf7 20.Qb5 Rab8 21.Nc4 a6 22.Qd5 Qxd5 Draw, Epishin–Van Wely, Bern 1993.

A) 6...Nc6

7.Bb5

7.Bd3 e5 8.h3 Qe8 9.O-O h6 10.Be3 b6 11.Re1 Nh5 12.Nc4 Nf4 13.Bf1 g5 14.a4 a5 15.Qd2 with advantage to White, D. Gurevich–Eagle, U.S. Open 1988.

7...a6

a) 7...Bd7 8.Qe2 h6 9.Bh4 a6 10.Bc4 e5 11.dxe5 Nxe5 12.Nxe5 dxe5 13.O-O a5 14.Rfd1 Qe7 15.a4 Rfd8 16.f3 Be6 17.Bxe6 Qxe6 18.Nc4 with advantage to White, Zhuravliov–Wojtkiewicz, Latvia 1980.

b) 7...h6 8.Bh4 a6 9.Ba4 b5 10.Bc2 Nd7 11.O-O Rb8 12.Re1 Qe8 13.a4 b4 14.a5 Na7 15.Nc4 bxc3 16.bxc3 Nb5 unclear, Cifuentes–Douven, Wijk aan Zee 1988.

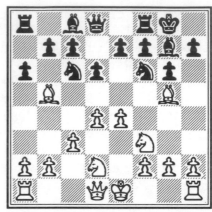

8.Ba4 Bd7 9.O-O h6 10.Bh4 Qe8 11.e5 Nh5

11...Nxd4? 12.cxd4 Bxa4 13.b3 with a decisive advantage to White.

12.Re1 d5 13.Bc2 Nd8 14.Nf1 Ne6 15.Ne3 c6 16.Bg3 Nxg3 17.hxg3 Qd8 18.Nh4 Qb6 19.Rb1 Ng5 20.f4 Ne4 21.Bxe4 dxe4 22.Qc2

With a large advantage to White, Darga–Ciocaltea, Siegen Olympiad 1970.

B) 6...h6

7.Bh4 Nc6

7...c5 8.Bd3?! (8.dxc5) 8...Nh5 9.Bg3 cxd4 10.cxd4 Nc6 11.Nb3 a5 12.a4 Qb6 13.Be2 Qb4+ 14.Kf1 e5 with advantage to Black, Machulsky–Asanov, Kazakhstan 1989.

8.Bb5 Bd7 9.O-O a6

9...Qe8 10.e5 dxe5 11.Bxc6 Bxc6 12.Nxe5 b6 13.Nxc6 Qxc6 14.Re1 Rfe8 15.Nf3 with advantage to White, Torre–Odendahl, Lone Pine 1980.

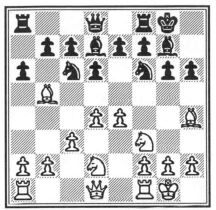

10.Bc4 e5 11.dxe5 dxe5 12.Re1 Qe8 13.a4 Nh5 14.Nb3 g5 15.Bg3 Rd8 16.Nfd2 Nxg3

If 16...Nf4, then 17.f3 h5 18.Bf2.

17.hxg3 Kh8 18.Qe2 Qe7 19.Nf1 Qf6 20.Nc5 Bc8 21.Ne3 Ne7 22.a5! Qg6 23.g4 b6 24.Nf5

Black has weaknesses on both sides of the board, Smyslov–Nunn, Tilburg 1982. The game continued **24...Nxf5 25.gxf5 Qc6 26.Nxa6 Bxa6 27.Bxa6 bxa5 28.Rxa5 Ra8 29.Rea1 Rfd8 30.Bc4 Rxa5 31.Rxa5 Kg8 32.Ra6 Qd7 33.Bd5 Qe7 34.Qh5 Rd6 35.Rxd6 cxd6 36.b4 1-0.**

C) 6...c5

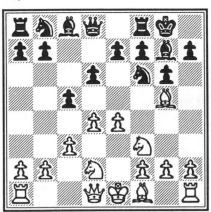

7.dxc5

7.Bd3?! cxd4 8.cxd4 Nc6 9.O-O

---

h6 10.Be3 Ng4 with advantage to Black, Zaitsev–Levitina, Moscow 1979.

7...dxc5 8.Bc4

8.Be2 Nc6 9.O-O

a) 9...b6 10.Qc2 Bb7 11.Bh4 Nh5 12.Rfd1 Qc7 13.Nc4 Bf6 14.Ne3 e6 Draw, Kasparov–Morovic, World Junior Championship, Dortmund 1980.

b) 9...Qc7 10.Qc2

b1) 10...Be6 11.Bc4 Bxc4 12.Nxc4 b5 13.Ne3 e6 14.a4 a6 15.Rfd1 c4 with equality, Glyanets–Timoshchenko, USSR 1988.

b2) 10...h6 11.Bh4 Nh5 12.Re1 Be6 13.Bf1?! (13.Bc4 with equality) 13...Rad8 with advantage to Black, Kiseler Yurtaev, Barnqul 1988.

For 8.Qc2, see Illustrative Game 84.

8... Nc6

8...h6 9.Bh4 Nc6 10.O-O Bg4 11.Qc2 g5 12.Bg3 Nh5 13.Rfe1 Nxg3 14.hxg3 e6 15.a4 Qc7 16.Be2 Bh5 with equality, Kortchnoi–L. Hansen, Jerusalem 1986.

9.O-O

9.Qe2 h6 10.Be3 b6 11.h3 Na5 12.Bd3 Qc7 13.Kh2 Rd8 14.Bc2 Nc6 15.O-O Nh5 16.Bb3 Nf4 with equality, Trifunovic–Smyslov, Dortmund 1961.

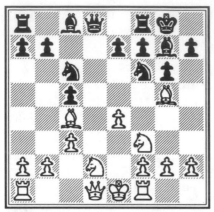

9...Na5

a) 9...Bg4 10.h3 Bxf3 11.Qxf3 h6 12.Be3 Qc7 13.Qe2 Rad8 14.f4 Na5 15.Bd3 Nh5 16.Rf3 e5 17.f5 Qd6 18.Bc4 with a large advantage to White, Trifunovic–Udovcic, Yugoslavia 1956.

b) 9...Qc7 10.Qc2 b6 11.Rfe1 Nh5 12.Rad1 Bb7 13.Bf1 Rad8 with equality, Kindermann–Nunn, Zurich 1984.

10.Be2 h6

For 10...Be6, see Illustrative Game 85.

11.Bf4 Be6 12.h3 a6 13.a4 b6 14.Ne5 Qc8

With equality, Malaniuk–Yurtaev, USSR 1986.

D) 6...Nbd7

7.Be2

a) 7.Bc4

a1) For 7...e5, see Illustrative Games 86 and 87.

a2) 7... c6

a21) 8.Bb3 b5 9.O-O Nb6 10.Re1 Qc7 11.Rc1 a5 12.a3 Ba6 13.e5?! Nfd5 14.exd6 exd6 15.Nf1 Nc4 with equality, Gulko–Westerinen, Moscow 1966.

a22) 8.O-O Nxe4 9.Nxe4 d5 10.Bd3 dxe4 11.Bxe4 Nf6 12.Bd3 Bg4 13.h3 with advantage to White, Malaniuk–Gurevich, USSR 1980.

a3) 7...h6 8.Bh4 c6

a31) 9.O-O e5 10.dxe5 dxe5 11.a4 a5 12.Qc2 Qc7 13.Ne1 Nc5 14.f3 b5 15.axb5 cxb5 16.Be2 Bd7 17.Bf2 Ne6 18.g3 Rfe8 with advantage to Black, Dzikiki–Chandler, Lucerne Olympiad 1984.

a32) 9.Bb3 Qc7 10.O-O e5 11.dxe5 dxe5 12.Qe2 Nc5? 13.Bxf6 Bxf6 14.Qe3 Nxb3 15.axb3 and White wins a pawn, Nun–Stohl, Stary Smokovec 1983.

b) 7.Bd3 e5 8.O-O

b1) 8...Qe8 9.dxe5 dxe5 10.b4 h6 11.Bh4 Nh5 with equality, Machulsky–Cvitan, Sibenik 1987.

b2) 8...h6 9.Bh4 Qe7 10.Re1 Nb6 11.Nf1 Re8 12.Ne3 Qf8 13.Qc2 Bd7 14.a4 a5 with equality, Kamsky–Cvitan, Palma de Mallorca 1989.

7...h6

7...e5 8.dxe5 dxe5 9.O-O

a) For 9...b6, see Illustrative Game 88.

b) 9...c6 10.Qc2 Qc7 11.Rfe1 Re8 12.Bf1 b6 13.a4 a5 14.Nc4 Bb7 15.Rad1 Re6 16.Bxf6 Nxf6 17.Ng5 Re7 18.Nd6 Ba6?! 19.Bxa6 Rxa6

20.Qb3 h6 21.Ndxf7 Rxf7 22.Rd8+ with a large advantage, Epishin–Kantsler, USSR 1989.

c) For 9...Qe8, see Illustrative Game 89.

8.Bh4 e5

8...Nh5 9.O-O Nf4 10.Bc4 c6 11.Re1 Nb6 12.Bf1 Qc7 13.a4 a5 14.e5 Be6 15.h3 Nh5 16.Ne4 Bd5 17.Qc1 f5 with equality, Rubinetti–Granda Zuniga, Buenos Aires 1992.

9.dxe5

Also good is 9.O-O:

a) 9...Re8 10.Qc2 g5 (weakening the f5 square) 11.Bg3 Nh5 12.Nc4 Nf4 13.dxe5 Nxe5 (13...dxe5 14.Ne3 Nf6 15.Bc4) 14.Nfxe5 Bxe5 (14...dxe5 15.Ne3 followed by Bg4) 15.Rad1 Qe7 16.Ne3 Be6 17.Bg4! Bg7 18.f3 a5 19.Bf2 a4 20.Nf5 with a large advantage to White because of the domination of the f5-square, Balashov–Vukic, Bugojno 1978.

b) 9...Qe8 10.Re1 Nh5 11.a4 a5 12.Nc4 exd4 13.Nxd4 Nf4 14.Bf1 Ne5 15.Ne3 c6 16.Qd2 with advantage to White, Rodriguez–Damljanovic, New York Open 1988.

9...dxe5 10.O-O Qe8

10...Qe7 11.Re1 Rd8 12.Qc2 b6 13.Bf1 Bb7 14.Nc4 Qe6 15.Nfd2 Qg4 16.Bxf6! Bxf6 17.Ne3 Qe6 18.Bc4 Qd6 19.Rad1 with advantage to White, Balashov–Sax, Rio de Janeiro Interzonal 1979.

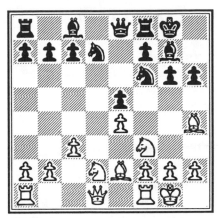

11.Re1

11.Qc2 Nh5 12.Rfe1 Nf4 13.Bf1 a5 14.a4 Nc5 15.Nc4 Bd7 16.b3 Qe6 17.Nfd2 Bf6 18.Bg3 with advantage to White, Averkin–Didyshko, USSR Championship 1981.

11...Nh5

11...Nc5 12.Qc2 Nh5 13.Nc4 Nf4 14.Bf1 Bg4 15.b4?! (15.Nfd2 with advantage to White) 15...Bxf3 16.bxc5 Bg4 with advantage to Black, Petursson–Pliester, London 1980.

12.Nc4 Nf4 13.Bf1 Nc5 14.b4 Na4

Cifuentes–Rubinetti, Pan American Championship 1981, continued 15.Qc2 Nb6 16.Na5 g5 17.Bg3 Qe7 18.Nd2 h5 19.f3 g4 20.fxg4 hxg4 21.Ndc4 Qg5 22.Ne3 with advantage to White.

Illustrative Game 84
GM Vladimir Malaniuk
IM Lanka Ravi

Calcutta 1993

1.d4 Nf6 2.Nf3 g6 3.Bg5 Bg7 4.Nbd2 O-O 5.c3 d6 6.e4 c5 7.dxc5 dxc5 8.Qc2 Nc6 9.Be2 Be6 10.O-O h6?!

Better is 10...Qc7.

11.Be3 b6 12.h3 Qc7

Better is 12...Ne8.

13.Nh2 Nd7

Better is 13...Ne8.

14.f4 f5 15.Bd3!

With the idea of Nhf3-h4.

15...Na5

The only move. Black is preparing ...c4.

16.Nhf3 c4 17.Be2

The d4-square has been opened for White's pieces.

17...fxe4 18.Nxe4 Bf7 19.Rad1 Rad8 20.Kh1 Nb7

The only move. If 20...Nc6, then 21.Qa4. If 20...Nf6, then 21.Ne5. If 20...e5, then 21.Nd6.

21.Nd4

Threatening f4-f5.

21...Ndc5

If 21...Nbc5, then 22.Bf3.

22.f5 Bd5

If 22...g5, then 23.Bf3.

23.Nxc5 Nxc5

If 23...bxc5, then 24.Nb5 Bxg2+ 25.Kxg2 Qc6+ 26.Rf3 Qxb5 27.Rxd8 Rxd8 28.f6 exf6 29.Qxg6 winning.

24.Bf3 Bxf3 25.Rxf3 e5

If 25...g5, then 26.Qe2 is winning.

26.fxe6 Rxf3 27.Nxf3 Rxd1+ 28.Qxd1 Nxe6 29.Qd5 Kf7 30.Bd4 Ke7 31.Bxg7 Nxg7 32.Ne5 Kf6 33.Ng4+ Ke7 34.Qe4+ Ne6 35.Qxg6 Qf4 36.Qxh6 Qf1+ 37.Kh2 Nf4 38.Qf6+ Ke8 39.Qc6+ Kf8 40.Ne3 Qf2 41.Nf5 1-0

Illustrative Game 85

GM Vladimir Malaniuk
IM Mihai Marin

Calimanesti 1992

1.d4 Nf6 2.Nf3 g6 3.Bg5 Bg7 4.Nbd2 O-O 5.c3 d6 6.e4 c5 7.dxc5 dxc5 8.Bc4 Nc6 9.O-O Na5 10.Be2 Be6 11.Re1 a6 12.Qc2

12.a4?! prevents ...b5 but weakens the b3-square.

12...b5 13.Nb3 Nxb3 14.axb3 Qc7 15.Bh4 h6 16.Nd2 Qb6 17.Nf1 Rfd8 18.Ne3 Ra7 19.Red1 Rad7 20.Rxd7 Rxd7 21.c4?!

This weakens the d4-square and the h8-a1 diagonal.

21...Rd4?

The Rook is exposed here. Better is 21...Nh7 followed by ...Bd4.

22.f3

With the idea of playing Bf2 followed by Nd5.

22...Rd7 23.Bf2 Nh5 24.g3 Bd4 25.f4 bxc4 26.Bxc4?!

Correct is 26.f5! with a slight advantage to White.

26...Bxc4 27.Qxc4 a5

Black has a large advantage because the Bishop is very powerful on d4 and White's pawns are weak.

28.Qc2

If 28.Nd5, then 28...Qd8.

28...Nf6 29.e5 Nd5 30.Nc4 Bxf2+ 31.Kxf2 Qe6

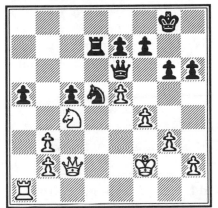

Now Black directs his attack at the exposed White King.

32.Qe2 Nb4 33.Kg1

If 33.Rxa5, then 33...Nd3+ 34.Kg1 Nc1 35.Qf3 Rd3 is strong.

33...Nc6 34.Qe3

If 34.Nxa5, then 34...Ra7 35.Qb5 Qd5 wins.

34...Nd4 35.Rxa5

If 35.Rd1, then 35...a4.

35...Qc6 36.h3

If 36.Nd2, then 36...Nxb3 37.Nxb3 Rd1+ 38.Kf2 Qh1 wins.

36...Nf5 37.Qe1 Rd3 38.Kh2 Rxg3 39.Qf2 Rxh3+ 0-1

Illustrative Game 86

GM Tigran Petrosian
GM Vlastimil Jansa

Bar 1980

1.d4 Nf6 2.Nf3 g6 3.Bg5 Bg7 4.Nbd2 d6 5.e4 O-O 6.c3 Nbd7 7.Bc4 e5 8.dxe5 dxe5 9.O-O h6

9...Qe7 10.Re1 Nc5 11.Bh4 Bd7 12.a4 a6 13.a5 b5 14.axb6 cxb6 15.Bd5 Rae8 16.Nc4 with advantage to White, Espig–Hazai, Leipzig 1983.

10.Bh4 Qe8 11.Re1 Nh5 12.a4 Bf6

Worth considering is 12...a5. Now White gains space on the Queenside.

13.a5 Qe7 14.Bxf6 Qxf6 15.Bf1 Rd8 16.Qe2 Nf4 17.Qe3 g5

This weakens the f5-square. But White was planning to play g3 followed by Nc4, tying Black down to the e5-pawn.

18.Red1 Re8 19.g3 Ng6 20.h3 Ndf8 21.Nh2 h5?

Weakening the Kingside. Better is 21...Be6.

22.Be2

Forcing Black to abandon the g4-square.

22...h4 23.Bg4 Kg7 24.Ndf1

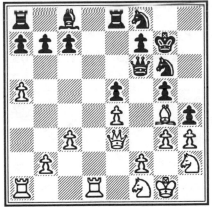

White maneuvers his Knights towards the weaknesses at g4 and f5.

24...Nh7 25.Rd3 Be6 26.Bxe6 Qxe6 27.Ng4 Nf6

Otherwise White plays Qf3 and Nf1-e3-f5.

28.Qxg5 Nxe4 29.Qh6+ Kg8 30.Rad1 Nf6 31.Nfe3 Nxg4 32.Nxg4 hxg3 33.Rxg3 Rad8 34.Re1 Qf5 35.h4 Re6 36.h5 Qf4 37.hxg6 1-0

Illustrative Game 87
GM Vassily Smyslov
IM Ketevan Arakhamia
Vienna 1993

1.d4 Nf6 2.Nf3 g6 3.Bg5 Bg7 4.Nbd2 O-O 5.e4 d6 6.c3 Nbd7 7.Bc4 e5 8.dxe5

Also possible is 8.O-O h6 9.Bh4 b6?! 10.Bd5 Rb8 11.Bc6 Qe7 12.Qa4 a6 13.Qa3 with a large advantage to White, Ye–Gufeld, Kuala Lumpur 1994.

8...dxe5 9.O-O h6 10.Bh4 g5?! 11.Bg3 Nh5 12.Re1 Nxg3 13.hxg3 c6 14.a4 Nc5 15.Qc2 Kh8

Black would like to start counterplay with ...f7-f5.

16.b4 Nxa4

If 16...Ne6, then 17.Nf1 followed by 18.Ne3.

17.Rxa4 b5 18.Ra5 bxc4 19.Nxc4

The Knights are superior to the Bishops in this position. Black will have trouble defending her weaknesses.

19...f6 20.Rea1 Rf7 21.Rd1 Rd7 22.Rxd7 Bxd7 23.Nfd2 Bf8 24.Nb3 Be6 25.Ne3 Qc7 26.Nc5

Bf7 27.Qa4 h5 28.Nf5 Kh7 29.Ra6 Bxc5 30.bxc5 Be8 31.Nd6 Bd7 32.Qa2 Rf8 33.Rxa7 Qd8 34.Qe6 1-0

White used only 59 minutes in this game compared with his opponent's 1 hour and 59 minutes.

Illustrative Game 88
GM Garry Kasparov
GM Slobodan Martinovic
Baku 1980

1.d4 Nf6 2.Nf3 g6 3.Bg5 Bg7 4.Nbd2 d6 5.e4 O-O 6.c3 Nbd7 7.Be2 e5 8.dxe5

Giving up the center but shutting in Black's King Bishop.

8...dxe5 9.O-O b6 10.Re1 Bb7 11.Qc2 h6 12.Bh4 Qe7 13.Bf1 Rfe8

It is important to defend the e5-pawn. Bad is 13...Rfd8 14.Nc4 Qe6 15.Nfd2 Qg4 16.Bxf6! Bxf6 17.Ne3 with a big advantage.

14.b4 a6 15.Nc4 Rac8?

Better is 15...Qe6 16.Nfd2 c5 with a slight advantage to White. Now White is able to create a bind on the Queenside.

16.a4 Qe6 17.Nfd2 Nh5 18.f3

Bf6?

Better is 18...Bf8, keeping an eye on the Queenside.

19.Bf2 Bg5 20.Ne3 Ndf6 21.c4 c6 22.Nb3 Nd7 23.c5 b5 24.Red1 Be7 25.Nc4!

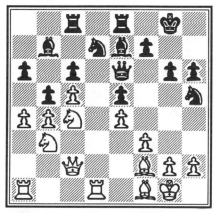

25...Rc7

Of course 25...bxc4 26.Bxc4 wins the Knight on d7.

26.Nd6 Rb8 27.axb5 cxb5

This leaves the a6-pawn weak, but worse is 27.axb5 28.Ra7 followed by Na5.

28.Nxb7 Rbxb7 29.Qa2 Nb8 30.Na5 Qxa2 31.Rxa2 Ra7

If 31...Rd7, then 32.Rd5.

32.c6 Ra8 33.Rc2 Bxb4 34.Rd8+ Kg7 35.Bb6 Bxa5 36.Bxa5 Rxc6 37.Rxb8 Rxb8 38.Rxc6 b4 39.Bc7 1-0

Illustrative Game 89

NM Diachkov

GM Yuri Balashov

Minsk 1993

1.d4 Nf6 2.Nf3 g6 3.Bg5 Bg7 4.Nbd2 d6 5.c3 Nbd7 6.e4 e5 7.dxe5 dxe5 8.Be2 O-O 9.O-O Qe8 10.Qc2 a5 11.b4

Grabbing space on the Queenside and taking the c5-square away from Black's pieces.

11...Nh5 12.Rfe1 Nf4 13.Bf1 Nf6 14.Nc4 axb4 15.cxb4 N6h5 16.Ne3 c6 17.Rad1 Be6

Better is first 17...Bf6 or 17...h6 18.Bh4 Bf6.

18.a4 h6 19.Bh4 f5 20.Nd2

Now a Knight is able to go to c4 and d6.

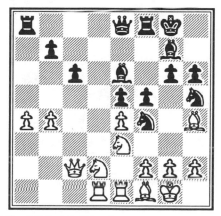

20...Nf6 21.Nec4

If 21.exf5, then 21...gxf5 22.Nxf5 Qh5 is unclear. The text is simpler. Now Black loses because of all the weaknesses in his position.

21...Nxe4 22.Nxe4 fxe4 23.Nd6 Qb8 24.Be7 Nd3 25.Bxd3 exd3 26.Qxd3 Rf4 27.Qxg6 Bg4 28.f3 Qa7+ 29.Kh1 b6 30.fxg4 Qxe7 31.Nf5 Qg5 32.Qxc6 Rf8 33.Rd7 R4xf5 34.gxf5 Qxf5 35.Qc4+ Kh8 36.Rdd1 Qh5 37.Qe2 Qh4 38.Rf1 Qxb4 39.Rxf8+ Qxf8 40.Qb5 Qb8 41.a5 Qc8 42.axb6 Qc2 43.Qb1 1-0

Conclusion: After 1.d4 Nf6 2.Nf3 g6 3.Bg5 Bg7 4.Nbd2 O-O 5.c3 d6 6.e4, all the main moves considered have been popular, but 6...c5 may be worth a second look.

Chapter 12

1.d4 Nf6 2.Nf3 g6 3.Bg5 Bg7 4.Nbd2 d6

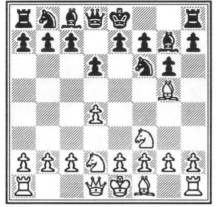

We now consider **A) 5.e4** and **B) 5.e3**.

A) 5.e4

5...h6

5...Nbd7 6.c3 h6 7.Be3 e5 8.dxe5 dxe5 9.h3 O-O 10.Bc4 Qe7 11.b4 (11.O-O b6 12.Qa4 unclear) 11...b6 12.O-O Bb7 13.Qc2 Ne8! with advantage to Black, Kovacevic–Polugaevsky, Vinkovci 1976.

6.Bh4

Less common alternatives are:

a) 6.Bxf6 Bxf6 7.c3 (more energetic is 7.e5!? Bg7 8.Bb5+ c6 9.Bd3 O-O 10.Qe2 c5 11.h4! cxd4 12.h5 g5 13.Qe4 with advantage to White, Guimard–Fischer, Buenos Aires 1960. Better was 9...Be6 unclear.) 7...Bg7 (7...O-O 8.h4 h5 9.e5 Bg7 10.Bc4 d5 11.Bd3 with advantage to White, Guimard–Geller, Gothenberg 1955) 8.Bc4 Nd7 9.O-O O-O 10.Qe2 e5 11.dxe5 dxe5 12.Rfd1 Qe7 13.Nf1 Nc5 14.Ne3 c6 with advantage to Black,

Simic–Vadasz, Smederevska Palanka 1977.

b) 6.Be3 Ng4 7.Bf4 e5 8.dxe5 Nxe5 9.c3 Nbc6 10.Bb5 O-O 11.O-O Qf6 with equality, Johansson–Bobotsov, Havana Olympiad 1966.

6...g5

Other moves should transpose to Chapter 11.

7.Bg3 Nh5 8.c3

8...g4 was threatened. For example, 8.Bd3 g4 9.Nh4 Bxd4 10.c3 Bf6 11.Nf5 Nxg3 12.fxg3?! (12.hxg3 e6 with advantage to Black) 12...e6 13.Ne3 h5 with a decisive advantage to Black, Hort–Fischer, Herceg Novi blitz 1970.

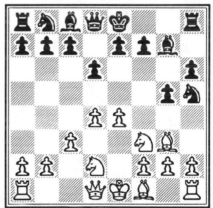

We will now examine **A1) 8...Nd7** and **A2) 8...e6**.

Alternatives are:

a) 8...O-O looks very risky, but has not been refuted:

a1) 9.Bc4 e6 10.e5 c5 11.Ne4! d5 12.Nfxg5 Nxg3 13.hxg3 dxe4 (13...hxg5? 14.Qh5 Re8 15.Nxg5 with a decisive advantage to White) 14.Nxe4 cxd4 15.Qg4 (15.Rxh6? Nd7! with advantage to Black, Z. Nikolic–Martinovic, Yugoslavia Championship 1980) 15...f5 16.Qg6 (16.exf6 Rxf6 with

138

advantage to Black) 16...fxe4 17.Rxh6 Rf5 18.Qxf5 (18.Rh7 Rf7) 18...Bxh6 19.Qg6+ Bg7 20.Bxe6+ Bxe6 21.Qxe6+ Kf8 22.Qf5+ Ke8 23.Qg6+ and White has at least a perpetual.

a2) 9.Nc4 e6 10.e5 Nxg3 11.hxg3 Nc6 12.Qc2 Re8 13.Ne3 dxe5 14.dxe5 Nxe5 15.Nxe5 Bxe5 16.Ng4 Bg7 17.Rd1 Qe7 18.Nxh6+ Kf8 19.Qh7 Qf6 20.Rd3 Bxh6 21.Rxh6 Qg7 22.Be2 with advantage to White, Balashov–Smiric, Sverdlovsk 1987.

b) An immediate 8...Nxg3 rules out a possible ...Nf4, but normally transposes to other variations. Then 9.hxg3 and:

b1) 9...c6 10.Bc4 d5 11.Bd3 Be6 12.Nf1 Qb6 13.Qe2 c5 14.dxc5 Qxc5 15.Nfd2 Nc6 16.exd5 Bxd5 17.Ne4 Bxe4 18.Qxe4 O-O-O 19.Qf5+?! Qxf5 20.Bxf5+ Kc7 21.Ke2 Rd5 22.Be4 Rd6 23.Bxc6 bxc6 with a more comfortable endgame for Black, Torre–Suetin, Sochi 1980.

b2) 9...e6 10.Bd3 Nc6 11.Qe2 Bd7 12.b4 Qe7 13.b5 Na5 14.Nb3 Nxb3 15.axb3 O-O 16.e5 f5 17.exf6 Qxf6 18.Qe4 with advantage to White, Karpeshov–Zilberstein, USSR 1983.

c) 8...c5?! 9.dxc5 Nxg3 10.hxg3 dxc5 11.Bc4:

c1) 11...Nc6? 12.Nxg5 hxg5 13.Rxh8+ Bxh8 14.Qh5 Bf6 15.f4 e6 16.e5 Bg7 17.Ne4 Qe7 18.Nxg5 Bd7 19.Rd1 O-O-O 20.Qxf7 with a large advantage to White, Trifunovic–Marovic, Yugoslavia 1961.

c2) 11...e6 12.g4 Bd7 13.Be2 Bc6 14.Qc2 Nd7 15.Nc4 Qc7 16.Rd1 Ne5 17.Nfxe5 Bxe5 18.Qd3 with advantage to White, Agzamov–Rash-

kovsky, USSR 1983.

A1) 8...Nd7

9.Nc4

a) 9.Bc4 e6 10.Qe2

a1) 10...Nf8 11.O-O-O Ng6 12.Ne1 Ngf4 13.Bxf4 Nxf4 14.Qf3 Ng6 15.Nf1 h5 unclear, Benko–Evans, U.S. Championship 1962/63.

a2) 10...Qe7 11.O-O-O a6 12.a3 Nb6 13.Bd3 Bd7 14.Rhe1 Nxg3 15.hxg3 g4 16.Nh2 h5 17.Nhf1 Qf6 18.Re2 O-O-O 19.Ne3 Qg5 unclear, Cifuentes–Hort, Amsterdam 1987.

b) 9.Bd3?! c5! 10.d5 O-O 11.a4 Ndf6 12.Nc4 Nxg3 13.hxg3 e6! 14.Ne3 exd5 15.exd5 Ng4! with advantage to Black, Espig–Uhlmann, Germany 1983.

9...e6

Spassky–Najdorf, Moscow 1967, continued 9...Ndf6 10.Qc2 Nxg3 11.hxg3 e6 12.O-O-O Qe7 13.Ne3 Bd7 14.e5 Nd5 15.Nxd5 exd5 16.exd6 Qxd6 17.Re1+ Be6 18.Qa4+ c6 19.Bd3 with a large advantage to White.

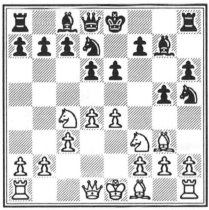

After the text, three examples:

a) 10.Qc2 Nf8 11.O-O-O Ng6 12.Ne3 Bd7 13.Ne1 Qe7 14.Be2 Nhf4 15.Bxf4 gxf4 16.Nc4 d5 17.Nd2 dxe4 18.Nxe4 Bc6 19.Bh5 O-O-O unclear, Yusupov–Tseshkovsky, Vilnius 1981.

b) 10.Bd3 Nxg3 11.hxg3 Qe7 12.Qa4 a6 13.Ne3 c6 14.Qc2 unclear, Chernin–Short, Wijk aan Zee 1986.

c) For 10.Nfd2 see Illustrative Game 90.

A2) 8...e6

This is the most flexible move, keeping open the possibility of the sharp move ...f5 or developing the Knight to c6 or d7.

9.Qb3

Preparing Queenside castling and also to meet 9...f5 with 10.exf5 exf5 11.Bc4 Qe7+ 12.Kd1!

a) 9.Bc4 fulfills the same aim.

a1) Psakhis–Zilberstein, Irkutsk 1983 continued 9...Qe7 10.O-O Nxg3 11.hxg3 Nd7 12.a4 h5 13.Qe1 Nf8 with advantage to White.

a2) 9...Nc6 10.Qe2 Bd7 11.O-O-O Qe7 12.Ne1 Nxg3 13.hxg3 O-O-O 14.Nc2 Kb8 15.Nb3, Yusupov–Vasiukov, Vilnius 1981.

b) 9.Bd3 Nd7 (9...O-O 10.O-O and now 10...Nc6 11.Nc4 f5 12.exf5 exf5 13.h3 f4 14.Bh2 with advantage to White, Ribli–W. Schmidt, Baile Herculane 1982 or 10...b6?! 11.Nc4 Bb7 12.a4 a6 13.Re1 Nd7 14.Nfd2 with advantage to White, Chernin–Gavrikov, Moscow 1985) 10.Nc4 Qe7 11.e5 Nxg3 12.fxg3!? g4 13.Nh4 dxe5 14.Qxg4 O-O 15.dxe5 Nc5 16.Bc2 b5 17.Ne3 Qg5! with equality, Gofman–Mih. Tseitlin, USSR 1982.

c) 9.Nb3 Nd7 10.Nfd2 Nxg3 11.hxg3 O-O 12.Bd3 a5 13.a4 f5 14.Qe2 Nf6 15.f4 gxf4 16.gxf4 Bd7 17.e5 Nd5 18.g3 Qe8! with

equality, Bronstein–Gufeld, Tallinn 1981.

9...Nc6 10.Be2 Qe7

10...f5?! 11.exf5 exf5 12.Ne5!

11.O-O-O a5 12.a4 Bd7 13.d5 Nd8

Now with 14.Nd4 White would have the better placed pieces. Balashov–Torre, Manila Interzonal 1976 continued with the weaker 14.h4?! Nxg3 15.fxg3 g4 16.Nd4 h5 17.Nc4 O-O 18.Bd3 unclear.

B) 5.e3

5...O-O

5...h6 6.Bh4 g5 7.Bg3 Nh5 and:

a) 8.Be2 O-O 9.c3 Bf5?! 10.O-O Bg6 11.Ne1! Nxg3 12.hxg3 Nd7 13.Bd3 Bxd3 14.Nxd3 c5 15.Qb3 Qc7 16.a4 Rac8 17.dxc5 with advantage to White, Larsen–Haik, Lanzarote 1976.

b) 8.c3 e6 (8...Nxg3?! 9.hxg3 Nd7 10.a4! Nf6 11.a5 Bd7 12.Bd3 e6 13.e4 g4 14.Nh2 h5 15.Nf1 Bh6 16.Qe2 e5 17.d5 c6 18.c4 c5 19.Ne3! with advantage to White, Ribli–Adorjan, Budapest 1981) 9.Bd3 Qe7 10.Qe2 Nc6 11.Nb3 Bd7 12.Nfd2 Nxg3 13.hxg3 O-O-O 14.Nc4 Kb8 15.O-O-O with advantage to White, Kovacevic–Ree,

Plovdiv 1983.

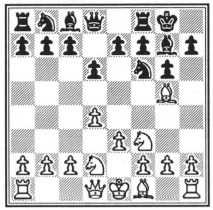

6.Bd3

a) 6.Be2 Nbd7 and now:

a1) 7.c3 e5 8.O-O h6 9.Bh4 Qe8 10.a4 e4 11.Ne1 Nh7 12.Nc2 f5 13.f3 Ndf6 14.Bxf6 Nxf6 15.fxe4 fxe4 16.a5 c6 17.Qe1 d5 with advantage to Black, Kovacevic–Gligoric, Yugoslavia 1979.

a2) 7.O-O e5 8.Bh4 Re8 9.c4 b6 10.Rc1 h6 11.h3 Bb7 12.d5 a5 13.b3 Nc5 14.a3 g5 15.Bg3 c6 16.b4 axb4 17.axb4 Nce4 unclear, Rongguang Ye–Dreev, Manila 1990.

b) 6.Bc4 Nbd7 7.O-O e5 (7...h6 8.Bh4 e5 9.c3 Qe7 10.a4 a5 11.Qe2 e4 12.Ne1 g5 13.Bg3 Nb6 14.Bb3 Bg4 15.f3 exf3 16.Nexf3 Rae8 17.Rfe1 Bd7 18.e4 Nh5 with equality, Kovacevic–Smejkal, Yugoslavia 1978) 8.dxe5 dxe5 9.Ne4 Qe8 10.Nxf6+ Bxf6 11.e4 Qe7 12.Bxf6 Nxf6 13.Qe2 Be6 with equality, Dreev–Khalifman, Vilnius 1988.

c) 6.c3

c1) 6...b6 7.Bd3 c5 8.b4 cxb4 9.cxb4 Nc6 10.a3 Bb7 11.O-O Qd7 12.Qe2 Rfc8 13.Rac1 Nd8 14.Bb5 Bc6? 15.Rxc6 Nxc6 16.Bxf6 Bxf6 17.d5 with a decisive advantage to White, Keres–Saidy, Tel Aviv

Olympiad 1964.

c2) 6...Nbd7 7.a4 h6 8.Bxf6 Bxf6 9.a5 a6 10.Qc2 e5?! (10...Bg7) 11.Bc4 Kh8 12.h4 h5? 13.Ne4 Bg7? 14.Neg5 with a large advantage to White, Petrosian–Ribli, Amsterdam 1973.

d) 6.a4 Nbd7 7.a5 a6 8.c3 e5 9.Be2 h6 10.Bxf6 Qxf6 11.O-O Qe7 12.dxe5 Nxe5 (Shirazi–Schussler, Haifa Olympiad 1976) 13.Nxe5 Qxe5 14.Bg4 Bxg4 15.Qxg4 with advantage to White.

e) 6.b4

b1) 6...Nbd7 7.Be2 Re8 8.O-O e5 9.c3 c6 10.Qb3 a5 11.a3 h6 12.Bh4 e4 13.Ne1 a4 14.Qd1 g5 15.Bg3 b5 with equality, Torre–Ftacnik, Lugano 1988.

b2) 6...Bg4 7.Be2 Nbd7 8.h3 Bxf3 9.Bxf3 c6 10.O-O e5 11.c3 a5 12.b5 Qb6 13.bxc6 bxc6 14.Rb1 Qa7 15.Qa4 Rfc8 16.Rb2 with advantage to White, Torre–Zuger, Biel 1988.

6...Nbd7

6...Nc6 7.O-O h6 8.Bh4 g5 9.Bg3 Nh5 10.c3 e6 11.e4 f5 12.exf5 exf5 13.Qb3 Kh8 14.h3 Bd7 15.Nc4 Rb8 with equality, Khalifman–Watson, Moscow 1985.

7.O-O

7.Qe2 h6 8.Bxf6 Nxf6 9.h3?! e5! 10.dxe5 dxe5 11.O-O-O Qe7 12.e4 a5 with advantage to Black, Kamsky–Yermolinsky, USSR 1987.

7...h6

7...b6 and:

a) 8.Re1 c5 9.c3 Bb7 10.a4 Qc7 11.a5 e5 12.e4 (12.dxe5 dxe5 13.e4 with equality) 12...cxd4 13.a6?! dxc3 14.Rc1 Bc6 15.Rxc3 Nc5 16.Bf1 Qd7 17.b4 Ne6 18.Bxf6 Bxf6 19.Nc4 Rfd8 20.Rd3 Qc7 with advantage to

Black, Dreev–Kir.Georgiev, Moscow 1985.

b) 8.c3 Bb7 9.Qe2 h6 10.Bh4 Qc8 11.e4 e5 12.dxe5 dxe5 13.Rfe1 Re8 14.b4 Nh5 15.Qd1 Bf6 16.Bxf6 Nhxf6 17.Nc4 Qd8 18.Qc2 Qe7 Draw, Torre–Nunn, Tilburg 1982.

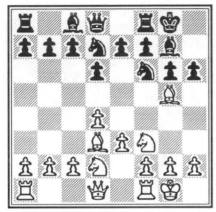

8.Bh4 e5 9.c3 Qe8

Better than 9...Re8?! 10.Qc2 Qe7 11.e4 with advantage to White. After 9...Qe8 10.Qc2 Nh7, 11.e4 will still be necessary. Taimanov–Jansa, Harrachov 1966, continued 11...Ndf6 12.dxe5 dxe5 13.Nc4 Nh5 14.Ne3 Nf4 15.Bc4 Bf6 with equality.

Illustrative Game 90
GM Valery Salov
NM Ilia Smirin

USSR Championship 1988

1.d4 Nf6 2.Nf3 g6 3.Bg5 d6 4.Nbd2 Nbd7 5.e4 h6 6.Bh4 g5 7.Bg3 Nh5 8.Nc4 Bg7 9.c3 e6 10.Nfd2 Nxg3 11.hxg3 Qe7 12.Ne3 Nf6 13.Qb3!

Tying the Bishop to b7. Not as strong is 13.f4 gxf4 14.gxf4 Bd7 15.Bd3 O-O-O 16.Qf3 Kb8 17.O-O-O e5 18.fxe5 dxe5 19.d5 h5 equal, Balashov–Tseshkovsky,

USSR 1975.

13...c6 14.O-O-O e5?!

This opens lines and weakens the f5-square. Better is 14...d5.

15.dxe5 dxe5 16.Ndc4 Be6

If 16...Nxe4, then 17.Qc2 Nf6 18.Nd6+ Kf8 19.Bc4 Be6 20.Nef5 is strong.

17.Nf5 Bxf5 18.Nd6+ Qxd6!

Black's only chance is to sacrifice his Queen. 18...Kf8 19.Nxf5 is hopeless.

19.Rxd6 Nxe4 20.Qxb7 O-O 21.Rdxh6 Nxf2 22.Qe7 Rad8 23.Be2 Nxh1 24.Rxh1 Be6 25.Qxg5 Bxa2 26.Rh4

Not 26.c4? Rd4. But now 27.c4 is threatened.

26...Be6 27.Bc4 Rd6 28.Rh6?!

White loses most of his advantage with this and his next move. Correct is 28.Qh5 Rfd8 29.Bxe6 Rxe6 30.Qh7+ Kf8 31.Rg4 Bh6+ 32.Kc2 Rd2+ 33.Kb3.

28...Re8 29.Bxe6?! Rdxe6 30.Rxe6 Rxe6 31.Qd8+ Bf8 32.Qa8 e4 33.Kd1 c5!

Black gives up his a-pawn and will blockade a passed Queenside pawn on the b6-square with his

142

Rook and Bishop. It is difficult for White to make progress in this position.

34.Qxa7 Kg7 35.Ke2 e3 36.Qb7 Bd6 37.Qd5 Be7 38.Qd7 Bd6 39.Qd8 Be7 40.Qd5 Kg8 41.Qd7 Bd6 42.Qb7 Kg7 43.g4 Be7 44.Qd5 Kg8 45.Qb7 Kg7 46.Qb5 Bd6 47.Qc4 Be7 48.b4 cxb4 49.cxb4 Bd8

Threatening to immediately force a draw with 50...Bb6.

50.Qd4+ Bf6 51.Qd3 Be5!

Threatening both ...Bf4 followed by ...Rd6 as well as ...Bc7-b6.

52.b5 Bc7 53.Qc3+ Be5 54.Qc5 Bd6 55.Qc4 Be5 56.Qc5 Bd6 57.Qd4+ Be5 58.Qc4 Bf6

Threatening 59...Bg5 followed by 60...Rf6.

59.Qd5 Bc3

Threatening ...Ba5-b6.

60.Qd8 Bf6 61.Qd3 Be5 62.g5

If 62.Kxe3, then 62...Bc7+ followed by 63...Bb6 is drawn.

62...Bc7 63.Qc3+ Be5 64.Qc5 Bd6 65.Qd4+ Be5 66.Qa7 Bc3 67.Qa4

If 67.b6, then 67...Bd4.

67...Be5 68.Qb4 Bc7 69.Qc3+ Be5 70.Qc5 Bd6 71.Qc4 Be5 72.Qb4 Bc7 73.Qc3+ Be5 Draw

Conclusion: Weakening the Kingside to win the Bishop pair is risky, but leads to sharp positions.

Chapter 13

1.d4 Nf6 2.Nf3 g6 3.Bg5 Bg7 4.Nbd2 d5

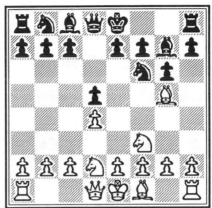

We consider A) 5.e3 and B) 5.c3. Usually these two moves can be interchanged, except it should be noted that the idea of the latter move is to discourage ...c5.

A) 5.e3

5...O-O

a) 5...Nbd7 6.b4 O-O 7.Be2 b6 8.b5 Bb7 9.O-O Ne4 10.Nxe4 dxe4 11.Nd2 h6 12.Bh4 g5 13.Bg3 e5 14.c3 f5 15.f3 f4 16.Bf2 exd4 17.cxd4 with advantage to White, Torre–Grunfeld, Zagreb 1987.

b) 5...Bf5 6.Bd3 Bxd3 7.cxd3 c6 8.O-O O-O 9.Qc2 Nh5 10.b4 f6 unclear, Taimanov–Gufeld, USSR 1966.

c) 5...c5 6.c3

c1) 6...b6 7.Bb5+ Bd7 8.Bd3 Nc6 9.O-O O-O 10.Re1 Bf5 11.Bxf6 Bxd3 12.Bxg7 Kxg7 13.dxc5 bxc5 14.Nb3 c4 15.Nbd4 Nxd4 16.exd4 Bf5 17.Qd2 Rb8 with advantage to Black, Shabalov–Kransenkov, Vilnius 1988.

c2) 6...Qb6 7.Qb3 O-O 8.Bd3 Nc6 (8...c4 9.Qxb6 axb6 10.Bxf6

Bxf6 11.Bc2 with advantage to White) 9.O-O Re8 10.Rfd1 Qxb3 11.axb3 e5 12.dxe5 Nxe5 with equality, Azmaiparashvili–Banas, Stary Smokovec 1983.

c3) 6...Nbd7 7.Qb3 O-O 8.Be2 b6 9.O-O Bb7 10.a4 a6 11.Rfd1 Qb8 12.Bf4 Qa7 13.Ne5 e6 14.Qa3 Rac8 15.b4 Nxe5 16.Bxe5 c4 17.Re1 Bc6 18.Bf3 Qb7 with equality, Timman–Kasparov, Linares 1991.

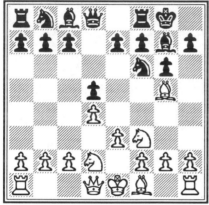

6.Bd3

a) 6.Be2

a1) 6...b6 7.c3 Ba6 8.Bxa6 Nxa6 9.O-O c5 10.Ne5 Qc8 11.Qa4 Nb8 12.b4 with advantage to White, Larsen–Kavalek, Tilburg 1980.

a2) 6...c5 7.c3 and:

a21) For 7...Nbd7, see Illustrative Game 91.

a22) 7...Qb6 8.Qb3 Nc6 9.O-O Bf5 10.Bxf6 Bxf6 11.Qxd5 cxd4 12.cxd4 Qxb2 13.Rfc1 e5 14.Qb3 with equality, Vaganian–Ftacnik, Hastings 1982/83.

a23) 7...cxd4 8.exd4 Nc6 9.O-O Qc7 10.Bd3 Bf5! with equality, Salov–Vaganian, Barcelona 1989.

a3) 6...Nbd7 7.O-O (for 7.b4, see Illustrative Game 92) 7...Re8 8.c4

a31) 8...h6 9.Bh4 e5 10.Rc1 exd4

11.Nxd4 dxc4 12.Nxc4 a6 13.Qc2 Qe7 14.Rfd1 with advantage to White, Ostenstad–Lechtynsky, Trnava 1989.

a32) 8...c5 9.Rc1 cxd4 10.Nxd4

a321) 10...Ne4 11.Bh4 Nxd2 12.Qxd2 dxc4 13.Bxc4 Ne5 14.Bb3 a5 with equality, Izeta–Adams, Dos Hermanas 1993.

a322) 10...Nf8 11.Qb3 Qa5 12.N2f3 Bd7 13.Bxf6 Bxf6 14.cxd5 e5 15.dxe6 Nxe6 16.Bc4 Ba4 17.Qa3 Nxd4 18.exd4 b5 19.b4 Qb6 20.Bb3 Bxb3 Draw, Chiburdanidze–Xie Jun, Kuala Lumpur 1994.

a33) 8...e5 9.Rc1 e4 10.Ne1 c6 11.cxd5 cxd5 12.Qb3 Qb6?! (12...Nf8 is better for White) 13.Nc2 Qe6 14.Nb4 Bf8? 15.Bb5! Rd8 16.Nxd5 with a decisive advantage to White, Salov–Kozul, Wijk aan Zee 1991.

a34) 8...c6 9.Rc1 h6 10.Bh4 g5 11.Bg3 Nh5 12.cxd5 Nxg3 13.hxg3 cxd5 14.Qb3 e6 15.Rc2 Nb6 16.Rfc1 Bd7 17.Bb5 Rc8 18.Ne5 Bxb5 19.Qxb5 Rxc2 20.Rxc2 Bxe5 21.dxe5 Qb8 22.b3 Rc8 23.Rxc8+ Qxc8 24.Qa5 Nd7 25.Qxa7 Qc1+ 26.Nf1 Nc5 27.Qb8+ Draw, Chiburdanidze–Rodriquez, Seville 1994.

b) 6.b4

b1) 6...Bg4 7.Be2 Nbd7 8.h3 Bxf3 9.Bxf3 c6 10.O-O e5 11.c3 a5 12.b5 Qb6 13.bxc6 bxc6 14.Rb1 Qa7 15.Qa4 Rfc8 16.Rb2 Nb6 17.Qb3 Rab8 18.Rfb1 Nfd7 19.Qd1 c5 with equality, Torre–Züger, Biel 1988.

b2) 6...Nbd7 7.h3 Re8 8.Be2 e5 9.O-O h6 10.Bh4 e4?! (10...exd4) 11.Nh2 with advantage to White, Malaniuk–Cehov, Warsaw 1989.

6...c5

a) 6...Nc6 7.c3 Re8 8.O-O h6 9.Bh4 Bf5 10.Bxf5 gxf5 11.Bxf6 Bxf6 12.Kh1 e6 13.Ne1 Ne7 14.Nd3 Ng6 15.f4 b6 16.Rf3 with advantage to White, Lein–Hernandez, Saint John 1988.

b) For 6...Nbd7, see Illustrative Game 93.

7.c3

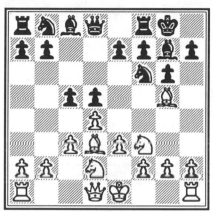

We now examine **A1) 7...Qb6** and **A2) 7...b6**. Alternatives are:

a) 7...cxd4 with:

a1) 8.exd4 Nc6 9.O-O h6 10.Bh4 Nh5 11.Re1 Qd6 12.Bb5 g5 13.Bg3 (better is 13.Bxc6 bxc6 14.Ne5) 13...Nxg3 14.hxg3 a6 15.Ba4 b5 16.Bc2 g4 17.Nh2 f5 with advantage to Black, Schüssler–Vaganian, Tallinn 1983.

a2) 8.cxd4 Nc6 9.O-O Qb6 10.Qb3 Qxb3 (10...Rd8 11.Rfc1 Bf5 12.Bxf5 gxf5 13.Qa3 Rdc8 14.Nb3 e6 15.Bxf6!? Bxf6 16.Nc5 Qc7 17.Qa4 with advantage to White, Gelfand–Ernst, Tallinn 1989) 11.Nxb3 Nb4 12.Bb1 b6 13.Ne5 Bb7 14.a3 Nc6 15.Bxf6 Bxf6 16.Nd7 Rfd8 17.Nxf6+ exf6 18.Bd3 with advantage to White, Dydyshko–Gelfand, Minsk 1989.

b) 7...Nbd7 8.O-O Qb6 (8...Qc7 9.Re1 [not 9.Bf4 Qb6 10.Rb1 Nh5 and ...e5] 9...b6 [not 9...e5 10.dxe5 Nxe5 11.Nxe5 Qxe5 12.Bf4 Qe7 13.e4] 10.Bf4 Qd8 11.h3 Bb7 12.Qb1 with advantage to White, Trifunovic–Bertok, Yugoslav Championship 1952) and:

b1) 9.Qb3 Rd8 10.Rfe1 Nf8 11.e4 Qxb3 12.axb3 cxd4 13.Nxd4 h6 14.Bxf6 Bxf6 15.e5 Bg7 16.b4 Ne6 17.N2b3 with advantage to White, Verdihanov–Ryskin, Nikolaev 1993.

b2) 9.Qc2 Re8 10.c4 cxd4 11.exd4 Qc7 12.Rac1 a6 13.Rfe1 e6 14.Bh4 b6 15.Bg3 Qc6 16.b4 dxc4 17.Nxc4 Bf8 18.Qb2 Qb5 19.Nd6 Qxd3 unclear, Smyslov–Vaganian, USSR Championship 1988.

c) 7...Nc6 8.O-O Nd7 (8...b6 9.a3 Bb7 10.b4 Qc8 11.Rc1 c4 12.Bc2 b5 13.a4 a5 14.axb5 Na7 15.b6 Nb5 16.Ba4 Nd6 17.Bxf6 exf6 18.Rb1 with advantage to White, Ionov Mih. Tseitlin, Leningrad 1983) 9.Re1 h6 10.Bh4 g5!? (10...Qb6 11.Qc2 e5 with equality) 11.Bg3 f5 12.c4 Nb4 13.Bb1? (better is 13.Bf1) 13...cxd4 14.a3 dxe3 15.axb4 exd2 16.Qxd2 Nb6 with advantage to Black, Konstantinopolsky–Kortchnoi, USSR Championship 1952.

A1) 7...Qb6

8.Rb1

a) 8.Qb3 Nc6 (9...c4) 9.O-O Re8 (9...c4 10.Qxb6 axb6 11.Bc2 Bf5) 10.Rfd1 Qxb3 11.axb3 e5 with equality, Ionescu–Ghinda, Timisoara 1987.

b) 8.Qb1 Nc6 9.O-O e5 10.Nxe5 Nxe5 11.dxe5 Ng4 12.Nf3 Nxe5 13.Nxe5 Bxe5 14.Qc2 Re8 with equality, Chekhov–Gorelov, Pavlodav 1987.

8...Nc6

8...Nbd7 and:

a) 9.Qa4 e5 10.Nxe5 Nxe5 11.dxe5 Ng4 12.Be7 Nxe5 13.Be2 Bd7 14.Qa3 Rfc8 15.Nf3 Bb5 with equality, Malaniuk–Georgadze, Lvov 1986.

b) 9.O-O e5 10.Nxe5 Nxe5 11.dxe5 Ng4 12.Nf3 Nxe5 13.Nxe5 Bxe5 14.f4 Bg7 15.f5 h6 16.Be7 Re8 17.f6 Be6 18.Qf3 Rxe7 19.fxe7 Re8 with compensation, Dreev–Dorfman, Moscow 1985.

9.O-O e5 10.Nxe5

10.dxc5 Qxc5 11.b4 Qd6 12.Bc2 Be6 13.Qe2 Rac8 14.Bb3 e4 15.Nd4 Ne5 with advantage to Black, Salov–Magem, Groningen 1984.

10...Nxe5 11.dxe5 Ng4 12.Nf3

12.c4?! Nxe5 13.cxd5 Nxd3 14.Nc4 Qa6 15.Qxd3 b5 16.Nd2 c4 with advantage to Black, Malaniuk–Romanishin, USSR 1983.

12...Nxe5 13.Nxe5 Bxe5 14.f4

14.Qf3 Be6 15.Bf6 Bxf6 16.Qxf6 Rfd8 17.b4 c4 18.Bc2 Bf5 with equality, Anastasov–Magerramov, Pavlodav 1987.

14...Bf6

14...Bg7?! 15.f5 with advantage to White.

15.Bxf6

15.Bh6? c4! (15...Re8? 16.f5 with advantage to White) 16.Bxf8 cxd3 17.Ba3 Qxe3+ 18.Kh1 Bf5 with a decisive advantage to Black, Neverov–Sideif-Zade, Baku 1986.

15...Qxf6 16.f5 Qe5

We have two examples:

a) 17.Qd2 Bd7 18.f6 Kh8 19.e4 d4 20.Bc4 Be6 21.Qh6 Rg8 unclear, Dreev–Khalifman, Moscow 1985.

b) 17.Rf3 Bd7 (17...g5) 18.Qd2 Rae8 19.f6 Qg5 20.Qf2 Re5 21.b4 c4 22.h4 with advantage to White, Neverov–Glek, Lvov 1985.

A2) 7...b6

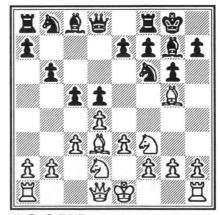

8.O-O Bb7

8...Nc6 9.a3 Qc7 10.Bf4 Qb7 11.h3 Nd7 12.Be2 a5 unclear, Salov–Lputian, Moscow 1987.

9.Ne5

a) 9.Qb1

a1) 9...Nbd7 10.b4 Qc8 11.h3 Re8 12.Rc1 e5 13.dxe5 Nxe5 14.Nxe5 Rxe5 15.Bf4 Re8 16.a4 a5

146

17.bxa5 bxa5 18.Ra2 Bc6 Draw, Agzamov–Hort, Potsdam 1985.

a2) 9...Nc6 10.b4 cxd4 11.cxd4 Qd6 12.a3 Rfc8 13.Bf4 Qe6 14.h3 Nd8 15.Qb2 Ne4 16.a4 f5 17.a5 with advantage to White, Loginov–Agzamov, Tashkent 1983.

a3) 9...a5 10.e4 cxd4 11.Nxd4 Nc6 12.Nxc6 Bxc6 13.Re1 dxe4 14.Nxe4 Qd5 15.c4 Qd7 with equality, T. Georgadze–Rashkovsky, Minsk 1979.

b) 9.a4 Ne4 (9...Nbd7 10.a5 Bc6 11.c4 dxc4 12.Nxc4 Ne4 with equality, Filip–Minev, Amsterdam (olympiad) 1954) 10.Bf4 Nd7 11.Qe2 Nxd2 12.Nxd2 (12.Qxd2 Re8 13.a5 with advantage to White) 12...e5 13.dxe5 Bxe5 14.Bxe5 Nxe5 15.Ba6 Bxa6 16.Qxa6 Re8 with equality, Malich–Stein, Kecskemet 1968.

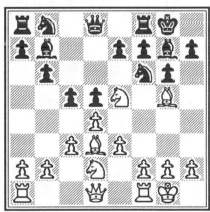

9...Nfd7

a) 9...Nbd7 10.f4 with advantage to White.

b) 9...Ne4 10.Nxe4 dxe4 11.Bc4 with advantage to White and now if 11...b5? 12.Qb3 with a decisive advantage to White or 11...cxd4 12.cxd4 Nd7 13.Nxf7 Rxf7 14.Qb3 Qe8 15.Rac1 with a large advantage.

10.Nxd7

10.Ng4 f6 11.Bh6 Bxh6 12.Nxh6+ Kg7 13.Nf5+ gxf5 14.Bxf5 Qe8 15.Qg4+ Kh8 16.Qh3 Rf7 17.Bg6 unclear, Cvetkov–Savon, USSR 1964.

10...Nxd7 11.f4 Qe8 12.Qg4 e6 13.Qh3 a6 14.Bh6 Bxh6 15.Qxh6 Qe7 16.Rae1 b5 17.Rf3 Rfc8 18.g4 b4 19.f5

White is better, Nikolic–Cvitan, Borovo 1981.

B) 5.c3
5...O-O

If 5...c5, then White can try to hold onto the pawn after 6.dxc5.

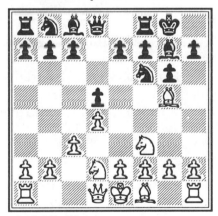

6.e3 Nbd7

a) 6...c5 7.dxc5 and now:

a1) 7...Bg4 8.Be2 Qc7 9.b4 b6 10.cxb6 axb6 11.Qb3 Rc8 12.Nd4 Bd7 13.c4 Nc6 14.Nxc6 Bxc6 15.Rc1 Qa7 16.Bxf6 Bxf6 17.cxd5 Bb5 18.Rxc8 Rxc8 19.Bxb5 Rc1+ 20.Ke2 Rxh1 21.Nf1 with advantage to White, Lputian–Khalifman, Kiev 1986.

a2) 7...Qc7 8.Nb3 (8.b4) 8...Ne4 9.Be2 Nxg5 10.Nxg5 e6 11.Qc2 Nd7 12.c4? Qe5 13.Nf3 Qxb2 14.Rc1 Nxc5 and Black was much better, Smyslov–Watson, New York

1987.

b) 6...b6

b1) 7.b4. Now 7...Nbd7 transposes back into the main variation. Dubious is 7...c5?! 8.bxc5 bxc5 9.Qa4 with advantage to White. Hug–Lutz, San Bernardino 1988, continued 9...Ne4 10.Nxe4 dxe4 11.Nd2 Bf5 (also possible is 11...h6 12.Bh4 f5) 12.Be2 h6 13.Bh4 Nd7 14.O-O g5 15.Bg3 Bg6 16.Rab1 cxd4 17.cxd4 e5 18.dxe5 Nxe5 19.Rfd1 Qd7 20.Qxd7 Nxd7 21.Nc4 Nc5 22.Ne5 Bf5 23.Nc6 Bf6 24.Rd5 1-0.

Worth considering is 7...Bf5. Machulsky–Gufeld, Moscow 1991, continued 8.c4?! (8.Be2 with equality) 8...c5! 9.bxc5 bxc5 10.cxd5 Ne4! with a large advantage to Black.

b2) For 7.Bd3, see Illustrative Game 94.

b3) For 7.a4, see Illustrative Game 95.

7.Be2

a) 7.b4:

a1) 7...b6 8.b5 Qe8 (8...Bb7 9.a4 Re8 10.Be2 e5 11.O-O h6 12.Bh4 c5 13.bxc6 Bxc6 14.Qb3 with advantage to White, Torre–Zapata, Brussels 1986) 9.Be2 e5 10.O-O Bb7 11.a4 Ne4 12.Rc1 a6 13.Bh4 axb5 14.axb5 Ra7 15.Bg3 Nxg3 16.hxg3 Qe7 17.Nxe5 Nxe5 18.dxe5 Bxe5 19.Nf3 Bd6 with equality, Torre–Kasparov, Brussels 1987.

a2) For 7...c6, see Illustrative Game 96.

a3) 7...Re8 8.Be2 e5 9.Nb3 b6 10.Bb5 e4 11.Bc6 Rb8 12.Nfd2 Bb7 13.Bxb7 Rxb7 14.b5 a6 15.a4 Ra7 16.O-O Qe7 with equality, Vaganian–Beliavsky, Erevan 1975.

a4) 7...Qe8 8.Bf4 c6 9.Bd3 Ng4!? 10.Be2 e5 11.Bg3 f5 12.dxe5 Ndxe5 13.Nd4 g5 unclear, Torre–Vaganian, Leningrad 1987.

a5) 7...a5 and:

a51) For 8.b5, see Illustrative Game 97.

a52) 8.Be2 Re8 9.O-O e5 10.Nb3 axb4 11.cxb4 e4 12.Nfd2 Nf8 13.Bh4 h5 14.Qc2 Bf5 15.Rfc1 Re7 16.a4 Ne6 unclear, Malaniuk–Dorfman, Lvov 1988.

b) 7.Bd3

b1) 7...Re8 and now:

b11) 8.e4 dxe4 9.Nxe4 Nxe4 10.Bxe4 c5 11.O-O cxd4 12.cxd4 Nf6 with equality, Popov–Tukmakov, Moscow 1983.

b12) 8.Bf4 Nh5 9.O-O Nxf4 10.exf4 c5 11.Ne5 Qb6 12.Qb3 Qxb3 13.axb3 cxd4 14.cxd4 f6 15.Nxd7?! (15.Nef3 with equality) 15...Bxd7 16.Ra5 Bh6 17.g3 e5 with advantage to Black, Yusupov–Vaganian, Moscow 1983.

b13) 8.h3 e5 9.dxe5 Nxe5 10.Nxe5 Rxe5 11.Nf3 Re8 12.O-O c6 13.Re1 Qb6 14.Bxf6 Bxf6 15.Qc2 Be6 with equality, Smyslov–Kamsky, Manila Interzonal 1990.

b2) 7...c5 8.O-O b6 9.b4 Bb7 10.Qb1 cxd4 11.cxd4 Rc8 12.a4 h6 13.Bh4 g5 14.Bg3 Nh5 15.Be5 f6 16.Bg3 Nxg3 17.hxg3 e5?! (17...e6) 18.Bf5 with advantage to White, Malaniuk–Loginov, Tallinn 1982.

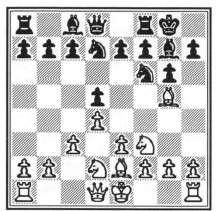

We now examine **B1) 7...Re8** and **B2) 7...b6**.

B1) 7...Re8

8.O-O

a) 8.b4

a1) 8...c6 9.O-O a5 10.a4 e5 11.b5 c5 12.dxe5 Nxe5 13.Rc1 h6 14.Bh4 Nxf3+ 15.Bxf3 c4 16.Bxf6 Bxf6 17.Re1 with advantage to White, Torre–Ftacnik, Novi Sad 1984.

a2) For 8...h6, see Illustrative Game 98.

b) For 8.Qb3, see Illustrative Game 99.

8...e5

8...c6 and:

a) 9.h3 e5 10.c4 h6 11.Bh4 exd4 12.Nxd4 Ne5 13.Rc1 Qb6 14.cxd5 Nxd5 15.Qc2 unclear, Tukmakov–Gavrikov, Mazatlan Quick Play 1988.

b) 9.a4 e5 10.dxe5 Nxe5 11.a5 h6 12.Bh4 Nxf3+ 13.Bxf3 Qe7 14.Qa4 g5 15.Bg3 Bf5 16.Rfd1 Rad8 17.h3 Nd7 18.Qa3 with equality, Rongguang Ye–Douven, Thessaloniki Olympiad 1988.

c) 9.b4 h6 10.Bh4 e5 11.Rc1 e4 12.Ne1 Nf8 13.b5 Ne6 14.bxc6 bxc6 15.c4 Qa5 16.Nc2 Nd7 17.Bg3 Bf8

18.c5 h5 19.Rb1 Ng7 20.Nb4 Re6 unclear, Torre–Thipsay, New Delhi 1990.

9.b4

a) 9.c4 with:

a1) 9...e4 10.Ne1 c5 11.Nc2 with advantage to White, Rongguang Ye–Tseshkovsky, Belgrade 1988.

a2) 9...exd4 10.Nxd4 Nc5 11.cxd5 Qxd5 12.Bf4 c6 13.Bf3 Qd8 with equality, Torre–Sokolov, Biel 1989.

b) 9.h3 c5 10.Bb5 Qb6 11.Qa4 a6 12.Bxf6 Qxb5 13.Qxb5 axb5 14.Bxe5 Nxe5 15.Nxe5 Bxe5 16.dxe5 Rxe5 17.b4 with advantage to White, Benjamin–Hellers, New York 1993.

c) For 9.dxe5, see Illustrative Game 100.

d) For 9.Nb3, see Illustrative Games 101 and 102.

e) For 9.Bh4, see Illustrative Game 103.

9...c6

For 9...h6 10.Bh4 e4 11.Ne1 see Illustrative Game 104.

10.Nb3

a) 10.a4 a5 11.Qb3 h6 12.Bh4 e4 13.Ne1 g5 14.Bg3 h5 15.h4 Ng4 16.hxg5 Qxg5 17.Bf4 Qg6 18.f3 exf3 19.Bd3 fxg2 20.Bxg6 gxf1=Q+ 21.Nxf1 fxg6 unclear, Salov–Gelfand, Linares 1990.

b) 10.Bh4 a5 11.a3 e4 12.Ne1 h6 13.Nc2 Nf8 14.c4 g5 15.Bg3 Ng6 16.bxa5 Rxa5 17.Nb4 Ra8 soon ended in a draw in Salov–Gelfand, Reggio Emilia 1991/92.

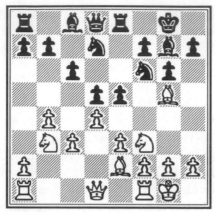

10...h6

10...Qb6 11.Bxf6 Bxf6 12.a3 Qc7 13.Rc1 e4 14.Nfd2 b5 15.a4 a6 unclear, Petrosian–Kortchnoi, Odessa 1974.

11.Bh4

11.Bxf6 Qxf6 12.Qc2 (12.Rc1 Draw, Vaganian–Nunn, Rotterdam 1989) 12...e4 13.Nfd2 Qg5 14.b5 Nf6 15.Kh1 Ng4?! 16.h3 Qh4 17.Kg1 Nf6 18.bxc6 bxc6 19.c4 Bf5 20.Rfc1 Rac8 21.c5 g5 22.Bf1 with advantage to White, Ostenstad–Basin, Trnava 1989.

11...g5 12.Bg3 Ne4 13.Rc1

13.Qc2 Nxg3 14.hxg3 e4 15.Nfd2 f5 16.c4 Nf6 17.a4 Qd6 18.b5? f4 with advantage to Black, Ostenstad–Stohl, Trnava 1989.

13...Nxg3 14.hxg3 e4

Torre–Uhlmann, Thessaloniki Olympiad 1988, continued 15.Nh2 f5 16.c4 Bf8 17.b5 cxb5 18.cxd5 Qb6 unclear.

B2) 7...b6
8.b4

a) 8.a4 a5 9.O-O Bb7 10.Re1 Re8 11.Qb3 e5 12.dxe5 Nxe5 13.Nxe5 Rxe5 14.Nf3 Re8 15.Red1 Qe7 with equality, Petrosian–Smejkal, Moscow 1981.

b) 8.O-O Bb7 9.Rc1 c5 10.Qa4 a6 11.Rfd1 Qc8 12.Qb3 b5 13.a4 Bc6 14.axb5 axb5 15.Ne5 c4 16.Qc2 e6 17.Nxd7 Qxd7 18.Bxf6 Bxf6 Draw, Granda Zuniga–Watson, New York 1987.

8...Bb7 9.O-O Qe8

9...Ne4?! 10.Nxe4 dxe4 11.Nd2 h6 12.Bh4 g5 13.Bg3 f5 14.f3 f4?! (14...Nf6) 15.Bf2 exf3 16.Bxf3 Bxf3 17.Nf3 fxe3 18.Bxe3 e5 19.Qb3+ Kh8 20.Qe6! Qc8 (20...Qe8 21.Qh3) 21.Rae1 Re8 22.Qg6 e4 23.Nxg5 hxg5 24.Rf7 1-0, Kavalek–Browne, U.S. Championship 1986.

10.Bxf6 Bxf6 11.b5 a6 12.a4 e5

Seirawan–Kudrin, U.S. Championship 1988, continued 13.dxe5 Nxe5 14.Nxe5 Bxe5 15.Qb3 axb5 16.axb5 d4 17.cxd4 Bxd4 18.Rxa8 Bxa8 19.Bf3 with advantage to White.

Illustrative Game 91
GM Vassily Smyslov
GM Maya Chiburdanidze

Aruba 1992

1.Nf3 Nf6 2.d4 g6 3.Bg5 Bg7 4.Nbd2 d5 5.e3 O-O 6.Be2 Nbd7 7.O-O c5 8.c3 b6 9.a4

9.Qa4 Bb7 10.Ba6 Qc8 11.Bb5 Rd8 12.Ne5 Nxe5 13.dxe5 a6!

14.Be2 Ne4 with advantage to Black, Vaganian–Timoshchenko, USSR Championship 1978.

9...a6

In order to meet 10.a5 with 10...b5.

10.b4 c4 11.b5!

Malaniuk–Dolmatov, Moscow 1992, continued 11.Ne5 Bb7 12.f4 with a slight edge for White.

11...Bb7 12.Qc2 e6 13.Qb2 axb5 14.axb5 Qe7 15.Ne5 Rfc8 16.Bf3

Threatening 17.Ndxc4.

16...h6 17.Bxf6 Nxf6 18.Rxa8 Rxa8 19.Ra1 Ra5

This is the best move although it weakens the b-pawn. 20.Rxa8 Bxa8 21.Ndxc4 was threatened and 19...Rxa1 20.Qxa1 allows White to penetrate with his Queen.

20.Rxa5 bxa5 21.Bd1!

White will now have a dominating passed pawn after Ba4 and Nc6.

21...Bf8 22.Ba4 Nd7

If 22...Qa3, then 23.Qxa3 Bxa3 24.b6 Bb2 25.Nb1 Ne4 26.Nd7 followed by Nc5 gives White a large advantage.

23.Nc6 Bxc6 24.bxc6 Nf6 25.Qb8 Ne8 26.g3 Nc7 27.Nf3 Kg7

If 27...f6, then 28.Nh4 Kg7 29.Bc2 f5 30.Nf3 followed by Ne5.

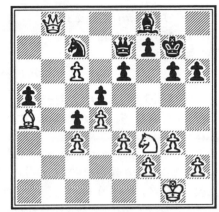

28.Ne5 Qd6 29.Qa7 Qd8 30.Qxa5 Bd6 31.Nd7 Qa8 32.Qxa8 Nxa8 33.Kf1 f6 34.Ke2 Nc7 35.f3 Kf7 36.e4 Be7 37.Kd2 Kg7 38.Nb6 Kf7 39.Bc2 Bd6 40.f4 f5 41.Nc8 Bn3 42.c5 h5 43.h3 Ke8 44.Ba4 Kd8 45.Nb6 Be7 46.Nd7 h4?!

This allows White to break through on the Kingside. It was better to sit tight.

47.gxh4 Ne8 48.Bd1 Ng7

Not 48...Bxh4 49.Nf8.

49.Nf6 Kc7 50.h5 gxh5 51.Bxh5 Nxh5 52.Nxh5

White's passed h-pawn is decisive.

52...Kxc6 53.Nf6 Bf8

If 53...Bxf6 54.exf6 Kd7, then White penetrates with his King on the Queenside.

54.h4 Kc7 55.h5 Kd8 56.Ng8 Ke8 57.h6 Kf7 58.h7 Kg7 59.Nf6 Be7 60.Ne8+ Kxh7 61.Nc7 Bd8 62.Nxe6 Ba5 63.Nc5 Kg6 64.Nb7 Bc7 65.Kc2 Kf7 66.Kb2 Ke7 67.Ka3 Kd7 68.Kb4 Kc6 69.Nd6 1-0

GM Ye Rongguang
GM Xie Jun

Kuala Lumpur 1994

1.d4 Nf6 2.Nf3 g6 3.Bg5 Bg7 4.Nbd2 d5 5.e3 O-O 6.Be2 Nbd7 7.b4

This move is very common in this type of position to prevent ...c5.

7...c6 8.O-O Re8 9.Rc1 a5 10.b5 c5 11.c4 cxd4 12.Nxd4 dxc4 13.Nxc4 Ne4 14.Bh4 Ne5 15.Nxe5 Bxe5 16.Qc2 Nd6 17.Rfd1 Qb6 18.Bg3 Bxg3 19.hxg3 e5 20.Nf3 Bg4 21.Qc5 Qxc5 22.Rxc5 Rac8 23.Rxc8 Nxc8 24 Kf1

White is better in the endgame because of his better placed Rook.

24...Kf8?

This allows White to start infiltrating into Black's position. Better is 24...f6 or 24...Be6.

25.Ng5 Bxe2+ 26.Kxe2 h6 27.Ne4 Ke7 28.Rc1 Kd8?!

Better is 28...f5 29.Nc5 b6 30.Na4 Kd7 with a difficult but solid position.

29.Nf6 Re6 30.Rd1+ Rd6?!

Black sacrifices a pawn with this move. Worse are 30...Kc7 31.Rd7+ and 30...Ke7 31.Ng8+ Kf8 32.Nxh6 f5 33.g4. However, 30...Nd6 is worth considering.

31.Ng4 Rxd1 32.Kxd1 Nd6 33.Nxe5 Nxb5 34.Nxf7+ Ke7 35.Ne5

If 35.Nxh6, then Black gets two connected passed pawns with 35...Nc3+.

35...Kf6 36.Nc4 Nc3+ 37.Kc2 Nxa2 38.Nxa5 b6 39.Nc6

Trapping the Knight. Black is forced to go into a pawn ending. However, perhaps White had a simpler win with 39.Nc4 b5 40.Nd6 b4 41.Ne4+ Ke5 42.f3.

39...Ke6 40.Kb2 Kd6 41.Kxa2 Kxc6 42.Kb3

With his connected passed pawn, White probably expected this position to be an easy win. However, this does not turn out to be the case.

42...Kc5 43.e4?

Better is 43.g4. Now Black is able to fix some of White's Kingside pawns.

43...h5 44.Kc3 b5 45.f4 Kc6 46.Kd4 Kd6 47.e5+ Kc6 48.Ke3

A winning method for White is not clear. If 48.Kc3, then 48...Kc5 49.Kb3 Kd5 50.Kb4 Kc6 51.e6 Kd6 52.Kxb5 Kxe6 53.Kc5 Kf5 draws.

48...Kd5 49.Kd3 b4 50.Kd2 Kc6 51.Ke2 Kc5 52.Ke3 Kd5 53.Kd3 Kc5 54.Kc2 Kc6 55.Kb3 Kb5 56.Kb2 Kb6 57.Kb3 Kb5 58.g4 hxg4 59.g3 Kc5 60.Ka4 Kd5 61.Kxb4 g5 Draw

Illustrative Game 93
GM Elizbar Ubilava
IM Ketevan Arakhami

Seville 1994

1.d4 Nf6 2.Nf3 g6 3.Bg5 Bg7 4.Nbd2 d5 5.e3 O-O 6.Bd3 Nbd7 7.O-O c5 8.c3 Re8 9.Re1 Qb6 10.Qa4?!

White felt that the b2-pawn would be poisoned, but this does not turn out to be the case.

10...c4

Not immediately 10...Qxb2? because of 11.Rab1 Qxc3 12.Rb3 trapping the Queen.

11.Bf1 Qxb2 12.Rab1 Qxc3 13.Rb4

Threatening to win the Queen with 14.Nb1. Black's next few moves are forced. If instead 13.Rec1, then Black is fine after 13...b5 14.Qxb5 Qa3.

13...a6 14.Nb1 b5 15.Qa5 Qc2 16.Na3 Qf5

Not 16...Qxa2 17.Re2 Qa1 18.Rb1 winning the Queen.

17.Nxb5 Rb8 18.Nc7?!

This wins back the pawn, but now White will have trouble saving this advanced Knight.

18...Rxb4 19.Qxb4 Rf8 20.Qxe7 Ne4 21.Bf4 Bf6 22.Qb4 g5 23.Bg3 Bd8 24.Na8 Qf6 25.Qa4 g4 26.Ne5 Nxe5 27.dxe5 Qe6 28.Qb4 Qc6

Winning the Knight which has strayed too far away.

29.Bf4 Qxa8 30.f3 gxf3 31.gxf3 Ng5 32.Re2 Nxf3+ 33.Kh1 Nh4 34.Bg2 Qb7 35.Qe1 Qd7 36.Qg3+ Qg4 37.Bxd5 Qxg3 38.Bxg3 Nf5 39.Bf4 Be6 40.Be4

Illustrative Game 94
GM Miquel Illescas Cordoba
GM Judit Polgar

Las Palmas 1994

1.d4 Nf6 2.Nf3 g6 3.Bg5 Bg7 4.c3 O-O 5.Nbd2 d5 6.e3 b6 7.Bd3 Bb7 8.O-O Nbd7 9.a4 Ne4 10.Bh4 Qe8?

Better is 10...a5 to prevent White's next move.

11.a5 h6 12.Qc2 Nxd2 13.Qxd2 Nf6 14.a6 Bc8 15.c4 dxc4 16.Bxc4 c6 17.Qc2 Bf5 18.Bd3 Be6

Better is 18...Bxd3. White's has a large advantage after the text.

19.Rac1 Rc8 20.b4 Nd7 21.Qe2 b5 22.Nd2 f5!?

Trying to discourage e3-e4.

23.e4 f4

If 23...Bxd4, then 24.Nf3 Bg7 25.exf5 Bxf5 26.Bxf5 Rxf5 27.Qe6+ gives White a large advantage.

24.d5 cxd5 25.Rxc8

Even stronger is 25.exd5 Bxd5 26.Bxe7 Rxc1 27.Rxc1 Rf7 28.Re1.

25...Qxc8 26.Bxe7 Re8 27.Bd6 dxe4 28.Qxe4?

Correct is 28.Bxe4 with a large advantage to White.

28...Nf6

Not 28...Bf7? because of 29.Qb7.

29.Qxg6

Not 29.Qb7? Rd8. If 29.Qxf4, then the position is equal after 29...Rd8 30.Ne4 Nxe4 31.Bxe4 Qxa6.

29...Bf7 30.Qf5 Qxf5 31.Bxf5

Rd8 32.Bxf4 Nd5

Now Black wins back her pawns and threatens to take over the initiative.

33.Bg3 Nxb4 34.Ne4 Nxa6 35.Nd6?!

Correct is 35.Rc1 b4 36.Rc8 Rxc8 37.Bxc8 Bd5 38.f3 with an equal position.

35...b4 36.Nxf7?!

Better is 36.h4 with just a slight advantage to Black.

36...Kxf7

Black's connected passed Queenside pawns are extremely dangerous.

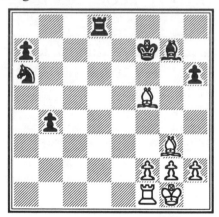

37.Re1?

White's best chance to try to hold is 37.h4, although after 37...b3 38.h5 b2 39.Bg6+ Kg8 Black has a large advantage.

37...Bc3 38.Be6+ Kg6 39.Rc1 Nc5 40.Ba2 a5 41.h4 a4 42.Kh2 a3

Slightly more accurate is 42...Rd2, which White prevents with his next move.

43.Bf4 Na4 44.g3

If 44.g4, then 44...Rd4 45.Kg3 Rxf4 wins.

44...Kg7 45.Kh3 Rd7

More accurate is 45...h5.

46.Kg4 Rb7 47.Bb3 Nc5 48.Bc4 Bb2 49.Re1 b3 50.Kh5 Rb6?

Correct is 50...a2 51.Bxh6+ Kh7 52.Re8 Rg7.

51.Re7+ Kf8 52.Ra7 a2 53.Be3! Na6! 54.Bxa6

If 54.Ra8+, then 54...Rb8!

54...a1=Q 55.Bc5+ Ke8 56.Ra8+! Rb8!

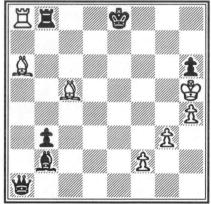

Judit Polgar demonstrates her tactical mastery. White is fine after either 56...Kd7? 57.Bc8+ or 56...Kf7? 57.Bc4+.

57.Rxb8+ Kd7 58.Be2?

Short on time, White misses his chance. Correct is 58.Bb5+! Kc7 59.Rb6! and White should equalize.

58...Bd4! 59.Bg4+ Kc7 60.Bxd4?

60.Rc8+ offered better chances.

60...Qa5+ 61.Kxh6 Kxb8 62.Kg6 Qb5 63.Bf5 b2 64.f4 Qxf5+ 65.Kxf5 b1=Q+ 66.Kg5 Kc8 67.g4 Kd7 68.h5 Ke6 69.h6

69.Be5, leaving the pawns where they are, would have offered more resistance.

69...Kf7 70.Bg7 Qc1 71.Be5

Kg8 72.Bg7

If 72.Kg6, then 72...Qc6+.

72...Kh7 73.Kf5 Qc2+ 74.Kg5 Qd2 75.Kf5 Qd5+ 76.Kf6 Qd8+ 77.Kf5 Qe7 78.g5 Qd7+ 79.Kf6 Qd3 80.Ke6 Kg6 81.Be5 Qf5+ 82.Kd5 Kf7 83.Kd4 Ke6 84.Ke3 Kd5 85.Kf3 Qh3+ 0-1

Illustrative Game 95

GM Vladimir Malaniuk
GM Georgy Timoshenko

Alushta 1994

1.d4 Nf6 2.Nf3 g6 3.Bg5 Bg7 4.c3 O-O 5.Nbd2 d5 6.e3 b6 7.a4 c5 8.a5 Na6 9.Be2 Bb7 10.O-O Ne4 11.Bf4 Nd6 12.h3 Nc7 13.axb6 axb6 14.Qb3 Ne6 15.Rxa8 Bxa8 16.Bh2 Qc7?!

The Queen is not well placed on the same diagonal as the h2-Bishop. Better is 16...c4.

17.Ra1 Bb7 18.Ne5 Ra8 19.Rxa8+ Bxa8 20.Qa2 Bb7 21.Nd3

White is better due to the pressure he gives on the h2-b8 diagonal, the a-file, and on the d5-pawn. Therefore Black decides to go into a speculative sacrifice, which backfires.

21...cxd4 22.exd4 Bxd4?! 23.cxd4 Qc2 24.Bxd6 exd6 25.Bf1 Qxd2 26.Qa7 Bc8?!

This loses a piece, but if 26...Bc6, then 27.Qxb6 Be8 28.Qb8 Ng7 29.Qxd6 is strong.

27.Qa8 Qc2 28.Nb4 Qc1 29.Na2 Qxb2

If 29...Qc2, then 30.Ba6 wins.

30.Qxc8+ Kg7 31.Nc1 Qxd4 32.Qc2 Qc5 33.Qb2+ d4 34.Nd3 Qc6 35.Qb4

Black's three isolated weak pawns are not sufficient compensation for the piece.

35...g5 36.Nb2 Qc5 37.Qb3 Nf4 38.g3 Ne6 39.Na4 Qa5 40.Nxb6 Nc5 41.Qb5 Qe1 42.Qe2 Qc1 43.Nc4 d3 44.Qb2+ Qxb2 45.Nxb2 d2 46.Bc4 f5 47.Kf1 Kf6 48.Ke2 Ne4 49.Bd3 d5 50.g4 Ke5 51.gxf5 h5 52.Nc4+ Kxf5 53.Nxd2 Kf4 54.Bxe4 dxe4 55.Nf1 h4 56.Nh2 e3 57.fxe3+ Kg3 58.Nf3 1-0

Illustrative Game 96

GM Eugenio Torre
GM Garry Kasparov

Thessaloniki Olympiad 1988

1.d4 Nf6 2.Nf3 g6 3.Bg5 Bg7 4.c3 d5 5.Nbd2 Nbd7 6.e3 O-O 7.b4 c6 8.Be2 Re8 9.O-O e5 10.a4?!

Better is 10.Nb3 to prevent ...a7-a5.

10...h6 11.Bh4 a5! 12.b5?!

This gives up the c5-square. Better is 12.Qb3.

12...c5 13.dxe5 Nxe5 14.Nxe5 Rxe5 15.Bxf6 Bxf6 16.Rc1 b6 17.Bg4 Bb7 18.Bf3?!

155

Better is 18.c4 d4 19.Bf3 with just a slight advantage for Black.

18...Qe7 19.c4 Rd8! 20.Qc2

According to Kasparov, Black has a large advantage after either 20.cxd5 Bxd5 21.Qc2 Bxf3 22.Nxf3 Red5 23.Rfd1 Qd7 or 20.Qb3 dxc4 21.Nxc4 Bxf3! 22.Nxe5 Bxe5 23.gxf3 Qg5+ 24.Kh1 Qh5 25.f4 Qf3+ 26.Kg1 Re8.

20...d4 21.Bxb7 Qxb7 22.exd4?!

Correct is 22.Nf3, although Black has a large advantage after 22...Rf5 23.exd4 Bxd4.

22...Rxd4 23.Rce1

If 23.Nf3, then 23...Rg4 and 24.h3 would be met by 24...Rxg2+ 25.Kxg2 Rg5+.

23...Rxe1 24.Rxe1 Qd7 25.Nf1 h5 26.g3

If 26.Ne3, then 26...Rd2 27.Rd1 Rxc2 28.Rxd7 Ra2 is strong.

26...h4 27.Ne3 Qe6 28.Qe2 Re4! 29.gxh4

This avoids ...h4-h3, but opens up the Kingside. White was in time pressure here.

29...Bc3! 30.Rd1 Rxh4 31.Qf3

If 31.Rd8+ Kg7 32.Qf3, then 32...Be5 is decisive.

31...Bd4 32.Ng2

If 32.Nd5, then 32...Kg7 33.Kg2 Qe5 34.h3 Rh5 wins.

32...Rh3 33.Qd5 Qf6 34.Ne3 Rf3

White cannot defend against the double threat of 35...Rxf2 and 35...Qg5+.

35.Kh1 Rxf2 36.Ng4 Qf3+ 37.Qxf3 Rxf3 38.Re1 Ra3 39.Re8+ Kg7 40.Rb8 Rxa4 41.Rxb6 Rxc4 42.Ra6 a4 0-1

Illustrative Game 97

GM Vladimir Malaniuk
NM Denisenko
Ukraine Team Championship, Alushta 1994

1.d4 Nf6 2.Nf3 g6 3.Bg5 Bg7 4.Nbd2 d5 5.e3 O-O 6.c3 Nbd7 7.b4 a5 8.b5 a4 9.Bd3

Torre–Jansa, Biel 1985 continued 9.Be2 c5 10.bxc6 bxc6 11.O-O c5 12.Rb1 with advantage to White.

9...c5 10.bxc6 bxc6 11.O-O Ba6

Exchanging off his bad Bishop.

12.Bxa6 Rxa6

One of the main keys to this game will be the control of the b-file. However, because White will be able to control the h2-b8 diagonal with his Bishop, the position must favor him.

13.Rb1 Qa5 14.c4 e6 15.Qc2 Raa8 16.c5 Rfb8 17.Bf4

With this move, White gains control of the b-file.

17...Rxb1 18.Rxb1 Ne8 19.a3 f6

Black intends ...e6-e5, intending to gain control of the b8-square for his Rook.

20.e4 g5

If 20...e5, then 21.exd5 exf4

(21...cxd5 22.c6) 22.dxc6 Nf8 23.Rb7 and White's pawns become dangerous.

21.Bg3 g4 22.exd5 cxd5

If 22...gxf3, then 23.dxc6 Nf8 24.Nc4 or 24.Nxf3 gives White some compensation for the sacrificed piece.

23.Ne1 e5

This weakens the d5-pawn, but a better move is hard to find.

24.Nd3 exd4 25.Qa2 Kf8 26.Qxd5?!

The soundness of this piece sacrifice is questionable. Better is 26.Nf4.

26...Qxd2 27.Bd6+

Black is fine after 27.Qxa8 Qxd3.

27...Nxd6 28.Qxd6+ Ke8 29.c6

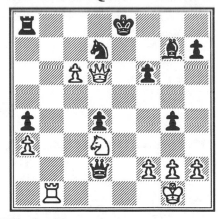

29...Qxd3

Worth considering is 29...Nf8. For example, after 30.Qxd4 Qa2 (not 30...Rd8 31.Qxa4) 31.Re1+ Kf7 32.Qxg4 Qxa3 33.Qc4+ Kg6 34.Qg4+ the game is drawn by perpetual check.

30.cxd7+ Kf7 31.Re1 Qc3 32.Qe6+ Kg6 33.h4

Despite being a piece down, White plays for a win because of his passed d-pawn and Black's ex-

posed King. He can draw by perpetual check with 33.Qxg4+ Kh6 34.Qh4+. The text avoids back-rank mates and the h-pawn can take part in a mating attack.

33...Rd8

Worth considering is 33...Kh6

34.Rd1

Threatening 35.Qe8+.

34...Qc2?!

34...Kh6 is still worth considering. After 35.Qxg4 Qxa3 36.Rxd4 Qe7 Black has a good position.

35.Rxd4 Qb1+ 36.Kh2 Qb8+ 37.g3 h5

38.Qe8+ and 38.Qg4+ have been stopped, but White still finds a strong move.

38.Rd5 1-0

Here Black lost on time. White is threatening 39.Rg5+ Kh6 40.Qf5 fxg5 41.hxg5#. Black can try defending with 38...Bh8 39.Qe4+ Kf7 40.Rxh5 Bg7 although the position is better for White.

Illustrative Game 98

GM Roberto Cifuentes Parada
GM Ilia Smirin

Wijk aan Zee 1993

1.d4 Nf6 2.Nf3 g6 3.Bg5 Bg7 4.Nbd2 O-O 5.c3 d5 6.e3 Nbd7 7.Be2 Re8 8.b4 h6 9.Bh4 g5 10.Bg3 Nh5 11.Nb3!?

Better is 11.Be5 g4 12.Ng1 Nxe5 (12...Bxe5 gives White a big advantage after 13.Bxg4 Nhf6 14.dxe5 Nxe5 15.Be2) 13.dxe5 f5 14.f4 with an unclear position.

11...Nxg3 12.hxg3 e5 13.Rc1

Better is 13.Nc5.

13...c6?!

157

Correct is 13...e4 14.Nfd2 f5 15.c4 c6 16.Nc5 Nf6 with the initiative to Black.

14.Nc5

Exchanging Knights will ease the pressure on White.

14...e4 15.Nd2 f5 16.Nxd7 Bxd7 17.c4 f4

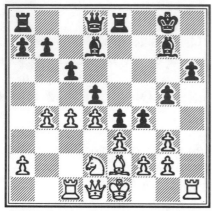

Black has a dangerous attack.

18.cxd5?

Correct is 18.Bg4 fxe3 19.fxe3 Qc7 20.Rh3 with an unclear position.

18...fxe3 19.fxe3 Qb8 20.O-O

The only move.

20...Qxg3 21.Qb3 cxd5 22.Qxd5+ Kh8

Better than 22...Be6 23.Qxe4 Bxa2 24.Rf3!

23.Qb3?!

The only move is 23.Rc3 although after 23...Bc6 24.Qf5 Rad8 25.Qg4 Rxf1+ 26.Nxf1 Qxg4 27.Bxg4 Bf8 28.a3 a5 Black has a large advantage.

23...Ba4 24.Qc3

If 24.Qa3, then 24...Bxd4 25.Nc4 Bb5 26.exd4 Qxa3 27.Nxa3 Bxe2 28.Rf7 e3 29.Rcc7 Bd3 wins.

24...Rac8 25.Qxc8 Qxe3+ 26.Kh1 Qxe2

Not 26...Rxc8 27.Rxc8+ Kh7 28.Bg4 and with the threat of 29.Bf5# White suddenly has a lot of play.

27.Qc3 Qh5+ 28.Qh3

Not 28.Kg1 Rd8 winning.

28...Qxh3+ 29.gxh3 Bxd4

Black's passed e-pawn and two Bishops give him a decisive advantage.

30.Nb3 Bg7 31.Kg2 e3 32.Rfe1 Bc6+ 33.Kg1 Be5 34.Rc2

If 34.Rxe3, then 34...Bh2+ 35.Kf2 Rxe3 36.Kxe3 Bf4+ wins.

34...Bg3 35.Ree2 Bf3 36.Nd4 Bxe2 37.Nxe2 Bd6 38.Rc4 Kg7 39.Rd4 Re6 40.Kf1 h5 41.Nc3 Be5 42.Rd7+ Kg6 43.Nd5 Rd6 44.Rxd6+ Bxd6 45.Ke2 Bf4 46.h4 Kf5 47.hxg5 Bxg5 48.a4 Kg4 49.Nc3 h4 50.Kf1 h3 0-1

Illustrative Game 99

GM Jan Timman
GM Gata Kamsky

Moscow 1992

1.d4 Nf6 2.Nf3 g6 3.Bg5 Bg7 4.c3 d5 5.Nbd2 O-O 6.e3 Nbd7 7.Be2 Re8 8.Qb3 c6 9.O-O

9.c4 Nb6 10.cxd5 Qxd5 11.O-O Bf5 12.Nc4 Be4 13.Bf4 Nh5 14.Bc7 Bxf3 is equal in Bronstein–Watson, London 1989.

9...e5 10.e4?!

This sacrifice is unsound. Better is 10.dxe5.

10...exd4 11.cxd4 dxe4 12.Bc4 Re7!

White would have compensation after 12...exf3 13.Bxf7+ Kh8 14.Bxe8 Qxe8 15.Rfe1.

13.Nxe4

If 13.Ne5, then 13...Nxe5

158

14.dxe5 Rxe5 15.Bxf7+ Kf8!

**13...Rxe4 14.Bxf7+ Kh8
15.Rae1 Qf8**

The only move. Not 16...Qb6
17.Qa3.

16.Ne5 Rxd4 17.f4

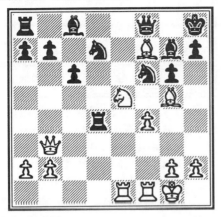

17...Rd5!

This is necessary to stem White's
attack. Black now threatens
18...Qc5+ and 19...Nxe5.

18.Bxd5

If 18.Nxg6+, then 18...hxg6
19.Qh3+ Nh7 20.Re8 Qxe8
21.Bxe8 Ndf6 wins.

18...Nxd5 19.Be7 Qg8

Not 19...Nxe7? 20.Nf7+ drawing.

**20.Nxd7 Bxd7 21.Qxb7 Qc8
22.Qxc8+ Rxc8 23.Bc5 a6
24.b3?**

This time pressure blunder
decisively weakens the c3-square.
Correct is 24.Rf2 with just a slight
advantage for Black. Now Black's
pieces get too much play.

24...Kg8 25.Rf2 Bc3

Forcing White to give up control
of the e-file.

**26.Rd1 Re8 27.h3 Re4 28.Kh2
h5 29.Rc1 Be1 30.Rfc2 Nxf4
31.Rc4 Rxc4 32.bxc4 Bg3+**

**33.Kh1 Bf5 34.Rc3 h4 35.Re3
Nd3 36.Bd4 Kf7 37.c5 a5 38.a4
Be1 39.Re2 Bb4 40.Bf2 Nxf2+
41.Rxf2 Bxc5 0-1**

Illustrative Game 100
**GM Vladimir Malaniuk
GM Gata Kamsky**
Moscow Active 1994

**1.d4 Nf6 2.Nf3 g6 3.Bg5 Bg7
4.c3 d5 5.Nbd2 O-O 6.e3 Nbd7
7.Be2 Re8 8.O-O e5 9.dxe5**

This leads to a less sharp of a
position than the other moves that
White has tried here.

**9...Nxe5 10.Nxe5 Rxe5 11.Nf3
Re8 12.h3 c6 13.a4 Qb6 14.Bxf6
Bxf6 15.Qd2 a5 16.Nd4**

White has a solid position but
nothing more.

**16...Bd7 17.Rfe1 Rad8 18.Bf1
h5 19.Qc2 Kg7 20.Rad1 Bc8
21.Nf3 Re7 22.Rd2 Rde8
23.Red1 Qc7 24.Nd4 Qe5
25.Nf3 Qc7 26.Nd4 Qb6 27.Be2
Be5 28.Nf3 Bb8?**

With the idea of lining up the
Queen and Bishop on the b8-h2
diagonal. However, now White
takes control of the a1-h8 diagonal
and takes the initiative.

**29.c4 dxc4 30.Bxc4 Bf5
31.Qc3+ Kg8**

31...Be5 might have been a better defense, although White has a strong initiative after 32.Nxe5 Rxe5 33.e4 Bxe4 34.Rd7.

32.Qf6 Qc7 33.Rd6

Blocking the b8-h2 diagonal.

33...Qc8

This results in a loss of time.

34.Ng5 Qc7

If 34...Bxd6, then 35.Bxf7+ wins.

35.e4?

This looks strong but only leads to a draw. Very strong would have been 35.Nxf7 Rxf7 36.Rd8 winning immediately, as 36...Qh2+ 37.Kf1 Qh1+ 38.Ke2 ends the spite checks.

**35...Bxe4 36.Nxe4 Rxe4
37.Qxg6+ Kf8 38.Qh6+ Ke7
39.Qf6+ Draw**

Illustrative Game 101

**GM Tony Miles
GM John Nunn**

London 1993

**1.d4 Nf6 2.Nf3 g6 3.c3 Bg7
4.Bg5 O-O 5.Nbd2 d5 6.e3
Nbd7 7.Be2 Re8 8. O-O e5
9.Nb3 c6 10.Rc1 a5 11.c4 a4
12.Nbd2 exd4 13.Nxd4 Qa5?**

Better is 13...Nb6. Now Black's Queen becomes misplaced.

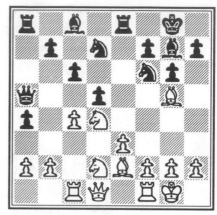

**14.cxd5 Qxd5 15.Bf4 Ne5
16.Qc2 Bg4 17.Bc4 Qa5**

17...Nxc4 18.Nxc4 loses the a-pawn after 18...Rad8 19.Nb6 or gives White a lot of pressure after 18...Qd8 19.h3 followed by 20.Rfd1.

**18.h3 Bd7 19.Be2 Rac8 20.Rfd1
b5**

If 20...c5, then 21.N4f3 Nxf3+ 22.Bxf3 b5 23.Bb7 winning the c-pawn.

21.N2f3 Nxf3+ 22.Bxf3 Nd5

If 22...c5, then 23.Bb7! cxd4 24.Bxc8 Bxc8 25.Qxc8 Rxc8 26.Rxc8+ Bf8 27.Bh6 Nd7 28.Rxd4 Qa6 29.Rxf8+ Nxf8 30.Rd8 winning.

**23.Bd6 Qb6 24.Qc5 Qxc5
25.Bxc5 Nf6**

Perhaps 25...Red8 26.b3 axb3 27.axb3 Be8 offered more resistance. White has a big advantage in the endgame because of his better placed pieces and the weakness at c6.

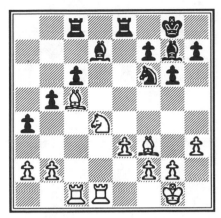

26.Ba3 Rb8

If 26...Ne4, then 27.Nxb5.

**27.Bd6 Rb6 28.Nxc6 Bxc6
29.Bxc6 Rc8 30.Bb4 Bf8
31.Bxf8 Kxf8 32.Bf3 Rc4
33.Kf1 Kc7 34.Kc1 Nd7 35.Bd5
Rxc1 36.Rxc1 b4 37.Rc7 Kd6
38.Ra7 Ne5 39.Bxf7 Nd3 +
40.Kd2 Nxf2 41.Rxa4 Ne4 +
42.Ke2 Rb7 43.Ra6 + Kc5
44.Bb3 Rd7 45.Ra5 + 1-0**

Illustrative Game 102

GM Anthony Miles
IM Jacek Gdanski

Iraklion 1993

**1.d4 Nf6 2.Nf3 g6 3.c3 Bg7
4.Bg5 O-O 5.Nbd2 d5 6.e3
Nbd7 7.Be2 Re8 8.O-O e5
9.Nb3 c6 10.Rc1 Qb6 11.Nfd2
Nf8 12.dxe5 Rxe5 13.Bf4 Re8
14.c4 Qd8 15.Bg3 h5 16.h3 Ne6
17.cxd5 cxd5 18.Be5**

White has a big advantage due to
the d4-weakness.

**18...Bd7 19.Nf3 Qb6 20.Qd2
Ba4 21.Qa5 Bxb3 22.Qxb6
axb6 23.axb3 Nd7 24.Bxg7
Kxg7 25.Rfd1 Nf6 26.Nd4 Nxd4
27.Rxd4 Rec8 28.Rb1 Rc2**

29.Bf3 Ra5 30. b4 Rb5

If 30...Ra4, then 31.Bd1 winning.
If 30...Ra2, then 31.Bxd5 Nxd5
32.Rxd5 Raxb2 33.Rxb2 Rxb2
34.Rb5 winning.

31.b3!

Taking advantage of the poor
position of the Rook on b5.
Black's next move is forced.

31...Ne4 32.Re1!

Black is fine after 32.Rxd5 Rxb4.

32...Rd2

Not 32...Nxf2 33.Be2 winning.
But worth considering is 32...Nc3.

33.Rd1 Rxd1 +?

Short on time, Black does not
find 33...Rb2.

34.Bxd1 Nc3

The only move.

35.Bf3 Kf6

Better is 35...Na2 although
White is winning after 36.Bd5

**36.Kf1 Ke5 37.Be2 Nxe2
38.Kxe2 f5 39.f4 + Kd6 40.h4
Kc6 41.Kd2 1-0**

White will play Kc2-b2-a3-a4
putting Black in zugzwang.

GM Ye Rongguang
GM Maya Chiburdanidze

Kuala Lumpur 1994

**1.d4 Nf6 2.Nf3 g6 3.Bg5 Bg7
4.Nbd2 O-O 5.c3 d5 6.e3 Nbd7
7.Be2 Re8 8.O-O e5 9.Bh4**

Avoiding an attack on the Bishop with ...Nf6-e4 at some point later in the game, or if Black plays ...e5-e4 and Nf8-e6.

9...c6 10.c4 exd4

Another idea is to keep the center closed with 10...e4 and later play for a Kingside attack.

**11.Nxd4 dxc4 12.Nxc4 Nc5
13.Qc2 Qe7 14.Rfd1 Bd7
15.Rac1 Rac8?!**

A hard move to understand. Don't Rooks belong on open files?

16.Na5 Ne6

16...b6 17.Bf3 is good for White.

17.Nf3

White can also grab the pawn. It is not clear how Black gets enough compensation after 17.Nxb7 Nxd4 18.Rxd4 Bf5 19.Qb3 Rb8 (if 19...Be6, then 20.Qb4) 20.Rb4 Bc8 21.Nd6. Instead White decides not to take any risks and seeks another way to exploit his advantage.

17...Nf8 18.Nc4

Clearly 18.Nxb7 Bf5 19.Qb3 Rb8 20.Ba6 Bc8 is now bad.

18...Bf5 19.Qd2 Rcd8 20.Nd6

Walking into a pin, but the Knight is a dangerous thorn in Black's position.

20...Rd7 21.Bc4

Worth considering is 21.Nxf5. Black would then be forced to ruin his pawn structure 21...gxf5. How-ever, the text is also strong.

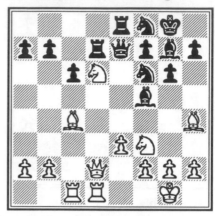

21...Be6 22.Ne5 Rxd6

This allows White to transpose into a favorable ending. But if 22...Rdd8, then White retains a large advantage with 23.Qb4 or 23.f4.

**23.Qxd6 Qxd6 24.Rxd6 g5
25.Bxg5 Ne4 26.Rxe6 Nxe6
27.Bf4 Nxf4 28.Bxf7+ Kf8
29.exf4 Rxe5 30.fxe5 Kxf7**

The smoke has cleared. White has a Rook and two pawns for two minor pieces, but most importantly his Kingside majority will be impossible to stop.

**31.Rc4 Ng5 32.f4 Ne6 33.f5 Nc7
34.Re4 h5 35.Kf2 Nd5 36.Kg3
Bh6 37.Kh4 Bc1 38.Kxh5 Bxb2
39.g4 Ne7 40.e6+ Kf6 41.Rb4
Ba3 42.Rxb7 a5 43.Rb3 Bc1
44.Rb8 1-0**

GM Gata Kamsky
GM John Nunn

Belgrade 1991

**1.d4 Nf6 2.Nf3 g6 3.Bg5 Bg7
4.Nbd2 O-O 5.c3 d5 6.e3 Nbd7
7.b4 Re8 8.Be2 e5 9.O-O h6
10.Bh4 e4 11.Ne1 g5 12.Bg3**

Nf8 13.Rc1 Ng6

Better is 13...g4 threatening ...h5-h4.

14.c4 c6 15.b5

According to Kamsky, better is 15.Qb3, and if 15...h5, then 16.cxd5 h4 17.dxc6 hxg3 18.fxg3 bxc6 19.Rxc6 Be6 20.Bc4 Bxc4 21.Nxc4 followed by 22.Nd6 with good play for the piece.

15...cxb5 16.cxb5 Re7 17.Nc2 g4 18.Nb4 h5 19.Qc2 Be6

Better is 19...Ne8 preventing 20.Bc7.

20.Bc7 Qd7 21.b6 Ne8

Not 21...a5 due to 22.Na6.

22.Qc5 Nxc7 23.bxc7 Rc8

If 23...b6, then White has a big advantage in the endgame after 24.Qb5 Qxb5 25.Bxb5 Rc8 26.Na6.

24.Qxa7 Rxc7 25.Qb6 Nh4

Threatening 26...Nf3+.

26.Nb3 Nf5 27.Nc5 Qd6 28.Na4

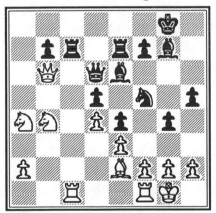

White has the advantage due to the weakness of the d-pawn.

28...Qd7 29.Qa5 Qd6 30.Qb6 Qd8 31.Rxc7 Qxc7 32.Qxc7 Rxc7 33.Nb6 Rc3

Better is 33...Ne7, although White still has a large advantage after 34.Bd1 f5 35.Bb3 Kf7

36.N6xd5 Nxd5 37.Nxd5 Bxd5 38.Bxd5.

34.N6xd5 Bxd5 35.Nxd5 Rc2 36.Re1 Nd6 37.a4 Ra2 38.Bd1 Kf8 39.Nf4 h4 40.Bxg4 Rxa4 41.Rb1 Ke7?!

Better is 41...Ra5.

42.g3?

Better is 42.Nd5+ Kd8 43.g3.

42...hxg3 43.hxg3 Ra5 44.Be2

White's plan is to play g4 followed by Nh5-g3, hitting the weak e-pawn.

44...Kd7 45.g4 Bh6 46.Nh5 Rg5?! 47.Kf1 b5?! 48.Rc1

Threatening 49.Rc5.

48...Rg6 49.Ng3 Bf8 50.Rc5 b4 51.Rc1 Be7 52.Rb1 Bh4 53.Nh5 1-0

Conclusion: After 1.d4 Nf6 2.Nf3 g6 3.Bg5 Bg7 4.Nbd2, 4...d5 is one of the best ways to play the King's Indian against the Torre.

Chapter 14

1.d4 Nf6 2.Nf3 g6 3.Bg5 Bg7 4.Nbd2 c5

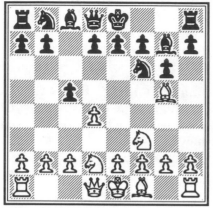

Black sometimes sacrifices a pawn with this move, often with good results. It is risky to delay this move until after 4...h6 6.Bh4: Mohr–Stull, Mitropa Cup 1988, continued 5...c5?! 6.Bxf6 Bxf6 7.Ne4 Bxd4 8.Nxd4 cxd4 9.Qxd4 O-O 10.Nc3 Nc6 11.Qd2 (gaining a tempo from the normal lines) 11...Kg7 12.e4 d6 13.h4 with a slight advantage to White.

After 4...c5, White has the choice between accepting the challenge **A) 5.Bxf6** or the more solid and passive **B) 5.c3** and **C) 5.e3**.

Worth considering is 5.dxc5 Qa5 6.c3 Qxc5 7.Bxf6 Bxf6 8.Ne4 Qc6 9.Nxf6+ Qxf6 10.Qd4 Qxd4 11.cxd4 b6 12.Kd2 Bb7 13.Rc1, Popchev–Kosanovic, Pernik 1987. However, 6...Na6 is probably better.

A) 5.Bxf6
5...Bxf6

5...exf6 weakens the d6 square: 6.Ne4 cxd4 7.Nd6+ Ke7 8.Qxd4 with advantage to White, Bellon–Pledina, Torremolinos 1977.

6.Ne4 Bxd4

a) 6...Qa5+ 7.c3 Bxd4 8.b4 Bxc3+ 9.Nxc3 cxb4 10.Qd5 Qb6 11.Na4 Qa6 12.Nc5 Qa3 unclear, Jonov–Livshits, Leningrad 1963.

b) A solid alternative is 6...Qb6 7.Nxf6+ Qxf6 8.c3 (8.e3 O-O 9.c3 d6 10.Be2 b6 11.O-O Bb7 12.a4 cxd4 13.exd4 a6 14.Re1 Nd7 15.Nd2 Rfc8 is equal, Taimanov–Gulko, Russian Championship 1976) 8...cxd4 9.Qxd4 (9.cxd4 O-O 10.e3 Nc6 11.Be2 d6 12.O-O Bd7 13.Qd2 Rfc8 is equal, Cifuentes–Zadrim, Malta Olympiad 1980) 9...Qxd4 10.Nxd4 Nc6 11.e3 d6 12.Be2 Bd7 13.O-O-O Rc8 14.g4 Ne5 15.Rhg1 a6 16.h4 b5 17.a3 h6 18.Rg3 Kf8 19.f4 Nc4 is equal, Torre–Timman, London 1984.

7.Nxd4 cxd4 8.Qxd4 O-O 9.O-O-O

a) 9.c4 with:

a1) 9...Nc6 10.Qd2 and now:

a11) For 10...d6, see Illustrative Games 105 and 106.

a12) 10...Qa5 11.g3 (11.Nc3 is better) 11...b6 12.Bg2 Ba6 (Better is 12...Bb7) 13.b3 Qxd2+ 14.Kxd2 Rac8 15.Rhd1 Rfd8 16.Nc3 Kf8 17.Kc2 Bb7 18.Kb2 Na5 19.Bh3 with advantage to White, Azmaiparashvili–Jiangchuan Ye, Beijing 1988.

a2) Stronger is the immediate 9...Qa5+ 10.Qd2 (10.Nc3 Qb4) 10...Qxd2 11.Kxd2 b6 12.Nc3 Bb7 13.e3 Na6 with advantage to Black, Tangborn–Nijboer, Reykjavik 1990.

b) 9.Nc3 Nc6 10.Qd2 Qb6! and now Miles–Gulko, Philadelphia

1987 continued 11.Rb1 Qd4! 12.Rd1 Qxd2 13.Rxd2 d6 14.Nd5 b5 with a slight advantage to Black. Instead, White should play 11.h4!? (Gulko) Qxb2 12.Rb1 Qa3 13.h5 unclear. Epishin–Mih. Tseitlin, Leningrad 1984, continued 11.b3 d6?! 12.Nd5 Qd8 13.e4 c6 14.Ne3 Qh4 15.Bd3 with advantage to White.

c) 9.Qd2 d5 10.O-O-O Qc7 11.Nc3 Be6 12.Nxd5 Bxd5 13.Qxd5 Nc6 14.e3 Rad8 with advantage to Black, Trifunovic–Karasloychev, Varna 1960.

d) 9.h4 Nc6 10.Qd2 d5 11.Ng3 e5 12.h5 Be6 13.O-O-O Qf6 14.e4 d4 15.Kb1 a5 16.a3 Rfb8 17.Qh6 Qxf2 18.Nc2 Qe3 with a large advantage to Black, Schwarz–Heinig, German League 1993/94.

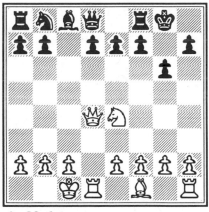

9...Nc6

9...Qa5?! 10.Nc3 Nc6 11.Qd2 d6 12.h4 Be6 13.Kb1 Rac8 14.e4 with a large advantage to White, Yusupov–Gorelov, USSR 1981.

10.Qd2 d5

a) 10...Qc7? 11.Nc3 e6 12.e4 f5 13.exf5 Rxf5 14.g3 with a slight advantage to White, Torre–Vogt, Baku 1980.

b) 10...Qa5 11.Nc3 d6 12.h4 Be6 13.Kb1 Ne5 14.e4 Rfc8 15.a3 Ng4 16.Nd5 Qxd2 17.Rxd2 Bxd5 18.exd5 h5 is equal, Panczyk–Sznapik, Poland 1982.

11.Qxd5

11.Ng3 Be6 12.e3 Rc8 13.Kb1 Qb6 and now Agzamov–Loginov, USSR 1986, continued 14.Ne2?! d4! 15.Nc1?! Nb4 16.Bd3 Nd5 with a slight advantage to Black. Instead White should play 14.Bd3 d4 15.exd4 Bxa2+ 16.Kxa2 Nb4+ 17.Kb1 Qa5 18.c3 Qa2+ and this is equal according to Loginov.

11...Qc7 12.Qc5

12.Qg5 Bf5 13.Nc3 Nb4 with compensation for the pawn, Nikolic–Damjanovic, Yugoslavia 1985. Not 12.Nc3 Qf4+.

12...b6

Not 12...Be6? 13.e3 with a large advantage to White, Blees–Nijboer, AVRO 1989.

13.Qc3 Qf4+ 14.Qe3

14.Nd2? Nb4 with a decisive advantage to Black.

14...Qxe3 15.fxe3 Ne5

Kovacevic–Stein, Zagreb 1972, continued 16.Nf2 Be6 17.g3 Rac8 Draw.

B) 5.c3

5...cxd4

Also possible is 5...O-O 6.Bxf6.

a) 6...Bxf6 7.Ne4 Qb6 8.Nxf6+ exf6 9.Qd2 d6 10.e3 Nbd7 is equal, Ostrovsky–Nezhmetdinov, USSR 1963.

b) 6...exf6 7.dxc5 f5 8.e3 f4 9.exf4 b6 10.Be2 bxc5 11.O-O d5 12.Nb3 Qd6 13.Ne5 Nc6 14.Nxc6 Qxc6 15.Bf3 Be6 is equal, Trifunovic–Spassky, Varna Olympiad 1962.

6.cxd4 Nc6

Queen moves like 6...Qa5 or 6...Qb6 are weaker. 6...d5 was Chapter 13.

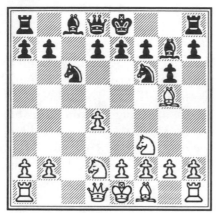

7.e3 O-O 8.Bd3

Other Bishop moves:

a) 8.Be2

a1) 8...d5 9.O-O Bf5 10.Qb3 Qb6 11.Qxb6 axb6 12.a3 Rfc8 13.Rac1 Ne4 (13...Nd7! is equal) 14.Nxe4 Bxe4 15.Bf4 f6 16.Bg3 e5 17.dxe5 Nxe5 18.Nd4 with advantage to White, Balashov–Hellers, Malmo 1988.

a2) 8...d6 9.O-O Bf5 10.Qb3 Rb8 11.Rac1 Be6 12.Qa3 Qb6 13.Rfd1 Rfc8 14.Bxf6 Bxf6 15.Ne4 Bg7 is equal, Trifunovic–Tan, Beverwijk 1963.

a3) 8...h6 9.Bh4 d6 10.O-O g5 11.Bg3 Nh5 12.Qb3 e5 13.d5 Ne7 14.e4 Nf4 15.Rfe1 Neg6 is equal, Trifunovic–Olafsson, Bled 1961.

b) For 8.Bc4, see Illustrative Game 107.

8...d6 9.O-O h6 10.Bxf6 Bxf6 11.Qb3

Black had problems in Trifunovic–Pavlov, Halle 1963. For example, 11...Kg7 12.Ne4 or 11...Na5 12.Qc2. Instead he played the dubious 11...e5?! White

correctly sacrificed a piece with 12.Bxg6 Na5 13.Qd5 Be6 14.Qe4 fxg6 15.Qxg6+ Kh8 16.Qxh6+ Kg8 17.Qg6+ Kh8 18.dxe5 dxe5 19.Ne4 with advantage to White.

C) 5.e3

Now we examine **C1) 5...O-O** and **C2) 5...b6**. An alternative is:

5...cxd4 6.exd4 Nc6 7.c3 O-O 8.Be2 d6 9.O-O h6 10.Bh4 and now:

a) 10...Qc7 11.Re1 Re8 12.Nc4 Nd5 is equal, Guimard–Reshevsky, Mar del Plata 1966.

b) 10...e5 11.dxe5 dxe5 12.Nc4 e4 13.Nfd2 Qe7 14.Qc2 g5 15.Bg3 Ne8 16.f3 e3 17.Nb3 b5 18.Nca5 Nxa5 19.Nxa5 f5 20.f4 with a slight advantage to White, Kovacevic–Kozul, Ljubljana 1989.

C1) 5...O-O

6.c3

a) 6.Bxf6

a1) 6...Bxf6 7.Ne4 Qb6 8.Nxf6+ Qxf6 9.c3 d6 10.Be2 b6 11.O-O Bb7 12.a4 cxd4 13.exd4 a6 14.Re1 Nd7 is equal, Taimanov–Gulko, USSR 1976.

a2) 6...exf6 7.Be2 f5 8.c3 b6 9.O-O Bb7 10.Nc4 d5 11.Nce5 c4

12.Ne1 Qe7 13.N5f3 f4 with advantage to Black, Arapovic–Paunovic, Yugoslavia 1983.

b) 6.Bd3 cxd4 7.exd4 Nc6 8.c3 d6 9.O-O h6 10.Bxf6 Bxf6 11.d5? Ne5 12.Nxe5 dxe5 13.Qb3 Bg7 14.Rad1 Kh7 15.Kh1 b6 16.Rfe1 Bb7 17.c4 f5 with advantage to Black, Filip–F. Olafsson, Varna Olympiad 1962.

6...b6

a) 6...cxd4 7.exd4

a1) 7...d6 8.Bd3 Nc6 9.O-O h6 10.Bh4 Nh5 11.Re1 f5 12.d5 Ne5 13.Bc2 Nf4 with advantage to Black, Timman–H. Olafsson, Malta Olympiad 1980.

a2) 7...d5 8.Bd3 Nc6 9.O-O Qc7 10.Re1 Nh5 11.Nf1 Nf4 12.Bb5 e6 13.Qd2 Nh5 14.Ng3 Nxg3 15.hxg3 a6 16.Bxc6 bxc6 17.Bh6 with a slight advantage to White, Trifunovic–Gligoric, Yugoslavia 1971.

b) 6...d6 7.Be2 h6 8.Bh4 Nbd7 9.a4 Qc7 10.Qb1?! e5 11.O-O Re8 12.dxe5 Nxe5 13.Nxe5 dxe5 with advantage to Black, Guimard–Keres, Buenos Aires 1964.

7.Bd3

a) 7.Bc4 Bb7 8.O-O d6 9.h3 Nc6 10.Qe2 Rc8 11.Ba6? (11.a3) 11...Qc7 12.Bxb7 Qxb7 13.Rfd1 Nd8 14.Rac1 Ne6 15.Bh4 Rc7 with a slight advantage to Black, Toran–Taimanov, Kapfenberg 1970.

b) 7.a4 Nc6 8.Bd3 Bb7 9.O-O h6 10.Bh4 d6 11.Qb1 Rc8 12.Rc1 cxd4 13.exd4 Nd5 14.Re1 Nf4 15.Bc4 Qd7 16.Bg3 g5 17.Bb5 a6 18.Bf1 with a large advantage to White, Ribli–Gheorghiu, Baile Herculane 1982.

7...Bb7 8.O-O d6 9.b4

9.Qe2 Nc6 10.Rfd1 cxd4 11.cxd4 h6 12.Bh4 Nb4 13.Bc4 a6 14.Bb3

Rc8 15.Rac1 b5 is equal, Hort–Smyslov, Wijk aan Zee 1972.

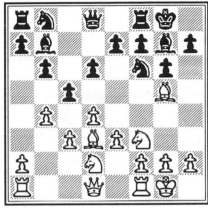

9...Nbd7 10.bxc5 bxc5 11.Qa4

11.Rb1 Qc7 12.Qa4 e5? (12...Bc6) 13.dxe5 dxe5 14.e4 with a slight advantage to White, Miles–Watson, New York 1987.

11...Nb6 12.Qa3 Qc7 13.Rab1 Rfc8

The position is equal, Pietzsch–Smyslov, Havana 1965.

C2) 5...b6

6.c3

6.Be2 O-O 7.O-O Nc6 8.c3 Re8 9.a4 Bb7 10.Bxf6 exf6 11.Nb3 Bf8 12.a5 Nxa5 13.Nxa5 bxa5 14.Qa4 cxd4 15.Nxd4 Re5! 16.Rfd1 Qb6 17.Qxd7 Rd8 18.Qa4 Bc5 19.Qc2 Be4 20.Bd3 Ba8 21.Bf1 Rb8 is equal, Lechtynsky–Vokac, Czechoslovakia 1984.

6...Bb7

6...O-O 7.Bxf6 exf6 8.dxc5 bxc5

a) 9.Nb3 Qb6 10.Qd5 d6 11.O-O-O Be6! 12.Qxd6 Rc8 13.Qxb6 axb6 14.Nfd2 Rxa2 with advantage to Black, Z. Nikolic–Bukic, Yugoslavia 1980.

b) 9.Bd3 f5 10.O-O Nc6 11.Qa4 Rb8 12.Rab1 Qc7 13.Rfd1 d6 14.b4 Bd7 15.Qa3 Ne5 16.Nxe5 Bxe5 is equal, Rustic–Krnic, Yugoslavia 1983.

7.Be2

a) 7.Qa4!? O-O 8.Be2 d6 9.O-O Nbd7 10.b4 Qc7 11.bxc5 bxc5 12.Rab1 Rfc8 13.Qa3 Nb6 14.Bd3 e6 (14...h6 15.Bh4 g5 16.Bg3 Nh5 17.Rfe1 Nxg3 18.hxg3 e6 is equal) 15.Rfe1 h6 16.Bh4 Nh5 17.Nf1 cxd4 18.cxd4 Bxf3?! 19.gxf3 Qc3 20.Qa6 with advantage to White, Kovacevic–Larsen, Bugojno 1984.

b) 7.Bd3 O-O 8.O-O d6 9.Qe2 Nbd7 10.Rfd1 h6 11.Bh4 g5 12.Bg3 Nh5 13.Ba6 Bxa6 14.Qxa6 f5 15.Nf1 Qe8 16.a4 e5 with a slight advantage to Black, Konstantinoposky–Zaitsev, Moscow 1966.

c) 9.Qc2 Nc6?! (9...cxd4 10.exd4 Nbd7 with the idea Rc8) 10.Rfe1 Rc8 11.Rad1 Qc7 12.Qb1 Rfe8 13.Bc4 a6 14.a4 Na5 15.Bf1 c4 16.e4 e5 17.h3 with advantage to White, Nikolac–Hartman, German League 1986.

d) 9.Re1 Qc7 10.a4 Nbd7 11.Bf1 e5?! (11...h6 12.Bxf6 [12.Bh4 g5 13.Bg3 Nh5 14.e4 Nxg3 15.hxg3 e6 is equal] Nxf6 13.e4 e6 is equal) 12.dxe5 dxe5 13.e4! a6 14.Bc4 Bc6 15.Bxf6 Nxf6 16.Qe2 Bb7 17.Bd3 Ne8 18.Nf1 Nd6 19.N3d2 Qd7 20.Nc4 with advantage to White, Platonov–Sideif-Sade, Tashkent 1980.

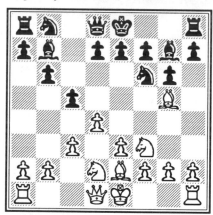

7...d6 8.O-O O-O

Now White has tried different plans:

a) 9.b4 Nd5 10.Qb3 cxb4 11.cxb4 h6 12.Bh4 Nd7 13.Bc4 N5f6 14.Rac1 a6 15.a4 e5 is equal, Moiseev–Savon, USSR Championship 1970.

b) 9.a4 h6 10.Bh4 g5 11.Bg3 Nh5 12.Qc2 Nxg3 13.hxg3 Nc6 14.g4 Qc8 15.Bd3 Ba6 16.Bxa6 Qxa6 17.d5 with advantage to White, Kovacevic–Doljanin, Stara Pazova 1988.

Illustrative Game 105

GM Nikola Spiridonov
GM Garry Kasparov

Skara 1980

1.Nf3 g6 2.d4 Nf6 3.Bg5 Bg7 4.Nbd2 c5 5.Bxf6 Bxf6 6.Ne4 Bxd4 7.Nxd4 cxd4 8.Qxd4 O-O 9.c4 Nc6 10.Qd2 d6 11.Nc3 Be6 12.e4 Qb6 13.Rd1?

Better is 13.Nd5 and if 13...Bxd5, then 14.exd5 Nd4 15.O-O-O with a good position for White.

13...Ne5 14.b3 f5 15.Be2

Better is 15.exf5 Rxf5 16.Qd4, although Black has the better ending after 16...Qxd4 17.Rxd4 Raf8 18.Rd2 Rf4.

15...f4 16.Nd5 Bxd5 17.Qxd5+ Kg7 18.O-O

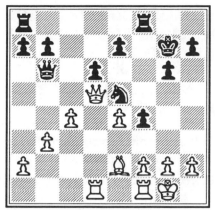

Black's Knight is superior to White's Bishop and White's only hope is the break c4-c5. For example, 18...a5 19.c5 Qxc5 20.Qxc5 dxc5 21.Rd5 Kf6 22.Rxc5 is fine for White.

18...Rac8?

Correct is 18...Kf6! Then 19.b4 Qxb4 20.Rb1 Qa3 21.Rxb7 Rab8 gives Black a big advantage.

19.b4 Qxb4 20.Rb1 Qa3 21.Rxb7 Kf6 22.h4

Threatening 23.Bg4.

22...h6 23.Rd1?

Correct is 23.Qd2 g5 24.Rb3 Qc5 25.Rb5 forcing the Black Queen away from its strong position.

23...Rb8

Not 23...Qxa2?? 24.Qxd6+!

24.Rc7 Rfc8 25.Rxc8 Rxc8

Now Black's positional superiority is clear.

26.Qb7 Qc5 27.Qb2?

27.Rb1 was more tenacious.

27...Qb6 28.Qc1 g5 29.Rd5 e6 30.hxg5+

Opening the h-file gives White more problems.

30...hxg5 31.Rd1 Ke7 32.Qc2 Rb8 33.Qa4 g4 34.Qa3 Qc5 35.Qc3 g3 36.Rf1 gxf2+

37.Rxf2 Rb1+ 38.Bf1 Qe3 39.Qxe3 fxe3 40.Rc2 Nxc4 0-1

Illustrative Game 106
GM Vassily Smyslov
IM Thomas Ernst

London 1988

1.d4 Nf6 2.Nf3 g6 3.Bg5 Bg7 4.Nbd2 c5 5.Bxf6 Bxf6 6.Ne4 Bxd4 7.Nxd4 cxd4 8.Qxd4 O-O 9.c4 Nc6 10.Qd2 d6 11.Nc3 Be6 12.e4 Qa5 13.Be2 a6 14.Nd5!

This leads to a better endgame for White due to a space advantage.

14...Qxd2+ 15.Kxd2 Bxd5 16.cxd5 Nd4 17.Bd3 Rfc8 18.Rac1 Kf8 19.Ke3 Nb5 20.g4 h6 21.h4 Na7

Black is hoping to exchange off Rooks on the c-file, but now White directs his attention to the Kingside.

22.Rcf1 Kg7 23.f4 Rc5 24.h5 Rh8

If 24...g5, then 25.fxg5 hxg5 26.h6+ Kg8 27.h7+ Kg7 28.h8=Q+ allows White a breakthrough at f7.

**25.hxg6 fxg6 26.Rhg1 Nb5
27.a4 Na7 28.Kd4 a5 29.e5 Nc8**
If Black tries to create
counterplay with 29...b5, then 30.f5
bxa4 31.f6+ exf6 32.exd6 is strong.
30.Rc1 Nb6
If 30...b6, then 31.Rce1 Rf8
32.f5. After the text, White's
central pawn majority will be
decisive.
**31.Rxc5 dxc5 32.Kxc5 Nxa4+
33.Kd4 Nxb2**
33...Rc8 34.d6 exd6 35.exd6 Rd8
36.Bb5! is also hopeless.
34.Bb5 a4
The only way to save the Knight,
as 35.Rb1 was threatened.
**35.d6 exd6 36.exd6 Rd8 37.d7
Kf6 38.Re1 a3 39.Kc3 Ra8
40.Re8 Na4 41.Bxa4 1-0**

Illustrative Game 107
GM Arthur Bisguier
GM Robert Fischer
U.S. Championship 1965/66

**1.d4 Nf6 2.Nf3 g6 3.Bg5 Bg7
4.Nbd2 c5 5.c3 cxd4 6.cxd4 Nc6
7.e3 O-O 8.a3 h6 9.Bh4 d6
10.Bc4 Bf5 11.h3 Rc8 12.O-O
e5 13.e4 Bd7 14.dxe5 dxe5
15.Ba2**
Better is 15.Bxf6. Now Black
shuts out this Bishop and starts a
Kingside attack.
**15...g5 16.Bg3 Qe7 17.Re1 Rcd8
18.Nh2 Be6 19.Bxe6 Qxe6
20.Nhf1**
White is hoping to transfer a
Knight to f5. He will never get the
chance, however.

**20...Rd3 21.Re3 Rd7 22.Qb3
Qe7 23.Nf3 Rfd8 24.Rae1 Nh5
25.Rc3 Qf6 26.Ne3?**
Better is 26.Bh2.
**26...Nd4 27.Nxd4 exd4 28.Ng4
Qg6 29.Rd3 Nxg3 30.fxg3?**
30.Rxg3 would have been a
tougher defense, although Black is
much better after 30...d3.
**30...Rc7 31.Nf2 Rdc8 32.Re2
Rc1 33.Kh2 h5**
Threatening 34...Be5 and
35...h4.
**34.Qb7 Be5 35.Qd5 R1c5
36.Qd7 h4 37.Nh1 Rc1 38.Rf3?**
38.Qg4 would have held out
longer.

38...g4!
Opening up the h-file.
**39.Qxg4 Qxg4 40.hxg4 Kg7
41.Rf5 Rxh1+ 0-1**
If 42.Kxh1, then 42...Rc1+
43.Kh2 Bxg3+ 44.Kh3 Rh1 mate.

Conclusion: After 1.d4 Nf6
2.Nf3 g6 3.Bg5 Bg7 4.Nbd2, 4...c5
is a sharp move championed by
both Fischer and Kasparov.

Chapter 15

1.d4 Nf6 2.Nf3 g6 3.Bg5 Ne4

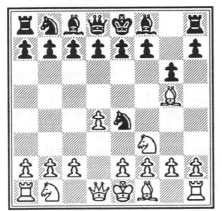

White has two reasonable ways to retreat the Bishop: **A) 4.Bf4** and **B) 4.Bh4.**

A) 4.Bf4
4...d5

4...c5 and:

a) 5.c3 Bg7 6.d5 (6.Nbd2 Nxd2 7.Qxd2 cxd4 8.cxd4 Qb6 9.e3 is equal, Zakharov–Kolpakov, Tashkent 1964) 6...O-O 7.Nbd2 Nf6 8.d6 Nc6 9.e3 Nh5 10.Bg5 f6 11.Bh4 g5 12.g4 unclear, Gurevich–Gulko, Batumi 1969.

b) For 5.e3, see Illustrative Game 108.

5.e3 Bg7

5...c5 6.c3 (6.Be5!? f6 7.Bxb8 Rxb8 8.Bb5+ Kf7 9.Bd3 Qb6 unclear, Bronstein–Aronin, Chigorin Memorial 1959) 6...Nc6 7.Nbd2 cxd4 8.Nxe4! dxe4 9.Nxd4 Qb6 (9...Nxd4 10.Qxd4 Qxd4 11.cxd4 with a slight advantage to White; 9...Bg7 10.Nxc6 Qxd1+ 11.Rxd1 bxc6 12.Bc7 with advantage to White) 10.Nxc6 Qxc6 11.Qb3 a6 (11...Be6 12.Bb5) 12.Bc4 e6

13.Be5 with a large advantage to White, Rytov–Vaganian, Tallinn 1979.

6.Nbd2 c5

6...O-O 7.Nxe4 dxe4 8.Nd2 f5 9.Bc4+ Kh8 10.h4 c5 11.c3 cxd4 12.cxd4 Nc6 13.h5 Qe8 is equal, Mikenas–Stein, USSR Championship 1965.

7.c3 O-O

a) 7...Qb6 8.Qb3 Nxd2 9.Nxd2 c4 10.Qxb6 axb6 11.Bxb8 Rxb8 12.e4 e6 13.Be2 b5 14.e5 Ra8 15.O-O with advantage to White, Kovacevic–Bertok, Zagreb 1969.

b) For 7...Nc6, see Illustrative Game 109.

c) 7...Nxd2 8.Qxd2 O-O 9.Be2 b6 10.Rd1 cxd4 11.cxd4 Bb7 12.Rc1 Nc6 13.O-O Rc8 14.Rc2 f6 15.Rfc1 Qd7 is equal, Lokvenc–De Lange, Leipzig Olympiad 1960.

8.Nxe4

8.Be2 Nc6 9.O-O Qb6 10.Qb3 Qxb3 11.axb3 Bg4 12.Bd1 Nxd2 13.Nxd2 Bxd1 14.Rfxd1 cxd4 15.exd4 a5 16.Nb1 Ra6 is equal, Vaganian–Mortensen, Esbjerg 1988.

8...dxe4 9.Nd2 cxd4 10.exd4 f5

Rodriguez–Westerinen, Alicante 1980, continued 11.f3 exf3

171

12.Bc4+ Kh8 13.Nxf3 Nc6 14.Qe2 Bd7 15.h4 h5 16.O-O with a slight advantage to White.

B) 4.Bh4

4...d5

a) 4...c5 and:

a1) 5.c3 Bg7 (5...Qb6 6.Nbd2 Nxd2 7.Qxd2 cxd4 8.Nxd4 e5 9.Nf3 f6 10.e4 Be7 11.Bc4) 6.Nbd2 Nxd2 7.Qxd2 cxd4 8.Nxd4 O-O (8...d5) 9.e4 Nc6 10.Nc2 d6 11.Be2 Be6 12.Ne3 Bh6 13.g4 unclear, Bellon–Fraguella, Lanzarote 1975.

a2) 5.Nbd2 d5 and:

a21) 6.e3 Bg7 7.c3 Bg4?! (7...Nc6; 7...O-O) 8.Qb3 Bxf3 9.Qxb7 Nxd2 10.Bb5+ Nd7 11.Bxd7+ with advantage to White, Psakhis–Konopka, Erevan 1986.

a22) 6.dxc5 Nxc5 7.Nb3:

a221) 7...Nc6 8.Nxc5 (8.c3?! Na4) Qa5+ 9.c3 Qxc5 10.e3 Bg7 11.Be2 O-O 12.O-O e5 13.Rc1 (with the idea b4-b5) 13...a5 14.Qa4 Bf5 15.Rfd1 h6 16.Nd2 Be6 17.Nb3 Qb6 18.Qb5 with advantage to White, Torre–Ermenkov, Thessaloniki Olympiad 1984.

a222) 7...Nxb3 8.axb3 Bg7 9.c3 O-O 10.e3 Nc6 11.Be2 O-O 12.O-O e5 is equal, Damjanovic–Markovic, Zagreb 1960.

b) 4...Bg7

b1) 5.e3 d5 6.Bd3 O-O 7.c4 Bf5 is equal, Filip–Stein, Stockholm 1962.

b2) 5.Nfd2 Nd6 6.c3 c5?! 7.dxc5 Nf5 8.Bg5 h6 9.Bf4 e5 10.Bg3 Qc7 11.Ne4 O-O 12.e3 Qc6 13.Nbd2 h5 14.Nd6 Nxd6 15.cxd6 Qxd6 16.Ne4 with a advantage to White, Gelfand–Kulaga, Minsk 1980.

b3) 5.c3 O-O 6.Nbd2 d5 7.e3 Bf5 8.Nxe4 Bxe4 9.Bd3 Bxd3 10.Qxd3 Qd7 11.O-O e6 12.Rac1 Na6 13.b4 c6 14.Ne5 Qe8 15.Bg3 Nb8 16.Nf3 Qe7 17.b5 a6 is equal, Lobron–Chiburdanidze, Brussels 1987.

c) 4...b6 5.Nbd2 Nxd2 6.Qxd2 Bb7 7.O-O-O Bg7 8.e4 O-O 9.e5 c5 10.d5 f6 11.exf6 exf6 12.Bg3 Ba6 13.h4 Bxf1 14.Rdxf1 Rf7 15.h5 g5 16.h6 Bf8 17.Re1 d6 18.Re6 with a large advantage to White, Timman–Sunye Neto, Amsterdam 1985.

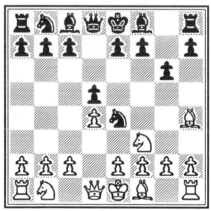

5.e3 Bg7 6.Nbd2 c5

For 6...Nd6 7.c3 c6 8.Be2, see Illustrative Game 110.

7.c3 cxd4

7...Nxd2 8.Qxd2 and:

a) 8...Qa5?! 9.b4 cxb4 10.cxb4 Qb6 11.Rc1 Bg4 12.Be2 Nd7 13.a4 Bf6 14.Bg3 O-O 15.a5 with a large advantage to White, Malaniuk–Semeniuk, USSR 1986.

b) 8...b6 9.Ne5 O-O 10.f4 Bb7 11.Bd3 Nd7 12.O-O Nf6 13.Rad1 unclear, Gereben–Trincardi, Reggio Emilia 1963/64.

8.exd4 O-O

8...Nc6 9.Nxe4 dxe4 10.Ng5 Bf6 11.d5 with advantage to White, Filip–Molnar, Lyons 1955.

9.Nxe4 dxe4 10.Nd2 f5 11.Bc4+ Kh8

a) Spassky–Berezhnoy, Kharkov 1963, continued 12.Bg5 Qe8 13.h4 e5 14.dxe5 Nc6 15.h5 Nxe5 16.hxg6 Qxg6 17.Qh5 Qxh5 18.Rxh5 Nxc4 19.Nxc4 Be6 20.Nd6 Be5 21.O-O-O with advantage to White.

b) For 12.Qe2, see Illustrative Game 111.

Illustrative Game 108

NM Andrei Rakhmangulov
IM Alexey Fedorov

Nikolaev, Ukraine 1993

1.d4 Nf6 2.Nf3 g6 3.Bg5 Ne4 4.Bf4 c5 5.e3 Bg7 6.Nbd2 d5 7.c3 Nc6 8.Nxe4 dxe4 9.Nd2 cxd4 10.cxd4 Qa5 11.a3

If 11.Be2, then 11...e5 is strong.

11...O-O 12.b4 Qf5

Threatening 13...Nxd4.

13.Bg3 Rd8 14.Rc1 e5 15.d5

The only move.

15...Ne7

If 15...Rxd5, then White wins his pawn back with 16.Qc2.

16.f3

White sacrifices a pawn to get activity for his pieces. Black would be better after 16.Qc2 Nxd5 followed by ...a5.

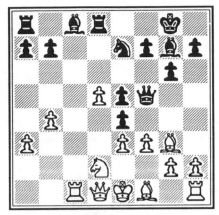

16...exf3 17.e4 fxg2 18.Bxg2 Qg5 19.O-O Bg4

If 19...Qe3+, then 20.Bf2 Qxa3 21.Bc5 gives White a strong attack.

20.Qe1 Rd7?!

Preventing Rc7, but the Rook is badly placed at d7, as White's next moves demonstrate. Better is 20...Rac8.

21.h3 Bh5 22.h4 Qh6 23.Nc4 f6 24.Bh3 Rdd8 25.Be6+

25.Na5 immediately would have been better.

25...Kh8 26.Na5

White has very strong Queen-side play and Black's only chance to save the game is with counterplay on the Kingside.

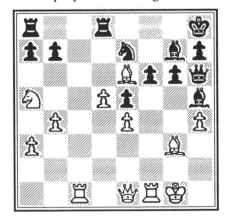

173

26...g5! 27.Nxb7 gxh4 28.Bxh4 Rg8 29.Nd6

29.Bxg8 Rxg8 30.d6 Ng6 31.Bg3 should win for White.

29...f5 30.Nxf5?!

If 30.Bxe7, then 30...Bf6+. White could still win with 30.Kh2. Now Black's desperate counterattack pays off.

30...Nxf5 31.Rxf5 Bf6+ 32.Bxg8 Rxg8 33.Kh2 Bxh4 34.Qxh4 Qxc1 Draw

White must force a perpetual check after 35.Qf6+ Rg7 36.Qf8+.

Illustrative Game 109

GM Tony Miles
IM Erling Mortensen

Aarhus, Denmark 1993

1.d4 Nf6 2.Nf3 g6 3.c3 Bg7 4.Bg5 Ne4 5.Bf4 d5 6.Nbd2 c5 7.e3 Nc6 8.Nxe4 dxe4 9.Nd2

9.Ng5 cxd4 10.exd4 Qd5 11.Qb3 e6 12.Qc2 (12.Bc4 Qf5) f5 13.f3 O-O 14.fxe4 fxe4 15.g3 e5 is equal, Keres–Botvinnik, Budapest 1952.

9...f5?!

Better is 9...cxd4 10.cxd4 Qa5 as in the previous game. Now Black will have trouble castling.

10.Qb3 cxd4 11.cxd4 Na5 12.Qc3

Threatening 13.Bc7.

12...b6 13.b4 Nb7 14.Rc1 Nd6?

Black should have used this opportunity to castle.

15.Qb3 Bb7 16.Be2 Rc8 17.O-O Rxc1 18.Rxc1 Qd7 19.Nc4 Nf7

This allows a decisive blow, although Black's position was hopeless in any case.

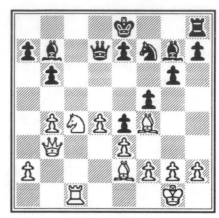

20.Nxb6! axb6 21.Rc7 Bd5 22.Qc2 Qe6 23.Bb5+ Kf8 24.Rc8+ Nd8 25.Rxd8+ Kf7 26.Rxd5 1-0

Illustrative Game 110

GM Tigran Petrosian
GM Semen Furman

USSR Championship 1958

1.d4 Nf6 2.Nf3 g6 3.Bg5 Ne4 4.Bh4 d5 5.e3 Bg7 6.c3 c6 7.Nbd2 Nd6 8.Be2 Nd7 9.O-O Nf5 10.Bg5 f6?! 11.Bf4 g5?!

If 11...e5, then 12.dxe5 fxe5 13.Bg5 followed by 14.e4.

12.Bd3 e6 13.Bxf5 exf5 14.Bd6 Nf8 15.Ba3 Be6 16.Rc1 Ng6 17.c4 Kf7 18.Ne1

The Knight is moved to c5.

18...Rc8 19.Nd3 Rc7 20.Nc5 Bc8 21.cxd5 cxd5 22.Qa4 b6

22...a6.

23.Na6 Bxa6 24.Qxa6 Qc8 25.Rxc7+ Qxc7 26.b3 Qd7 27.Rc1 Rd8 28.Qa4

Accepting doubled pawns to control the c-file.

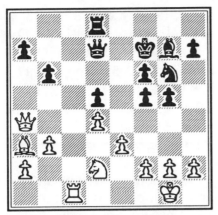

28...f4 29.Qxd7+ Rxd7 30.g4
Bf8 31.Bxf8 Kxf8 32.Kf1 Ke7
33.Ke2 fxe3 34.fxe3 Nh4 35.Nf3
Nxf3 36.Kxf3 Kd6 37.Rc8 Rf7
38.Rd8+ Ke6 39.e4 dxe4+
40.Kxe4 Ke7 41.Ra8 Ke6
42.d5+ Kd6 43.Re8 Rc7
44.Re6+ Kd7 45.Rc6 1-0

Illustrative Game 111

GM Vladimir Malaniuk
IM Viktor Varavin

Alushta 1994

1.d4 Nf6 2.Nf3 g6 3.Bg5 Bg7
4.c3 Ne4 5.Bh4 O-O 6.Nbd2 d5
7.e3 c5 8.Nxe4 dxe4 9.Nd2 cxd4
10.exd4 f5 11.Bc4+ Kh8
12.Qe2 Nc6 13.f3 Qb6 14.Bb3
e5 15.Nc4 Qc7 16.d5 b5!
17.dxc6 bxc4 18.Bxc4 exf3
19.gxf3 Rb8 20.O-O-O

The King will soon come under a
ferocious attack, although White
should be able to defend with accurate play. Worth considering is
20.Bd5 Qa5 21.O-O-O e4 22.Be7
Ba6 with an unclear position.

20...e4

Opening the diagonal for the
King's Bishop and threatening
21...Qf4+.

21.Kb1?

Now White is in serious trouble.
Correct is 21.Bf2. After 21...Qxc6
22.Bd4 Be6 23.Bxe6 Qxe6 24.Kb1
Bxd4 25.Rxd4 Qc6 26.fxe4 Qxc3
the position is equal.

21...Bxc3 22.Bb3 Be6!

Black sacrifices a piece in order
to slash open the position of the
White King.

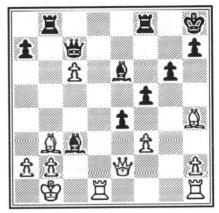

23.bxc3?

23.Qc2 offered more resistance
although Black is much better after
23...Bg7.

23...Bxb3 24.axb3 Rxb3+ 25.Kc2 Qa5!

Not 25...Rxc3+? 26.Kxc3 Qa5+
27.Kd4 and White is winning.

26.Bf6+

Temporarily displacing the Rook
is forced as 26.Kxb3 Rb8+ 27.Kc4
Qb5+ wins the White Queen.

26...Rxf6 27.Kxb3 Rxc6 28.Qe1

The best chance. Other moves
lose. For example, if 28.Qe3, then
28...Rb6+ 29.Kc4 Qb5+ 30.Kd4
Rd6# or if 28.Rc1, then 28...Rb6+
29.Kc2 Qa4+ 30.Kd2 Rb2+
31.Ke1 Rxe2+ 32.Kxe2 Qc4+
wins.

28...Rb6+ 29.Kc4

Not 29.Kc2 Qa2+ followed by mate.

29...Rc6+ 30.Kb3 Rb6+ 31.Kc4 Qb5+

Short on time, Black misses 31...Qa4+!. After 32.Kd5 Rb5+ 33.Ke6 Qc4+ 34.Kf6 Qc7! White will get mated.

32.Kd4 Re6 33.fxe4

Not 33.Rb1 because 33...Qd3+ will lead to checkmate.

33...Rxe4+?

Black could have retained his large advantage with 33...Qd7+ 34.Kc4 Rxe4+ 35.Qxe4 Qa4+ 36.Kc5 Qxe4 37.c4 f4.

34.Qxe4 fxe4 35.c4 Qc6 36.Rc1 Kg7 37.c5?!

Simpler is 37.Rhe1 with an equal position.

37...Kf6 38.Rhe1 Kf5 39.Re3 Qa4+ 40.Kd5 Qd7+ 41.Kc4 Qa4+ 42.Kd5 Qd7+ 43.Kc4 Ke5 44.Kb3 Qb5+ 45.Ka3 Kd4 46.Rcc3

White has set up a blockade with his Rooks on the third rank which Black will find impossible to break through.

46...Qc6 47.h3 g5 48.Kb3 a5 49.Rg3 h6 50.Rge3 h5 51.Rg3

g4 52.hxg4 hxg4 53.Ka3 a4 54.Kb4 Qa6 55.Ka3 Qc6 56.Kb4 Ke5 57.Rxg4 Qb7+ 58.Ka3 Qb1 59.Rgg3 Qa1+ 60.Kb4 Kd5 61.c6 a3 62.c7 Qb2+ 63.Rb3 Qd4+ 64.Kxa3 Qa7+ 65.Kb2 Qxc7 66.Rb5+ Kd4 Draw**

Conclusion: 3...Ne4 is inferior and less popular than the other ways of playing against the Torre.